ENGINEERING SCIENCE SERIES

Direct-Current Machinery

THE MACMILLAN COMPANY
NEW YORK · BOSTON · CHICAGO · DALLAS
ATLANTA · SAN FRANCISCO
MACMILLAN AND CO., Limited
LONDON · BOMBAY · CALCUTTA · MADRAS
MELBOURNE
THE MACMILLAN COMPANY
OF CANADA, Limited
TORONTO

Early Edison Dynamo

Direct-Current Machinery

ROYCE G. KLOEFFLER, S.M.
Head, Department of Electrical Engineering

RUSSELL M. KERCHNER, M.S.
Professor of Electrical Engineering

JESSE L. BRENNEMAN, E.E.
Formerly Professor of Electrical Engineering

KANSAS STATE COLLEGE

REVISED EDITION

New York The Macmillan Company 1949

Preface to Second Edition

The importance of direct-current machinery has increased since the first edition of this book was written in 1934. The total capacity of d-c machines other than fractional horsepower produced by one of the largest electrical manufacturers in America increased from 30 per cent to a maximum of over 53 per cent of combined d-c and a-c output in 1944. While the war production was responsible for this peak, there is good reason for believing that d-c machines will continue to occupy a prominent place in the electric power field. The generation, transmission, and distribution of electric power will continue via the alternating-current system. However, new and efficient electronic and other methods of rectification make possible the utilization of the superior torque and speed characteristics of the d-c motor in many applications where accurate control is desirable.

This revision of the text contains the latest information available on new theories, developments, and applications in the direct-current field. In machines, the amplidyne, multifield exciters, welding generator, and airplane generators have been added. The newer theories of commutation and current methods of automatic starting and control are treated in some detail. The order of treatment has been changed to assist the student in the laboratory work that accompanies the recitation, and the problems have been increased in number and scope. All circuit diagrams, both old and new, conform to the graphical standards approved by the American Standards Association.

The authors are grateful to many users of the text who have given helpful suggestions for this revision. Many thanks are due to Professor W. E. Meserve of Cornell University for his constructive criticisms.

R. G. Kloeffler
R. M. Kerchner

Manhattan, Kansas

Preface to the First Edition

This book is intended for use as a text in courses on direct-current machines for junior students in electrical engineering. The contents of the book and the intellectual level of the presentation are designed to suit the preparation and needs of the average junior engineering student. In those engineering schools where the fundamental theory of electricity and magnetism is covered in the sophomore year or before the time of studying direct-current machinery, the student will be prepared to begin at Chapter I and proceed to the last chapter. For those colleges in which the fundamental theory of electricity is covered at the beginning of the course on direct-current machinery, the student should proceed from Chapter I to the Appendix on "Units and Fundamental Concepts" and then return to Chapter II.

This text differs from other treatments of this subject in the order and style of presentation of the material, and through the addition of recent theories and applications of direct-current machines. Theory and discussion of a design nature have been largely eliminated. The differences between alternating-current and direct-current machines have been emphasized and the complete treatment of the subject aims to prepare the student for his future study of alternating currents. The characteristics of direct-current dynamos are shown quantitatively by new and simple graphical methods involving constructions in a single plane. The characteristics of loads are likewise treated through similar graphical constructions. Since students are inclined to confuse the theory of armature reaction and reactance voltage, these subjects are treated in separate chapters and in a new way. Some of the theory of commutation is needed early in a study of direct-current machines, yet the entire subject is too long and difficult for a complete treatment at that time. This difficulty has been met by giving the necessary theory early in the text under the title of "Reactance Voltage and Interpoles" and by treating the subject in a more extensive manner in a later chapter on commutation. The text contains a special chapter which shows in a qualitative way the relationships between speed, capacity, weight, and ratings of direct-current machines. These relationships are illustrated by curves prepared from the data on several lines of manufacturers' standard machines. Many specialized and modern applications of direct-current machines are treated in a chapter on "Special Direct-Current Dynamos and Applications."

The authors feel especially grateful to Professor D. C. Jackson, of Massachusetts Institute of Technology, for his constructive criticisms and suggestions made during the preparation of the manuscript. Many thanks are due to Professors C. E. Tucker and C. E. Lansil, of Massachusetts Institute of Technology, for their helpful suggestions regarding the contents and arrangement of the manuscript. The authors are appreciative of the courtesies of the General Electric Company, Westinghouse Electric and Manufacturing Company, and the Century Electric Company, in furnishing photographs, cuts, and data used in the preparation of the manuscript.

R. G. K.
J. L. B.
R. M. K.

Manhattan, Kansas
October, 1934

List of Symbols

a, paths in a winding.

A, cross-sectional area.

AT, ampere-turns.

B, flux density; sometimes number of commutator bars

B_m, maximum flux density.

cp, commutator pitch.

d, distance.

e, instantaneous voltage.

e_a, rotational emf in coil undergoing commutation.

e_i, instantaneous induced emf.

e_L, induced emf due to self-induction.

E, electromotive force.

E_g, generated emf.

E_m, potential in electromagnetic (cgs) units.

E_r, emf due to residual magnetism.

emf, electromotive force.

f, force; sometimes frequency cycles per second.

F, force; sometimes mmf.

g, conductance.

G_o, resultant conductance.

H, magnetizing force.

i, instantaneous current.

I, current (usually in amperes).

I_a, total armature current.

I_f, field current.

I_m, current in electromagnetic (cgs) units.

I_n, current in neutral.

K, constant, also used with subscripts to denote different constants.

K_h, constant of proportionality for hysteresis loss.

l, length.

L, self-inductance.

m, m', pole strengths.

M, mutual induction.

M_e, equivalent mutual inductance.

$mmf.$, magnetomotive force.

n, speed revolutions per second; sometimes per minute.

N, number of turns.

N_f, turns per pole on field.

N_s, series-field turns.

p, number of poles.

P, power.

P_e, eddy-current loss.

P_m, motor power in watts.

P_m', motor power in horsepower.

Q, quantity of electricity.

Q_m, quantity in electromagnetic (cgs) units.

$\mathcal{R}$, reluctance in the magnetic circuit.

R, resistance.

r, resistance; sometimes radius.

R_a, armature resistance; sometimes armature circuit resistance between points of shunt field connection.

R_{a_o}, armature circuit resistance including all fields in series with the armature but not the starting resistor.

R_c, resistance of commutating pole field.

R_f, field resistance.

R_m, resistance in electromagnetic (cgs) units.

R_o or r_o, resistance at 0 C.; sometimes initial resistance in a discussion; sometimes resultant resistance.

R_{rheo}, resistance of field rheostat.

R_s, series-field resistance.

r_s, total armature circuit resistance including any external resistor.

R_x, resistance of starting resistor.

RV, reactance voltage.

S, number of slots.

viii

t, time; sometimes thickness; sometimes temperature.

T, torque, for Z inductors.

T', torque, for one inductor.

T_c, time of commutation.

U, drop in magnetic potential.

v, velocity; sometimes instantaneous voltage.

V, difference of potential; sometimes terminal voltage; sometimes volume.

V_m, electromagnetic (cgs) unit of potential.

V_o', specific terminal voltage at no load.

w, energy; sometimes slot width.

W, weight; sometimes work; sometimes watts.

Y_b, back pitch.

Y_f, front pitch.

Z, inductors or conductors (total).

Z_a, conductors in series per path.

α, temperature coefficient of resistance; sometimes angle of brush shift from mechanical neutral.

δ, air gap radial length.

η, efficiency.

θ, angle.

λ, flux-linkages.

μ, permeability.

ρ, resistivity or specific resistance; sometimes distance to element (polar coordinates).

ϕ, flux.

ASA Graphical Symbols

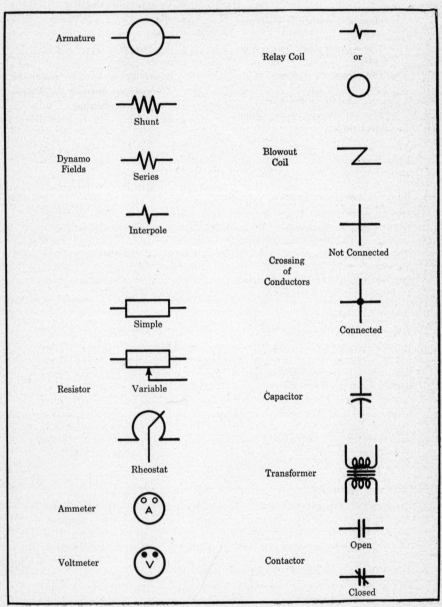

Armature

Shunt

Dynamo Fields — Series

Interpole

Resistor — Simple

Variable

Rheostat

Ammeter

Voltmeter

Relay Coil — or

Blowout Coil

Crossing of Conductors — Not Connected

Connected

Capacitor

Transformer

Open

Contactor

Closed

Contents

CONTENTS

Series, Parallel, and Series-Parallel Circuits—Kirchhoff's Laws—The Magnetic Circuit—Magnetomotive Force—Reluctance—Magnetization of Materials—Magnetization of Iron—Calculation of the Magnetic Circuit—The Magnetization Curve—Hysteresis Loop—B-H Curves—Hysteresis Loss—Eddy-Current Loss—Calculation of the Magnetic Circuit in Iron—Self Inductance—Mutual Inductance—Energy Stored in a Magnetic Field.

Direct-Current Machinery

CHAPTER I

The Dynamo

Definition. Machines called **dynamos** may be defined upon the basis of either use or construction. From the functional point of view, the dynamo is a rotating machine for converting mechanical energy into electrical energy, or the reverse process — electrical energy into mechanical energy. The first case represents electrical generating action and the dynamo so used is called a **generator.** In the second case, the dynamo is developing mechanical power and when so used is called a **motor.** From the structural point of view, a dynamo may be defined as a rotating machine which functions by producing a relative motion between electrical conductors and a magnetic field. The magnetic field structure may be stationary and the electrical conductors revolve, or the electrical conductors may be stationary and the magnetic field structure may revolve. It is also possible for both the conductors and the magnetic field to be in motion.

The induced emf and associated current in the active conductors of the ordinary type of dynamo are always alternating in direction.* Through the use of a commutator it is possible to make the electric current unidirectional in the external circuit of the dynamo. Dynamos are classified with respect to the kind of current external to the machine itself. If the dynamo operates from or delivers alternating current, it is termed an **alternating-current machine.** Conversely, if the current in the external circuit is unidirectional (or direct), the dynamo is called a **direct-current machine.** Fundamentally, the direct-current dynamo is an alternating-current machine with a commutating device. The addition of the commutator gives rise to certain differences in the operating characteristics and applications of the machine so that it has become customary to treat direct and alternating-current machines separately. This text will be confined to the discussion of direct-current machines.

The flux in the magnetic circuit of the dynamo may be produced by permanent magnets or electromagnets. Those machines using permanent magnets are called **magnetos.** Magnetos are small in size and capacity because of the

---

* The induced emf and associated current are not alternating in certain types known as acylic dynamos.

1

limited strength of permanent magnets. A large number of alternating-current magnetos are used for magneto telephone systems and ignition systems of gas engines. A smaller number of direct-current magnetos are used for various forms of speed-indicating devices.

The typical direct-current dynamo uses powerful stationary electromagnets for producing the fields. The conductors for the generation of the emf are carried on a rotating element called the **armature.** The field structure and the armature of an early Edison bipolar dynamo are illustrated in the frontispiece. The field electromagnets of this machine consisted of two long vertical spools of wire wound on iron cores. This form of large heavy electromagnet has been superseded by the more economical and efficient shape described in the following article.

Magnetic Circuit of a Dynamo. The magnetic circuit of a four-pole dynamo is illustrated in Fig. 1. The principal parts of the magnetic circuit are the poles, the field yoke, the armature core, and the air gap. The field yoke acts as a

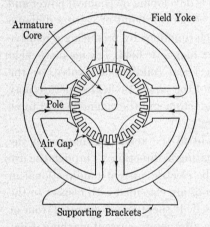

mechanical support for the poles and frequently also for the end pieces, which carry the bearings. Because of this mechanical function, the yoke and the supporting feet is called the **frame.** The path and direction of the flux through the magnetic circuit are indicated by the lines and arrows. It should be noted that the flux through each pole divides when passing through the yoke and the armature core. Thus, the flux which passes through the cross section of the yoke and the armature core is approximately one half that passing through the poles.

Fig. 1. Magnetic Circuit of a Dynamo.

The details of the magnetic circuit of a dynamo are illustrated in the cross-sectional view of Fig. 2. The yoke of dynamos has been constructed of cast iron, cast steel, and rolled steel. Cast iron was used for the frames of early machines in power-houses or any application where the weight of the heavy machine was not objectionable. Cast steel with its higher permeability later replaced cast iron for yokes. Since 1920, there has been a drift toward the use, of fabricated frames made of rolled steel for all except very large dynamos. Figures 3 and 4 show dynamos with cast and fabricated yokes respectively. Uniformity of the magnetic circuit is uncertain when castings are used because of the possibility of concealed blowholes and of embedded slag. The rolled-steel frame has a higher permeability as well as greater uniformity of

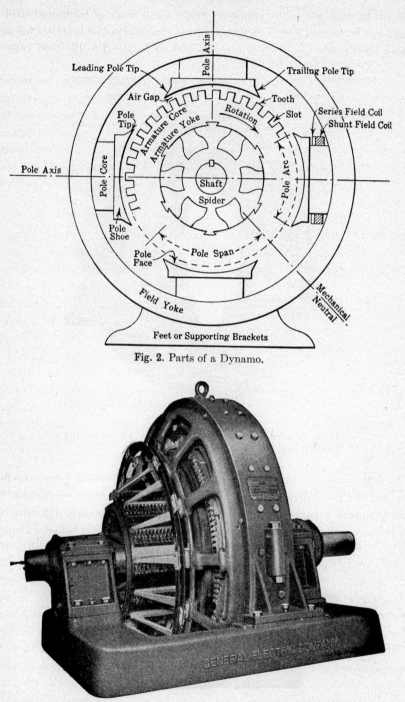

Fig. 2. Parts of a Dynamo.

Courtesy General Electric Company

Fig. 3. Dynamo with Cast Frame and Base and Bracket-Type Brush Mounting.

material. In some special dynamos the field yoke is made of laminated steel to permit quick changes in flux in the magnetic circuit. Feet or brackets for supporting the dynamo are usually integral with or fastened to the field yoke.

Courtesy Westinghouse Electric Corporation

Fig. 4. Dynamo with Rolled-Steel Frame, Compensating Windings and Interpoles.

In some early machines and in some small ones of recent years, the field yoke and the pole cores have been integral. Aside from these exceptions, the poles have been separate pieces attached to the yoke. The early dynamos had cast poles (usually cast steel) made in one piece. They gave satisfactory opera-

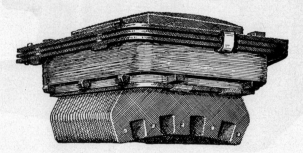

Fig. 5. Laminated Pole Core with Series and Shunt Field Coils.

tion when used with smooth-core armatures. The introduction of the slotted armature with a shorter air gap made it necessary to laminate the pole faces to reduce the eddy-current loss produced by the rapidly moving tufts of flux from the armature teeth. The earlier procedure was to fasten laminated pole shoes to a cast pole core. Later practice has shown it to be simpler and more economical to make the pole core and shoe integral and to make them of laminated steel, as shown in Fig. 5. The pole shoes spread out beyond the pole core to reduce the reluctance of the air gap, establish the desired flux distribution and to provide a mechanical support for the field coils. The smaller cross section of the pole core reduces the amount of copper required for the field coils. The tips of the pole shoes are termed **leading** and **lagging pole tips,** in accordance with the direction of rotation of the armature.

Courtesy Westinghouse Electric Corporation

Fig. 6. Laminated Steel Armature Core Being Assembled on a Cast-Iron Spider. Wedges Assure Alignment of Segments of Laminations.

Fig. 7. Assembled Armature Core and Spider.

The magnetic circuit through the armature consists of laminated steel, and is called the **armature core.** The laminations are necessary to limit the magnitude of the eddy currents which result from the rapid flux changes in the rotating armature. The outer surface of the laminated armature consists of teeth and slots as shown in Fig. 2 and Fig. 6. The part of the armature core at the base of the teeth is called the **armature yoke.** On small machines the armature punchings are circular disks which are keyed directly to the central shaft.

On large machines armature laminations are stamped complete or in segments and are fastened to a central spider either by dovetailing as shown in Fig. 6, or by other means as illustrated in Figs. 7 and 8. This construction represents a saving in laminated steel since all of the radial distance to the shaft yields a greater cross-sectional area of iron than is needed for the magnetic circuit. In addition, reductions in armature weight and cost are obtained. Also, because of providing better ventilation, the temperature rise of the machine is reduced.

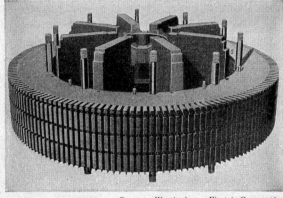

Courtesy Westinghouse Electric Corporation

Fig. 8. Laminated Steel Armature Core Being Assembled on a Fabricated Spider.

The space between the armature and the pole shoes is called the **air gap.** The radial length of the air gap is the distance from the top of the teeth to the pole face. This distance varies with the size of the machine and is of the order of $1/16$ to $\frac{1}{4}$ inch.

Field Coils. The flux for the magnetic circuit is provided by coils or spools of wire placed on the pole cores. These coils conform to the shape of pole cores (circular or rectangular) and are held in place by the poles, as shown in Fig. 5.

Fig. 9. Form-Wound Armature with Skewed Slots.

The field coils for a given dynamo are connected in series so that adjacent poles are of opposite polarity and the circuit so formed is called the **field circuit.** The field circuit may be connected in parallel with the armature (shunt field), or in series with the armature (series field). The field coils of the *shunt field* consist of many turns of wire of small cross section and have a relatively high resistance. The coils of the *series field* consist of a few turns of conductors of large cross section and have a low resistance. Figure 5 shows a shunt coil and a series coil mounted on a laminated pole core.

Armature Construction. The armature is the rotating unit of the direct-current dynamo. It consists of four principal parts, namely, the shaft, the iron core, the armature winding (conductors), and the commutator (see Figs. 9 and 10).

Fig. 10. Random-Wound Armature with Skewed Slots.

The armature laminations of the iron core are generally assembled so as to produce slots parallel to the shaft, as in Fig. 6. In some cases the laminations are assembled to produce skewed slots, as in Fig. 10. The latter construction reduces the changes in reluctance between the pole face and armature, and hence, causes the machine to be more quiet in operation. The armature conductors are wound into coils (see Chap. IV, Fig. 7) and placed in the slots of the armature core. The ends of these coils are connected to segments on the commutator. The conductors are held in the slots by bands of wire wrapped around the armature (Fig. 9), or by wedges driven into the slot (Fig. 10).

The Commutator. The commutator consists of a large number of copper segments which are insulated from each other and from the armature shaft. These segments (Fig. 11) are wedge-shaped, so that they may be assembled in the form of a cylinder. On the under side, the segments have two V notches, which serve for clamping the segments together and for holding them against the centrifugal forces due to rotation. The rising projection (*r*) is called the **riser** and its function is to connect to the ends of the armature coils. The parts of the commutator and their assembly can be visualized from the exploded view of Fig. 12. Beginning on the right of this figure, the first part is a cast-iron spider which is keyed to the shaft

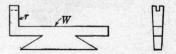

Fig. 11. Commutator Segment.

and which serves as the main support for the entire commutator. The second part from the right is a micanite V ring which insulates the commutator segments from the supporting spider. The next part is the assembly of commutator bars insulated from each other by micanite strips.

Fig. 12. Exploded View of Commutator.

These strips are usually undercut slightly so as to preclude the possibility of their projecting above the copper segments. High micanite strips cause the brushes to make poor contact with the copper segments, thereby causing arcing at the commutator.

The next part is a micanite cylinder which insulates the under side of the commutator bars from the supporting spider. The second part from the left is

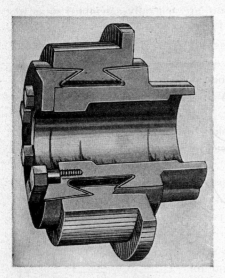

Fig. 13. Sectional View of Commutator.

another micanite V ring which insulates the segments from the clamping ring on the left side. The clamping ring on the extreme left is held to the supporting spider by cap screws or bolts. The complete assembly of a commutator is illustrated in Fig. 13.

Commutators for fractional horsepower dynamos are often made by molding the commutator segments into an insulating compound such as bakelite. In this case the insulating compound forms the insulation and the complete supporting base for the commutator.

If the commutator is long, the centrifugal forces may become so great as to cause the segments to bulge at the center. This weakness may be overcome by placing an insulated shrink ring upon the commutator, as shown in Fig. 14. This figure also shows two rows of ventilating fins soldered into the commutator bars to help reduce the temperature rise under load.

Brushes and Brush-Holding Mechanism. The current in the armature circuit is led to or from the machine through brushes which bear upon the commuta-

Fig. 14. Shrink-Ring on Commutator. Riser from Commutator Bars to Armature Coils Shown.

tor. These brushes are rectangular in form and are made of carbon or graphite, reinforced by other ingredients. On low-voltage machines brushes made of copper particles embedded in graphite are used. The brushes are held in position by brush holders like those illustrated in Figs. 15 and 16. The brush holder has a rectangular sleeve which serves as a guide for any radial motion of the

Fig. 15. Brush-Holder for Mounting on Stud.

brush resulting from the vibration or eccentricity of the armature. An adjustable spring on the brush holder bears on top of the brush and maintains the desired contact pressure of the brush upon the commutator. In some small dynamos, the current passes from the brush to the brush holder through the sliding contact between them and also through the spring which keeps the brush in contact with the commutator. The general practice, however, is to provide for a positive connection from the brush to brush holder through a flexible copper cable called a **brush shunt,** or a **"pig tail."** The brush shunt is supplied integral

with the brush and its free end has a terminal which can be attached to the brush holder.

The brush holders are held in position by various forms of mechanism. The average machine requires several brushes at each brush position in order to secure sufficient contact area to carry the full current rating of the machine. The brushes for each position are generally mounted on a brush-holder stud. A stud and its insulating members are illustrated in Fig. 17. The brush-holder stud and its assembled brush holders and brushes must be maintained in its proper position on the commutator by some adjustable mechanism. One form of such mechanism is the rocker arm illustrated

Fig. 16. Brush-Holder for Mounting on Bracket.

in Fig. 18. This figure shows three studs, each having four brush holders mounted on a rocker arm. A ring on the rocker arm usually fits in a circular groove on the bearing housing so that the rocker arm may be rocked or rotated to bring the brushes into the proper position where it may be clamped. In

Fig. 17. Brush Stud and Insulating Members.

Fig. 18. Rocker Arm for Four-Brush Studs.

large machines the brush-holder stud becomes too flexible, so that brush-holder brackets are used instead. Figure 19 shows a bracket with seven brush holders mounted in place on a bracket ring. The assembled construction of brackets and rings for another machine is illustrated in Fig. 20.

In some small machines the rocker arm is omitted. Here the brush-holder studs or the brush holder itself (where only one is required per position) is attached to but insulated from the frame or end housing of the dynamo.

Courtesy Westinghouse Electric Corporation

Fig. 19. Bracket with Seven Brush-Holders Mounted on a Bracket Ring.

PROBLEMS

1. Draw a cross-sectional view of a four-pole dynamo and label all parts.

2. Use a compound motor as an example and name all parts in the armature circuit in the order in which the current reaches the part, proceeding from the terminal board to the point in the armature where names of parts begin to repeat.

3. Why are pole cores usually made laminated instead of solid?

4. Why are risers generally used on large armatures instead of making connections of coil leads direct to the commutator bars?

5. Why were field coils formerly made round and now rectangular in periphery outline?

6. Why are field yokes frequently made of cast steel instead of cast iron, although the steel costs more per pound?

7. Why are brush shunts used? Would it not be cheaper to permit the current to flow directly from the brush holder into the side of the brush in all cases?

Courtesy Westinghouse Electric Corporation

Fig. 20. Brackets and Ring Mounted on Machine.

CHAPTER II

Dynamo Principles

Motor and Generator Action. The instantaneous emf induced in a conductor of length l moving with a velocity v within and perpendicular to a magnetic field of density B is

$$e = Blv \quad \text{[see 27, Appendix]} \tag{1}$$

Also the force on a conductor of length l when carrying a current i within and perpendicular to a magnetic field of density B is

$$f = Bil \quad \text{[see 17, Appendix]} \tag{2}$$

Dividing equation 1 by equation 2, yields

$$ei = fv \tag{3}$$

The left member of equation 3 represents electrical power while the right member represents mechanical power. Because of the reversible quality of the energy conversion as shown in equation 3 it is possible for the motion of armature conductors carrying current in a magnetic field to produce either generator or motor action. Therefore the same machine may operate as either a generator or motor and the amount of generator or motor action may be calculated in terms of either electrical or mechanical units. Quantitative calculations of these quantities are considered in detail in Chap. IX.

The Elementary Dynamo as a Motor. Since a conductor carrying a current in a magnetic field is acted upon by a force, an elementary motor may be formed by placing a single coil or loop of wire (two conductors) between the two poles of a magnet, as shown in Fig. 1. The coil is free to rotate about its central axis and its ends are connected to slip rings. The slip rings are connected through the brushes bb' to a battery. The potential of the battery will produce a current through

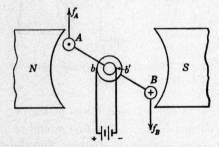
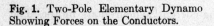

Fig. 1. Two-Pole Elementary Dynamo Showing Forces on the Conductors.

13

the closed circuit which will be "in" or toward the paper along conductor B and "out" from the paper along conductor A. The conductors A and B carrying current at right angles to the magnetic field between the poles N and S will be acted upon by forces. The application of any one of several rules (see Appendix, page 356) will show these forces to be in direction of

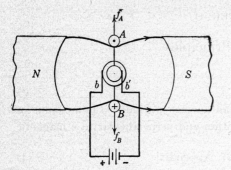

Fig. 2. Two-Pole Elementary Dynamo Showing Forces on the Conductors.

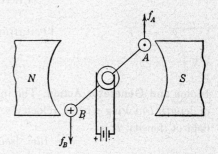

Fig. 3. Two-Pole Elementary Dynamo Showing Forces on the Conductors.

f_B and f_A. These two forces create a couple tending to rotate the coil clockwise. Since the coil is free, it will rotate until its plane becomes perpendicular to the magnetic field, as in Fig. 2. In this position the forces f_A and f_B still exist, but the couple is zero. If the coil structure has sufficient inertia, it will overrun this position and momentarily assume the one shown in Fig. 3. Here the forces remain unchanged in direction, but they are now producing a counter torque tending to restore the coil to the previously considered position of 2. Thus, if the coil has sufficient inertia, it may oscillate about and finally come to rest in the position of Fig. 2.

It is obvious that if the direction of current in the coil could be reversed at the instant the coil goes through the position of Fig. 2, the coil would continue

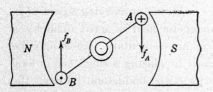

Fig. 4. Two-Pole Elementary Dynamo Showing Forces on Conductors.

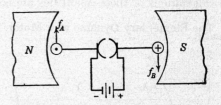

Fig. 5. Elementary Dynamo with a Two-Segment Commutator.

to rotate in the clockwise direction because of the reversed forces of Fig. 4. Such a reversal of current can be produced in two ways. The first would be through the use of an alternating-current source instead of a battery, and the dynamo would function as an alternating-current synchronous motor. The second method of reversing the current through the moving coil is to replace the slip rings with a commutator.*

Motor with Two-Segment Commutator. The coil of the elementary dynamo may be connected to two semi-circular segments insulated from each other as shown in Fig. 5. The forces f_A and f_B will cause the coil to rotate to the vertical position of Fig. 6. In this position the circuit to the coil has been opened and

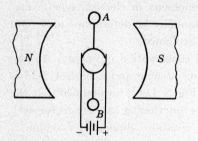

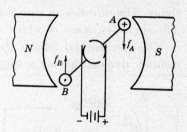

Fig. 6. Elementary Dynamo with a Two-Segment Commutator.

Fig. 7. Elementary Dynamo with Two-Segment Commutator with Armature in Position where Torque Is Produced.

no force is exerted upon the conductors. If the coil has sufficient inertia, it will move on to a new position, such as that shown in Fig. 7, where each commutator segment is touching the other brush. Here the direction of current through the coil has been reversed, the direction of the electromagnetic forces upon the conductor has been reversed, and the moment of the forces continues the clockwise rotation. After a half revolution from the position of Fig. 6, the commutator will open the circuit again and will be ready to return the current to its original direction through the coil. Thus, the two-segment commutator and a single coil may produce continuous rotation with intermittent torque. The two positions of zero torque in each revolution are objectionable since they present two "dead" positions for starting and are likely to make the motor noisy. It is apparent from Fig. 6 that a short circuit (zero resistance) between the brushes may occur if both brushes should be permitted to touch the same commutator segment at the same time. These objections can be eliminated by using several coils in series instead of one, and by having them distributed throughout 360 degrees. More commutator segments will be required, the torque will be more nearly continuous and uniform, and the danger of a direct short circuit through the commutator will be eliminated.

The Elementary Dynamo as a Generator. A conductor moving across a magnetic field has an emf generated in it equal to

$$E = BlvN10^{-8}. \qquad\qquad [(29), \text{Page } 362.]$$

* The word "commutator" is derived from the Latin word *mutare*, meaning "to change."

If the flux linking a coil of wire changes, an emf will be induced in that coil in accordance with the equation

$$E = -N \frac{d\phi}{dt} 10^{-8}.$$ [31, Page 362.]

The determination of the direction of the induced emf in any conductor or coil is very important in analyzing the phenomena in electromagnetic machines. The direction of each emf in a dynamo may be determined in several different ways, some of which will now be explained.

The first method follows the law of the conservation of energy. An elementary dynamo having a single loop or coil of wire and a bipolar field is

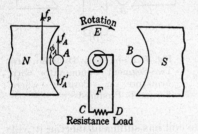

Fig. 8. Elementary Dynamo for Determining Direction of Induced Emf.

shown in Fig. 8. Let it be assumed that the dynamo is functioning as a generator with clockwise rotation. Since the machine is delivering energy, according to the law of conservation of energy, it must receive an equal or greater amount of energy. To receive energy a mechanical force f_A must be applied in the direction of rotation in order to overcome the force f_A' caused by electromagnetic action between the field flux and armature current. From Newton's third law of motion a force of f_p equal and opposite to f_A' must act on the north pole N. By definition, the direction of a magnetic field is the direction in which a north pole is urged. Hence the current established in conductor A by generator action is producing an encircling field in the direction of ϕ_A or f_p. The application of Ampere's right-hand rule shows that such a clockwise field is produced by a current "into the paper" or away from the observer. Since the current in a generator is driven by the induced emf, the direction of the induced emf for conductor A must be "into" the page.

The second method of determining the direction of the emf depends on Lenz's law. Figure 9 shows the elementary generator for the same conditions as in the previous example. The slip rings and the load have been omitted for the sake of simplifying the drawing. In the position shown, no flux from the field links the coil AB. As the coil turns clockwise from this position, flux from

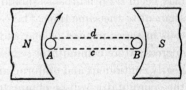

Fig. 9. Elementary Generator.

the field NS will begin to link the coil AB in the direction from side c to d. This change in flux linkages will induce an emf and current in such a direction as to oppose the change in linkages (*Lenz's law*). Such a current must be "*in*" at conductor A and "*out*" at B. The induced emf must have the same direction as the induced current and this deduction checks the one obtained by the first method.

A third method of determining the direction of the emf makes use of the electron theory of electricity. Under this theory an **electric current** is a *movement of electrons* in the circuit. However, the electrons move in a direction opposite to the conventional direction of current in electric circuits. Hence, while *protons* (positive charges of electricity) do not move in solids, it is proper to say that the conventional direction of an electric current is the direction in which a proton is *urged*. Similarly, the direction of an induced emf may be defined as the direction in which a proton is urged.

The electron theory can be applied to this problem by fixing attention on a single isolated proton which exists as a part of conductor A in Fig. 9. As this proton is carried upward by the rotation of the coil AB, it constitutes an electric current having the direction and path shown by the arrow. This current will produce a magnetic field around itself which, according to Ampere's right-hand rule, will urge the north pole N outward from the paper. The reaction to this force upon the proton itself must be *"in"* toward the paper, and this by definition is the direction of the current flow, and hence of the induced emf.

The three methods just given form the fundamental bases for obtaining the direction of an induced voltage. In many cases some of these methods may be difficult to apply and a fourth or *conventional method* will be added. This conventional method is justified only by the fact that it is simple, easy to apply, and always yields correct results.

The application of this method makes a fictitious assumption that the lines of force in the magnetic field may be likened to stretched rubber bands, as illustrated in Fig. 10. To determine the direction of the induced emf, note that the *motion of the conductor A* will cause the lines (bands) to be bent or distorted around the conductor. Now grasp the conductor with the fingers of the right hand bent around the conductor in the same direction as the distorted flux. The extended thumb will indicate the direction of the induced emf. One must be certain to conceive the mechanical distortion of the flux as being due to motion of the conductors and not that caused by electromagnetic action.

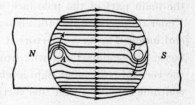

Fig. 10. Fictitious Distortion of Field for Determination of Direction of Induced Emf by a Conventional Method.

Another method of determining the direction of induced emf is known as **Fleming's right-hand rule.** The forefinger, middle finger, and thumb of the right hand are extended in such a way as to make them mutually perpendicular. Then if the forefinger is pointed in the direction of the flux, the thumb in the direction of motion of the *conductor*, the middle finger will point in the direction of the induced emf. If the left hand is used and the middle finger pointed in the direction of current flow in the conductor, the rule is applicable to motor operation.

Generated or Counter Emf. The coil and field poles representing motor action in Fig. 1 are identical with those representing generator action in Fig. 8. Since the rotation is in the same direction and the conductors are moving in similar magnetic fields, an emf is induced in the conductor A of Fig. 1 in the same direction as in Fig. 8. The induced emf is into the paper, and hence opposite or counter to the flow of current, which is out of the paper in Fig. 1. The induced emf is also opposite or counter to the impressed voltage drop which is the voltage driving the current in the conductor. These facts give rise to the term **counter** or **back emf** for the generated emf when a dynamo is acting as a motor. A study of the preceding relations shows that a change from motor to generator action for the *same* direction of rotation and polarity of the field is due only to a *reversal* of armature current. In the generator, the current flows in the direction of the induced emf, while in the motor it is opposite.

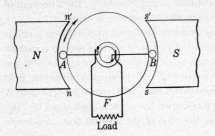

Fig. 11. Elementary Alternating-Current Generator.

The Direct-Current Generator.

The typical direct-current dynamo has an armature with an iron core and an air gap which is fairly uniform in the vicinity of the center of the pole and which becomes larger as the pole tips are approached. This construction gives a nearly uniform flux distribution under the main part of the pole face with a reduction in the flux at the pole tips. Under these conditions the elementary dynamo of Fig. 11 will have a uniform emf induced in its conductors A and B while they are moving under the pole faces. This induced emf will drop to zero when the conductor moves through the vertical position at right angles to that shown in Fig. 11. As the conductors continue clockwise past this vertical position, they cut the field flux in the op-

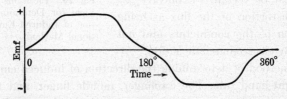

Fig. 12. Emf Wave Impressed on Load of Elementary Generator of Fig. 11.

posite direction and the induced emf reverses in direction. The reversed direction of the emf continues until the conductor A reaches the bottom of the figure, where it falls to zero and then reverses to its original direction as the clockwise rotation continues. Thus, the induced emf for the coil AB will be an alternating emf inside of the coil and also in the external circuit if slip rings are used. A picture of the emf induced in the conductor A for a single revolution beginning with the coil at position F, is given in Fig. 12. The current flowing in the load resistance would be of the same alternating form as the induced emf. The induced current and the terminal potential may be made unidirectional or direct in the external or load circuit by the addition of a two-segment commutator described earlier in this chapter. Such a commutator is illustrated in Fig. 13. It will change the potential in the external circuit to the form illustrated in Fig. 14. The load current will be pulsating and will have two zero values for each revolution of the coil.

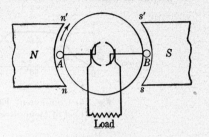

Fig. 13. Elementary Direct-Current Generator.

A new coil CD may be added to the armature at right angles to AB, as shown in Fig. 15. If this coil is provided with a separate two-segment commu-

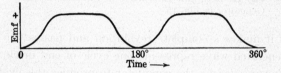

Fig. 14. Emf Wave Impressed on Load of Elementary Generator of Fig. 13.

tator and parallel brushes, it will generate an emf which is out of time-phase with that of coil AB. Thus, when the emf of coil AB is zero, that of CD will be at a maximum, and vice versa. The potentials produced by these coils with separate commutators are pictured in Fig. 16. The commutators of coils AB and CD may be connected in series to produce the resultant potential in the external circuit, as shown in Fig. 17. This new wave form is unidirectional, has no zero values, and has twice as many ripples as that of Fig. 14. Hence it is much superior to the latter form. The ripples or pulsations can be reduced in magnitude (and increased in number) by adding many more coils on the armature, by connecting them in series, and by distributing them uniformly around the periphery of the armature, as explained in a subsequent chapter. This construction will give a smooth current wave form and a smooth voltage wave form in the external circuit. Thus, it appears that a direct-current dynamo must have a commutator and the armature conductors should be uniformly distributed around its periphery.

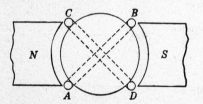

Fig. 15. Elementary Direct-Current Generator Having Two Armature Coils at Right Angles.

Electrical and Mechanical Degrees. The complete circle about a point represents 360 mechanical degrees. **Mechanical degrees** are measured by the arc
swept out in a plane. The conductor A in Fig. 11 generates the voltage wave

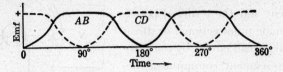

Fig. 16. Component Emf Waves in External Circuit of
Each Coil of Generator in Fig. 15.

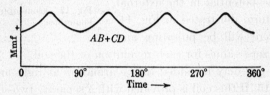

Fig. 17. Resultant Emf Wave in External Circuit of
Generator in Fig. 15.

of Fig. 12 as it makes a complete revolution and passes two complete pole
spans. The generated wave represents one cycle of emf or current generated
and the distance moved by the conductor to produce this cycle is called 360
electrical degrees. In the case cited, 360 electrical degrees are equal to 360
mechanical degrees. A dynamo having four poles would produce two complete
electrical cycles in a single revolution. Thus, there would be $2 \times 360 = 720$
electrical degrees in a single revolution through 360 mechanical degrees.

A conductor must pass two poles to produce a cycle. Hence the number of
electrical degrees per revolution is as follows:

$$\frac{\text{Electrical degrees}}{\text{Revolution}} = \frac{\text{poles}}{2} \times 360.$$

PROBLEMS

1. Base your argument upon the law of conservation of energy and find the direction
of emf generated in Fig. 18.

2. Use the proton theory as a basis of argument and find the direction of emf in Fig. 18.

3. Which way are electrons urged in Fig. 18? Adapt the argument of Prob. 2 to this
case and show all steps in the argument in logical sequence.

4. Find the direction of emf in Fig. 19 while the coil is moving from position a to
position b.

5. After switch S is closed in Fig. 20 and while the battery current is being established,
which end, A or B, of the resistance has positive potential? Give your reasoning in
logical sequence.

6. Let switch S in Fig. 20 be closed until the current becomes steady. Then open switch S and determine by a process of reasoning whether A or B is the positive end of the resistance. Make your argument independent of the conclusion found in Prob. **5.**

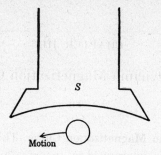

Fig. 18. See Problems 1, 2 and 3.

7. The earth's magnetic field at a certain location dips 60 degrees below the horizontal and the horizontal projection of the field vector deviates 15 degrees east of north.

a. A power line carries a current horizontally due north. Find the precise direction in which the wire is urged by the earth's field.

b. A power line carries a current horizontally due west. Find the precise direction in which the wire is urged by the earth's magnetic field.

c. If a horizontal north and south wire swings east, what is the direction of the emf generated?

d. Is there any direction in which a north and south wire might be moved parallel to itself without producing any emf? If there is, describe the motion precisely.

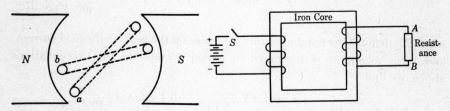

Fig. 19. See Problem 4.   **Fig. 20.** See Problems 5 and 6.

8. A reciprocating engine causes a 12-pole generator armature to oscillate 2 mechanical degrees from its average position based upon uniform motion. What is the oscillation in electrical degrees?

CHAPTER III

The Dynamo Magnetization Curve

Definition of the Dynamo Magnetization Curve. The magnitude of the emf generated by a dynamo is determined by the equation

$$E = Z_a \frac{\Delta\phi}{\Delta t} 10^{-8}, \text{volts} \qquad [31, \text{page } 362, 363],$$

where Z_a is the effective number of inductors per path in the armature, $\Delta\phi$ is the flux per pole in maxwells or lines, and Δt is the time in seconds required for the armature to turn the distance of one pole span. For any given machine operated at constant speed, Z_a and Δt are of constant value; hence the emf generated depends directly upon the flux per pole $\Delta\phi$. The flux per pole, in turn, depends upon the magnetomotive force of the field winding and the reluctance of the magnetic circuit. Thus,

$$\Delta\phi = \frac{\text{mmf}}{\mathcal{R}} = \frac{0.4 \; \pi N_f I_f}{\mathcal{R}} \qquad [55, \text{page } 372],$$

where N_f denotes the number of turns per pole on the field, I_f the field current, and $\mathcal{R}$ the reluctance of the magnetic circuit. Combining the two equations above, we find

$$E = Z_a \frac{\Delta\phi}{\Delta t} 10^{-8} = \frac{Z_a}{\Delta t} \frac{0.4 \; \pi N_f I_f}{\mathcal{R}} 10^{-8} = \frac{0.4 \; \pi Z_a N_f I_f}{\mathcal{R}\Delta t} 10^{-8} \text{ volts} \qquad (1)$$

For a dynamo running at constant speed all of the terms in equation 1 except I_f and $\mathcal{R}$ are constant. The magnetic circuit of a dynamo consists of a short air gap and relatively long paths through iron. The reluctance of the air gaps are constant but the reluctance of the iron portion of the path varies with the field-flux density which is produced by the field current I_f. Therefore, the relation which exists between the generated emf and the field current or excitation is not a linear one. *The dynamo magnetization curve is the graph which shows the relationship between the emf generated by the armature and the field excitation produced by the field current.* This curve is often called the **saturation curve** of a dynamo, and is sometimes referred to as the no-load characteristic of a dynamo.

22

A magnetization or saturation curve for increasing field currents of a commercial dynamo is shown in Fig. 1. This curve has a trend similar to the $B-H$ curves for iron. However, there is a decided difference in both the function and the exact trend of the two types of curves. The $B-H$ curves cover a single sample of iron in which the cross section is constant, the flux density is uniform, and the magnetizing force per unit of length is constant throughout the specimen. As a complete contrast, the magnetization curve of a dynamo covers a path made partly of air and partly of different grades of iron, a path of varying cross section, a path of varying flux densities, and a path of varying magnetizing force per unit of length.

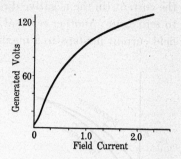

Fig. 1. No-Load Saturation or Magnetization Curve of a Generator.

Sometimes it is desirable to plot the magnetization curve to other coordinates than those shown in Fig. 1. Thus, since E is proportional to the flux per pole, the latter may be used for ordinates in the place of E. Calculations for the design of the excitation of fields are usually made in terms of ampere-turns, so that this unit is often substituted for field amperes as abscissa.

Experimental Determination of the Magnetization Curve. The magnetization curve of a dynamo which has been assembled and completed for service can be determined experimentally by means of the circuit shown in Fig. 2. The dynamo is driven at constant speed by some source of mechanical power. The reversing switch is placed in one position and the field rheostat is varied from zero to a maximum by small steps. Simultaneous readings of field current (A)

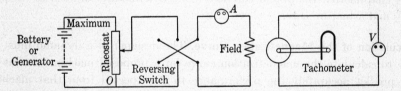

Fig. 2. Connections for Experimental Determination of Magnetization Curve of a Generator.

and generated volts (V) are taken for each step. The data thus obtained will give the necessary points for plotting the magnetization curve. If the field current is decreased in steps after reaching the maximum value, the descending curve for these decreasing values will be above that due to rising values, as shown in Fig. 3. The higher curve for the decreasing values is due to the hysteresis in the iron or the lagging of the flux behind the magnetizing force produced by the field current.

A complete cycle of magnetization of the field of the dynamo may be secured by reversing the field current after it comes back to zero, then increasing the current (in the negative direction) to its maximum, and then decreasing it to zero again. Another reversal to the original direction and an increase of the field current in steps to a maximum will give the complete hysteresis loop.

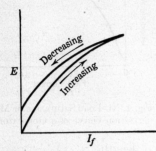

Fig. 3. Hysteresis Effect on Magnetization Curve when Obtained by Increasing and then Decreasing the Field Current.

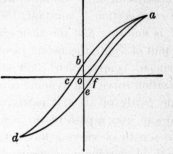

Fig. 4. Magnetization Curve and Complete Hysteresis Loop.

The complete hysteresis loop shown in Fig. 4 is *abcdefa*. In order to avoid errors caused by the hysteresis effect, the field current should be changed continuously in one direction from *o* to *a*, then from *a* to *bcd*, and also from *d* to *efa*.

The area of the hysteresis loop described above gives no indication of the losses in the dynamo. While the form of the hysteresis loop depends to a considerable extent upon the hysteresis of the iron in the pole core and yoke, no losses occur in these parts of a properly designed dynamo. It will be shown in a later chapter that the iron or core losses of a dynamo are confined to the pole faces and armature core.

Calculation of the Magnetization Curve. The designer of a dynamo must be able to calculate the magnetization curve for a proposed machine so that he can predict accurately the performance to be expected from that machine when it has been built. Before studying the details of any method of making calculations in many types of practical problems, it should be recognized that exact solutions of many such problems are impossible. In many instances, it is necessary to make certain approximations and simplifying assumptions. Just what is done in any case may be based upon experience, results of tests, standard practice, or simply the judgment of the engineer. In these cases it is reasonable to expect the methods and practices of various engineers to differ. These differences when based upon sound and reasonable judgment cause little variation in the over-all results. The calculation of the magnetization curve of a dynamo is a problem of this nature. One method along with certain simplifying assumptions that have been used to yield reasonable results will be outlined.

The first question to be decided when making calculations in magnetic circuits involving iron concerns which relation between B and H should be used since the value of H for some given value of B depends upon the previous magnetic history of the iron. Unless there is a specific reason for doing otherwise, it is customary to base calculations on the *normal B–H* curves (see page 380).

The calculations for the magnetization curve of a dynamo require a knowledge of the rating of the dynamo and a complete set of physical dimensions of the proposed magnetic circuit. The general method of procedure is to divide the magnetic circuit into its component parts, such as the armature

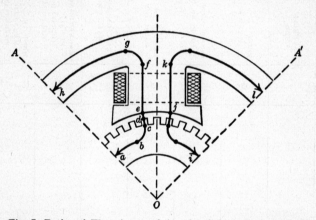

Fig. 5. Paths of Flux Assumed for the Calculation of Mmf Required to Produce a Given Flux in the Magnetic Circuit of a Dynamo.

yoke, teeth, air gap, pole core, and field yoke, and then to determine consecutively for each part the total flux, the cross section, the length of path, the flux density, the magnetizing field, and the magnetomotive force. These quantities can be visualized better through reference to a section of the magnetic circuit, as shown in Fig. 5, and the steps can be more readily understood and carried out through the use of a tabular form, as shown in Table I.

The following steps should be taken in calculating the magnetization curve.

1. An emf is assumed and the corresponding flux per pole is calculated from equation 30, page 362, or from equation 8, page 65. The value of flux thus calculated is the flux per pole which links the armature coils and is effective in the generation of the emf. This flux passes through the armature coils, through the armature teeth, and through the air gap. Therefore, it is entered opposite these items as they appear in Table I. Only one half of this flux is

entered in the table opposite "armature yoke" because the flux from the pole is assumed to divide equally, as indicated in Fig. 5.

The flux through the pole cores and field yokes is equal to the flux through the armature plus the flux which leaks between the pole tips. The ratio of this combined flux through the pole cores to that through the armature coils is called the **coefficient of leakage,** or the **dispersion coefficient.** This ratio varies from 1.05 for large modern machines with short pole cores to 1.25 for small

TABLE I

PORTION OF MAGNETIC CIRCUIT	MATERIAL USED	(1) FLUX (MAXWELLS) ϕ	(2) CROSS SECTION OF PATH (CM.²) A	(3) LENGTH OF PATH (CM.) l	(4) FLUX DENSITY (MAX./CM.²) $B = \dfrac{\phi}{A}$	(5) MAGNETIZING FIELD (OERSTEDS) OR (GILB./CM.) H	(6) DROP IN MAGNETIC POTENTIAL (GILBERTS) $U = Hl$	
Arm. yoke								
Arm. teeth								
Air gap								
Pole core								
Field yoke								
						Total drop =		Gilberts

machines. Therefore the pole-core flux is determined by multiplying the effective flux through the armature coils by the coefficient of dispersion. One half of this pole-core flux goes through each arm of the field yoke, as indicated in Fig. 5.

2. The cross section of each part of the magnetic circuit is determined from the physical dimensions of the proposed machine. The cross section of the armature yoke is the distance from the bottom of the slots to the armature spider multiplied by the net axial length of *iron* in the armature (over-all length minus space occupied by ventilating ducts and any scale or insulation on lamination.)

The cross section of the teeth will include only those teeth or fractions of teeth which are under one equivalent pole face. The average width of each tooth between the root and the face of the tooth will be assumed as a fair approximation to the effective width. Because of fringing at the edges of the pole face the equivalent pole face is larger than the actual. To account in an

approximate way for this fringing, the equivalent pole face will be considered
to have the dimensions shown in Fig. 6.

The axial length of the tooth is the net axial
length of the armature iron (over-all length minus
ventilating ducts minus total space occupied by
any oxide or insulation on the laminations). Hence
the cross section of the teeth is:

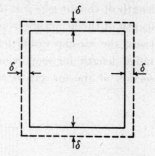

(Teeth under equivalent pole face) x (average
   width of tooth) x (net axial length of armature).

The proper value to use for the cross section of
the air gap is very difficult to determine accurately on account of the irregularities produced by
the slots and ventilating ducts. The manner in
which the flux fringes around the teeth is illustrated in Fig. 7. Obviously, it would not be proper
to take the entire pole face as the area of the air

Fig. 6. Full Lines Represent
Radial Projection of Actual
Pole Face on the Armature
Core. Dotted Lines Show
Equivalent Pole Face to
Account Approximately for
Fringing. δ Is the Radial
Length of Air Gap.

gap nor would it be correct to take the area of the face of the teeth. If
the teeth and slots are about equal in width, and the air gap is about one
third of the slot width (which is near the usual proportions), it will be
satisfactory to imagine that each tooth is increased in width on each side
by one third of the air gap and then assume that the flux passes in parallel

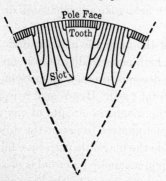

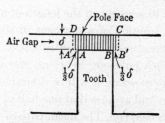

Fig. 7. Approximate Distribu-
tion of Flux in Air Gap Showing
Tufting or Fringing at Armature
Teeth.

Fig. 8. Imaginary Increase of
Tooth Width for the Determination of Air Gap Cross-Section.

lines across the gap opposite this imaginary tooth. This assumption is illustrated in Fig. 8. If there are ventilating ducts in the armature the flux will
fringe at the edges of the iron bordering these ducts. This also tends to increase the cross section of the air gap. For purposes of determining the air-gap
cross section one might imagine the iron at the ventilating ducts increased

by one third of the air-gap radial length as suggested in Fig. 9, and then to imagine the flux passing from pole to armature along parallel lines. The axial length of the air gap will then be approximated by adding to the gross axial length of the armature iron minus the total axial length of ventilating ducts, twice the air-gap radial length (see Fig. 6), plus two thirds of the air-gap radial length for each ventilating duct (see Fig. 9.) The equivalent cross section of the air gap is then the axial length as defined above times the

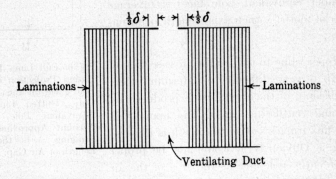

Fig. 9. Imaginary Increase of Iron at a Ventilating Duct for Calculating Air Gap Cross-Section.

number of teeth under the equivalent pole face (see Fig. 6) multiplied by the width $A'B'$ for the equivalent tooth shown in Fig. 8.

The cross sections of the pole core and the field yoke are calculated directly from the physical dimensions.

3. The lengths of the various sections of the magnetic path are difficult to determine accurately, but on account of the high permeability of iron, an error of 5 or 10 per cent in the length of a section does not produce an error of more than a fraction of a per cent in the final total result. Hence any reasonable approximation will be satisfactory. Since the magnetic circuits of the north and south poles are in series, and the magnetomotive forces of the adjacent coils are in series, it will be desirable to divide the magnetic path by a line OA (Fig. 5) and assume that one half of the drop in magnetic potential is produced by each field coil. The mean path of the flux is represented by the lines $abcdefgh$ or $ijkl$.

The mean length of the path in the armature is taken as abc. The arc ab has the armature axis O as a center. The point c is at the bottom of the slots and in a midway position beneath the left half of the pole face. The arc cb has a radius of one half the depth of the armature yoke.

The length of the air gap is the distance from the pole face to the armature teeth (de). The length of the pole core is taken as fe in Fig. 5. The length of the field yoke is taken as hgf. The arc hg is along the mean radius for the field yoke, and the arc gf is on a radius equal to one half the thickness of the field yoke.

4. The flux density in each part of the magnetic circuit is determined directly from the calculations in parts 1 and 2. Thus $B = \phi/A$.

5. The magnetizing force H for each of the iron portions of the magnetic circuit is obtained from the $B–H$ curves (Fig. 24, Appendix) corresponding to the value of B (part 4) and the particular material used. The value for H in the air gap is numerically equal to B and is expressed in gilberts-per-centimeter for the metric system. The magnetizing force in the air gap is 0.313 B ampere turns per inch for the English system of measurement.

6. The drop in magnetic potential for each portion of the magnetic circuit is the product of the magnetizing force H and the length of path l. The sum of all the drops in potential gives the total drop in potential, which must be balanced by the magnetomotive force of the coil on each pole.

7. The preceding steps give the method for determining the mmf per pole to produce a flux which will generate the assumed value of emf. Several other values of emf may be assumed and like calculations completed. The results of these calculations will give the field mmf's corresponding to the generated emf's and make available the necessary data for plotting the magnetization curve.

Shape of the Magnetization Curve. The shape of the magnetization curve has an important bearing on the characteristics of the dynamo. The shape of the curve can be controlled through the selection of materials and by the dimensions of the magnetic circuit, as indicated by the various components of the magnetization curve in Fig. 10. The emf is proportional to the flux, and, since the air gap does not become saturated, the ampere-turns required for it will be directly proportional to the flux, as shown by line OA. The ampere-turns required for the other portions of the magnetic circuit must be added to get the resultant magnetization curve. The curve usually consists of three parts: a lower portion which is approximately straight, a central portion

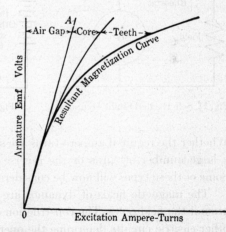

Fig. 10. Ampere-Turns Required for the Components of the Normal Magnetization Curve.

having considerable curvature caused by the approach to saturation of some portion of the magnetic circuit, and the upper portion which is nearly straight. Since the permeability of iron at low flux densities is very high, the magnetization curve in its lower part comes very close to the line OA, which represents the air gap only. This may be illustrated by the case of a dynamo with an air gap of 0.15 inch and an iron portion of the magnetic circuit 20.0 inches long with a permeability of 1000 at low flux densities. The drop in magnetic potential in the iron is equivalent to 20 inches divided by the permeability, or 20/1000 or 0.02 inch of air. Thus, the drop in the air gap is 0.15/0.17, or 88 per cent of the total drop in magnetic potential.

The slope of the lower part of the magnetization curve is determined primarily by the width of the air gap. The point of maximum curvature on the curve is called the **knee of the curve.** The portion of the curve far above the knee approaches a slope equal to that which would be produced by an air-cored circuit. A dynamo operating at the densities represented by this slope is said to be saturated. The iron part of the circuit determines primarily the shape of the upper part of the magnetization curve.

Forms of Dynamo Excitation. The previous discussion has shown how to determine the ampere-turns required to produce a certain flux in a dynamo.

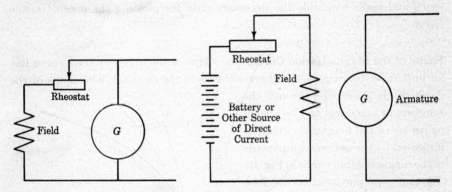

Fig. 11. Self-Excited Shunt Dynamo.   **Fig. 12.** Separately-Excited Dynamo.

Whether the required ampere-turns are secured by using a small current with a large number of turns or the reverse depends upon the type of dynamo. Some of these types will now be considered.

The magnetic fields of dynamos are produced or excited by coils placed around the field poles. The construction of these coils and their connection to other electric circuits determine the operating characteristics of the machine. One type of field coil has many turns of relatively small wire, has high resistance, and is designed to have normal line potential impressed across its circuit. This type of coil is connected "in shunt" or in parallel with the armature or a supply line, as shown in Fig. 11. Fields of this type are called **shunt fields** and machines using these fields exclusively are called **shunt dynamos.**

Instead of receiving excitation current from the dynamo of which it is a part, the field may be excited from an entirely separate source, as illustrated in Fig. 12. Such sources as a battery, rectifier, another machine, and the like may be used. A dynamo excited in this manner is called a **separately excited dynamo.**

Some field coils are designed to be connected in series with the armature, as shown in Fig. 13. These coils are called **series-field coils** and the dynamo using this form of field exclusively is called a **series dynamo.** Series-field coils are wound with relatively few turns of conductor of large cross section and they have a low resistance.

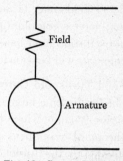

Fig. 13. Series Dynamo.

Many dynamos use a combination of a shunt and a series field upon their poles, as illustrated in Fig. 14, 1 and 2. This combination gives rise to the terms **compound field** and **compound dynamo.** In part 1 of Fig. 14, the shunt field is connected in parallel with the armature only, and the connection is called the **short-shunt connection.** In part 2 of the same figure, the shunt field is connected in parallel with a circuit consisting of both the armature and the series field; this gives rise to the term **long-shunt compound connection.** There is very little difference in the operating characteristics of the short-shunt and long-shunt connections. The short-shunt generator is probably the more common, since it causes less complication in the switchboard circuits.

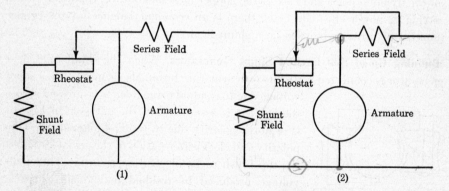

Fig. 14. (1) Short-Shunt Compound Dynamo. (2) Long-Shunt Compound Dynamo.

The compound dynamo may be classified on the basis of the relative direction of the excitation produced by the series and the shunt fields. If the series field is connected so that its mmf will be in the same direction as that of the shunt field, the machine is said to be *cumulatively compounded,* and the machine is called a **cumulative compound dynamo.** A series field connected so as to oppose the shunt field gives rise to the term **differential compound dynamo.**

The field coils of a dynamo may be self-excited or separately-excited. Figure 11 illustrates a self-excited shunt dynamo. If the machine is acting as a generator, the armature is supplying the current for energizing the field, while under motor action the same source of potential is applied to both the armature and the shunt field circuit. The separately excited dynamo (Fig. 12) has its field excited from a source entirely independent of the armature circuit. Series fields may be separately excited in special cases, and a single machine may have a combination of self and separate excitation of its fields. The form of excitation used has an important bearing on the characteristics of the machine, as will be shown in a later chapter.

Field Turns and Current. The ampere-turns required for a field pole can be obtained with a large current and a small number of turns, or vice versa. In a series dynamo, where the series field carries the same current as the armature, the number of turns required is the quotient of the ampere-turns required divided by the full-load current. In the case of the shunt dynamo the field is in parallel with the armature and there is no definite restriction regarding the number of turns since the product of ampere-turns may be secured by an infinite number of combinations of coil turns and field current. However, the field is subject to the full-line potential and the power lost in the field is the product of line potential times field current. It is desirable to keep this loss small, so that a large number of field turns with a relatively high resistance is used. However, as the number of field turns is increased indefinitely, the length of the dynamo poles and cost of the copper increases out of proportion to the saving in power effected. Thus, there is an economic balance for the proper number of turns to be used on a shunt field.

Building Up of Self-Excited Shunt Generators. When the shunt field of a generator is connected across its own armature terminals, as in Fig. 15, a small

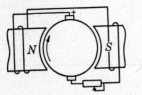

Fig. 15. Self-Excited Shunt Dynamo.

voltage due to residual magnetism is impressed across the field. It is assumed that the left pole in Fig. 15 is of north polarity due to residual magnetism. This polarity and clockwise rotation of the armature cause the top brush to be of positive polarity. The small voltage produced by residual magnetism causes a small current to flow through the field turns which, in turn, causes an mmf that acts upon the residual flux of the field. As indicated in Fig. 15, a proper connection of the field across the armature terminals will cause this mmf to assist the residual magnetism. If the resistance of the field winding is sufficiently low for the speed at which the dynamo is running, the field flux will be increased. This increase of flux causes an increase in the generated emf, which, in turn, causes an increase in field current, more flux, and hence a further increase in the generated voltage. This process, called **building up of a generator,** is cumulative and continues to a point of equilibrium. Equilibrium will be reached when the generated voltage causes a current in the field which corresponds to the exact excitation required for the generation of this emf. More can be learned about this process by considering a magnetization curve and a field-resistance line or excitation line, as shown in Fig. 16.

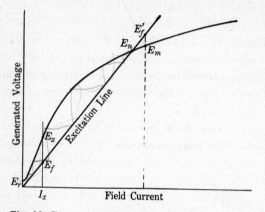

Fig. 16. Construction Illustrating the Building-Up Process of a Shunt Generator.

Since the building-up process starts with residual magnetism and proceeds in the direction of increasing potentials across the field, the ascending branch of the magnetization curve will be used in all discussions relating to the building up of generators. The excitation line is plotted from the equation

$$I_f = \frac{E_f}{R_f},$$

where R_f is the total field resistance including that of the rheostat. This is a straight line passing through the origin. The residual magnetism causes the generation of a voltage E_r which sets up a current in the field. This field current produces a flux which is added to the residual magnetism and thus generates a voltage greater than E_r. Of any instantaneous voltage E_x impressed on the field, E_f is sufficient to overcome the field-resistance drop due to I_x, and the difference $E_x - E_f$ is available for accelerating and increasing the field current. As long as any difference exists between E_x and E_f, the field current will continue to increase. The accelerating voltage ($E_x - E_f$) is opposed by an emf of self-induction induced in the field by the change of field flux.

Thus

$$E_x - E_f = N_f \frac{d\phi_f}{dt}. \tag{2}$$

Since $E_f = I_f R_f$,

$$E_x = (E_x - E_f) + E_f = N_f \frac{d\phi_f}{dt} + I_f R_f. \tag{3}$$

Equation 3 is the equation governing any change of voltage and current in an inductive circuit.

As the generated voltage rises along the magnetization curve, the point E_n is finally reached. At this point the voltage generated is just equal to that required to produce an excitation which will cause it. The stability of this point can be shown by considering what would happen if the voltage should overrun to some point E_m. Point E_m on the magnetization curve corresponds to a field excitation which requires a field voltage of E_f'. Obviously, this field voltage is not available for self-excitation and a generated voltage of E_m cannot be maintained. Therefore the intersection of the field-excitation line and the magnetization curve represents the voltage to which a self-excited generator will build at no load.

In this connection it should be noted that some curvature of the magnetization curve is essential for stable operation of a self-excited shunt generator at no load. If the magnetization curve were perfectly straight the intersection of the field-resistance line and the magnetization curve would be indefinite and a stable no-load voltage would not exist. On the other hand, a considerable curvature of the magnetization curve makes the intersection with the field-resistance line definite and a stable no-load operating point is assured. In a subsequent chapter it will be noted that one of the important factors that determines the maximum load a self-excited shunt generator is capable of supplying is dependent upon the distance between the field-resistance line and the magnetization curve. This distance is determined by the degree of curvature of the magnetization curve. As shown in Chap. III, the curvature of the magnetization curve was determined by the saturation of one or more parts of the magnetic circuit. Hence in certain instances saturation of a magnetic circuit is a highly desirable and essential quality.

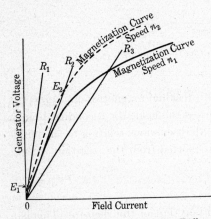

Fig. 17. Field Resistance Lines for Different Values of Resistance.

Critical Resistance and Speed. The building up of a shunt generator depends upon the variables of field resistance and the speed. A shunt generator having a speed n_1 and a field-resistance line (excitation line) as given by OR_3 of Fig. 17, will build up as explained in the preceding article. However, if the resistance of the field circuit be increased by the addition of resistance in a field rheostat, the excitation line may be shifted in the counterclockwise direction to positions such as OR_2 and OR_1. For the condition represented by the excitation line OR_1, the generator would not build up because no accelerating voltage would be present to cause the field current to grow. At the position OR_2, the generator would be on the verge of building up but still no accelerating voltage is present*. However, for any position of the field-resistance line to the right of OR_2, the generator would build up, while for positions to the left it would not. Thus the position OR_2 is a critical one for the speed represented by magnetization curve n_1, and the field resistance which produces a line OR_2 is called the **critical resistance.**

If the speed of the generator of Fig. 17 be raised from n_1 to n_2, the magnetization curve would rise to a new position shown by the dotted line. The field resistance represented by the excitation line OR_2 is no longer a critical one because the generator will now build up to a voltage of E_2. A further increase in speed might raise the magnetization curve to a point where the generator would build up for the resistance represented by line OR_1. R_2 was called the **critical resistance** for the speed n_1, yet it is equally logical to think in terms of speed and say that speed n_1 is the critical speed for the field resistance R_2. Obviously the terms are purely *relative* and depend on which quantity is con-

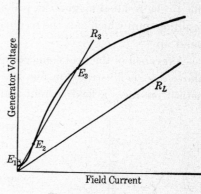

Fig. 18. Field Current.

sidered as fixed for the purpose of making a definition. The **critical speed** for a given field resistance is that speed above which the generator builds up and below which it fails to do so.

A generator may fail to build up at a resistance below its critical value due to a pronounced bend in the magnetization curve at low flux densities. This condition is illustrated in Fig. 18 for the excitation line R_3. This generator will not build up past the voltage E_1 unless some method is employed to get the voltage above E_2. Once above point E_2, the voltage would rise to E_3 due to the accelerating voltage present between E_2 and E_3. The simple and usual method of getting the voltage past E_1 and E_2 is to lower the field resistance temporarily to a point corresponding to some line such as R_L, and then to raise the resistance to R_3. The generator voltage will be stable through the range from E_2 to E_3.

* While this condition is detrimental in ordinary generators, it is useful in special machines to be discussed in Chapter XIV.

Effect of Field Connections, Direction of Rotation, and Residual Magnetism on Building Up. A shunt generator having a proper field resistance and speed may still fail to build up, or it may build up with an undesired polarity due to improper field connections, direction of rotation, or residual magnetism.

In Fig. 19, assume that the residual magnetism has the field polarity as indicated by N and S, the direction of rotation as shown by the arrow, and

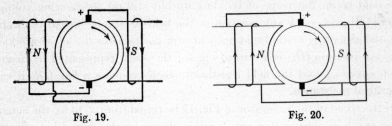

Fig. 19.   Fig. 20.

that this combination makes the upper brush positive, as shown. The voltage due to the residual magnetism will cause a current in the field winding with a resulting mmf which aids the residual magnetism. Therefore the generator will build up.

A reversal of the field connections, with all other factors unchanged for the above case, is illustrated in Fig. 20. Here the voltage due to the residual magnetism produces a field current and a mmf which opposes the residual magnetism. This opposing mmf will serve to reduce the terminal voltage to a lower value, but not to zero. Quantitatively, the terminal voltage may be determined by a method similar to that shown in Fig. 21. Since the mmf of the field current tends to produce a flux opposite to that of residual magnetism, the field resistance line must be drawn in the second quadrant as shown in Fig. 21. The point of equilibrium, as previously explained, is the intersection of the field resistance line and the magnetization curve. Hence the terminal voltage drops from V_R to V_O when the field circuit is connected incorrectly across the armature. Obviously the generator will never build up under these conditions.

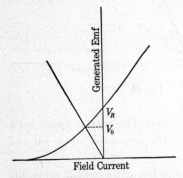

Fig. 21. Building Down of a Self-Excited Shunt Generator with an Incorrectly Connected Field.

A reversal of the direction of rotation for the conditions shown in Fig. 19 will reverse the polarity of the generated voltage due to residual magnetism. This reversal of polarity of the voltage will reverse both the direction of current and the mmf in the field winding. Thus the resultant flux will be less than the residual flux, and the generator will not build up.

A reversal of both the field connections and the direction of rotation for conditions of Fig. 19 is illustrated in Fig. 22. An analysis of these figures shows that the polarity of the brushes has been reversed due to the reversal of rotation, but that the reversal of the field connections counteracts this change. Hence the direction of the mmf due to the field current remains the same as in Fig. 19 and aids the residual magnetism. Thus the generator will build up but with a reversed polarity.

The effect of a reversal of the residual magnetism upon building up may be analyzed from Figs. 19 and 23. In Fig. 19, the generator built up satisfactorily. A reversal of the residual magnetism is shown in Fig. 23. This causes a reversal of polarity of the generated voltage, and, in turn, a reversal in the direction of the field current and the field mmf. A reversed mmf will be in the right direc-

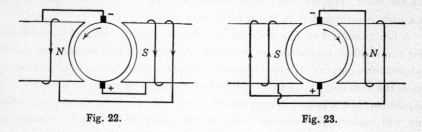

Fig. 22.   Fig. 23.

tion to aid a reversed residual magnetism. Thus the generator will build up but with a reversed polarity.

It is important to note that the building up of the generator is determined solely by the relation between the direction of rotation and the connection of the field, and it is independent of the polarity of the residual magnetism. The polarity of the generated voltage is controlled by the direction of rotation and by the polarity of the residual magnetism.

Failure of a Self-Excited Generator to Build Up. The following is a summary of the factors which determine the building up of generators.

1. The generator field must have residual magnetism.

2. The field resistance must be less than the critical resistance for the speed used or the speed must be greater than the critical speed for the resistance used.

3. There must be a proper relation between the direction of rotation and field connections. The polarity of residual magnetism is immaterial except in determining the polarity of the generated emf.

A generator which fails to build up should be tested by connecting a voltmeter across the terminals of its armature. This test should first be made with the shunt field disconnected. If the voltmeter fails to give any reading, either the voltmeter circuit is open, the residual magnetism is zero, or the armature is open-circuited or short-circuited. The voltmeter circuit should be tested on a separate source. A separate excitation from some dry cells or other source will determine if the excitation is zero. An open circuit on the armature may be due to a faulty brush contact on the commutator. This could be remedied by pressing on the brushes with the fingers.

If the initial test with the voltmeter shows a voltage due to residual magnetism, the action should be carefully noted when the field circuit is closed. If the voltmeter drops to zero, the field circuit is probably short-circuited. If the voltmeter reading drops very slightly, it suggests a high-resistance brush contact which can be remedied as explained above. If the voltmeter reading drops to nearly one-half the value it had before closing the field, the field connections are probably reversed. If the voltage rises somewhat upon closing the field circuit, the field is correctly connected but the resistance of the field circuit is too high, causing the excitation line to intersect the magnetization curve at a low value. This condition may be due to a high brush-contact resistance or to a high resistance left in the field rheostat.

A low potential of $1\frac{1}{2}$ volts or less due to residual magnetism indicates that the residual magnetism is too weak. A weak residual magnetism can be restored by separate excitation from an external source. A 6-volt battery placed across the field may prove to be insufficient to restore or strengthen the residual magnetism, but a proper connection in series with the field circuit and armature will usually give enough boost to the generated voltage to cause the machine to build up and thus restore its own residual magnetism. •

A new, experimental, or recently repaired machine may fail to build up to its rated voltage because of reversed connections on one or more field coils. A polarity test of the field poles by means of a compass will locate any erroneous field-circuit connections.

Froelich's Equation. It is sometimes desirable to represent the magnetization curve of a dynamo by means of an equation. One type of equation for this purpose has a hyperbolic form and is known as **Froelich's equation.** This equation is

$$\phi = \frac{cF}{b + F} \tag{4}$$

where ϕ denotes the flux, F the excitation expressed as mmf or field current, and c and b are empirical constants.

Since emf is proportional to flux for constant dynamo speed, a more useful form of this equation for use with direct-current dynamos is

$$E = \frac{aF}{b + F}. \tag{5}$$

The constants a and b can be determined from two points on the magnetization curve. Substituting the values of emf for two such points, we obtain the two equations

$$E_1 = \frac{aF_1}{b + F_1}, \qquad E_2 = \frac{aF_2}{b + F_2}$$

which may be solved simultaneously to determine the constants a and b. It is good practice to plot the equation obtained to ascertain how closely it fits the actual magnetization curve over the range desired. Perhaps a calculation at two other points will modify the constants a and b sufficiently to make the equation fit the actual curve better.

Froelich's equation has some limitations. When the excitation is zero, it gives zero voltage, whereas a small voltage due to residual magnetism does exist. At an infinite excitation, the equation gives a curve whose slope is zero, while the magnetization curve has an actual slope equivalent to that of an air-cored circuit. The accuracy of Froelich's equation may be improved by adding terms to it, as follows:

$$E = \frac{aF}{b + F} + d + eF + \cdots.$$

These additions complicate the use of the equation. The reader will find other forms of equations in texts devoted to methods for finding equations of experimental curves.

Field-Discharge Resistances. The shunt fields of a dynamo consist of a large number of turns of wire placed on an iron core. Hence they have a large self-inductance. When the field circuit is broken, the field flux established is left to decrease to zero. This decrease in flux linking with the field turns produces a large change in flux linkages and produces an emf of self-induction in accordance with Lenz's law:

$$E = -L\frac{di}{dt}.$$
[71, page 386].

If the field circuit were broken instantly without arcing, di/dt would be infinite and the induced voltage would be infinite. This condition is impossible, but

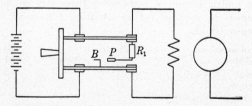

Fig. 24. Field-Discharge Resistance and Switch.

the rate of change of current and flux linkages when the field is broken may be sufficient to cause an induced voltage which will damage the insulation of the field coils. To prevent such damage, a field-discharge resistance is sometimes used in large machines. This arrangement is illustrated in Fig. 24, where the blade B makes contact with the point P, thus connecting the field across the resistance R before the contact with the source opens. Then the emf of self-induction equals the IR drop across both the external resistance R_1 and the field resistance. Thus we have

$$I(R_1 + R_f) = -L\frac{di}{dt}. \tag{6}$$

The rate di/dt at which the current decreases is determined by equation 6. If the external resistance is made equal to the field resistance, the voltage across the field cannot exceed normal line voltage.

In some instances a small number of short-circuited turns are placed on each pole of a shunt field. These turns, amounting to only a small percentage of the total on the shunt field, serve to keep the voltage induced in the field within safe limits. If the field circuit is opened, the flux tends to drop rapidly. The change in flux linkages in the shorted turns induces a voltage which causes a current to flow which, in turn, produces an mmf in the same direction as the field flux. This mmf produced by the short circuited turns retards the rate of decrease of the field flux.

In applications involving automatic control equipment where the field circuit may be interrupted suddenly, shunt fields should be protected by field discharge resistors. Such protection may be given by (1) a discharge resistor connected across the field permanently, (2) a discharge resistor inserted automatically by the control equipment, or (3) by connection across the field of a type of resistor with special characteristics such as thyrite. Thyrite is a material which possesses a very high resistance at normal operating voltages but a relatively low resistance when the voltage rises appreciably above normal operating values.

PROBLEMS

1. Calculate by the metric system of units using Table I, page 26, the excitation in gilberts, and ampere-turns required for an armature voltage of 500 for a machine having the following constants:

Diameter of armature core over top of teeth	23.4 in.
Number of slots	91
Coils per slot	3
Turns per coil	1
Simplex wave winding for 6 poles.	
Pole face = 0.6 of pole span (radial projection).	
Slot depth	1 in.
Air gap	0.132 in.
Armature yoke path (ac, Fig. 5)	3.85 in.
Cross-section of armature yoke net	25 sq in.
Tooth width equals slot width at air gap.	
Slots have parallel sides.	
Pole-core length (ef in Fig. 5)	7 in.
Pole-core cross-section net	40 sq in.
Field-yoke cross-section	25 sq in.
Field-yoke magnetic path (fh in Fig. 5)	9.5 in.

Speed	600 rpm
Axial length of core	9.25 in.
Leakage coefficient	1.10
Ventilating ducts	None
Scale and varnish between laminations	10% of stack

The field yoke is made of cast steel and the cores of laminated steel whose B–H curves are shown in Fig. 24, Appendix page 377.

Correct for fringing around teeth and edge of pole face, both along circumference and at ends of armature core.

2. Repeat Prob. 1 using English units.

3. In Prob. 1, what is the ratio of the drop in magnetic potential in the air gap to the magnetomotive force of a pole?

4. What kind of designs would yield sharp knees, and what kind rounded knees, on the magnetization curves of a direct-current machine?

5. Using Froelich's equation, determine the constants to make this equation represent the lower 100 per cent magnetization curve shown on page 131. Plot the curve as given by your equation and find the maximum deviation from the original curve over the range given.

6. A generator running at 1150 rpm has a magnetization curve as follows:

Emf	5.2	30	48.5	60	78	98	115	125	140	150	173.5
Field current	0	0.22	0.4	0.52	0.72	0.96	1.18	1.33	1.59	1.82	2.6

    a. The field resistance is 66.6 ohms. To what voltage will the dynamo build?

    b. This generator is rated at 125 volts. How much resistance must be inserted in the field to bring the generator to rated voltage at no load?

    c. How much resistance must be inserted in the field to prevent the generator from building up to more than 50 volts?

7. The magnetization curve data in Prob. 6 were taken at 1150 rpm. If the field of this machine is connected directly across the armature terminals, at what speed will the generated voltage at no load be 125 volts?

8. *a.* When the field, without any external resistance added, of the dynamo in Prob. 6 is connected across the armature, what is the greatest value the voltage accelerating the field current ever attains?

    b. If resistance is inserted in the field so that the no-load voltage is 125 volts, what would be the greatest accelerating voltage?

9. *a.* Find the critical field resistance of the dynamo for which data is given on pages 129–131 when operated at 100 per cent speed.

    b. Find the critical speed of the dynamo when the field is hot.

    c. Find the critical speed of the dynamo when the field is cold.

10. The dynamo specified on pages 129–131 is to operate in the cold state and build up to 200 volts when self-excited. At what speed must it operate?

11. To how many volts would the generator specified on pages 129–131 build up when operated self-excited in the cold state if the speed is held at 900 rpm?

12. *a.* When the dynamo specified on pages 129–131 is operated at 100 per cent speed in the hot state, to what voltage will it build if self-excited?

    b. What is the field resistance drop when the terminal voltage is 174 volts as the generator is building up? (Neglect armature circuit $I_a r_a$ drop due to the field current.)

Explain the physical significance of the difference between the terminal voltage and field resistance drop under these conditions. How much is this difference?

13. Calculate a and b in Froelich's equation (5) for the magnetization curve given in Prob. 6 if the 60- and 150-volt points are used. Use the equation thus found and calculate the emf for 1.33 amp. Compare your result with the actual emf.

14. The field of a four-pole dynamo has 4.2×10^6 maxwells of flux per pole produced by a field current of 2.3 amp from a line of 225 volts. The field coils are in series and have 2200 turns per pole. Assume the magnetization curve approximates a straight line.

    a. What is the self-induction of the field circuit?

    b. What is the kinetic energy of the field current?

    c. How much power is required to maintain the flux?

    d. How much energy was required to establish the flux?

    e. When the field switch was closed on a supply potential of 225 volts, what was the rate at which the field current was changing at the instant after closing the switch?

    f. After closing the field switch on a line potential of 225 volts, what was the rate at which the field current was changing at the instant the field current had reached 1.5 amp?

    g. If the normal field current is stopped in 1/10 sec what is the average induced emf produced?

    h. If a field discharge resistance of 80 ohms is used connected as in Fig. 24, find the maximum voltage induced in the field circuit, the maximum potential across the field circuit, and the maximum voltage across the field discharge resistance when the switch is opened.

    i. Repeat questions in part *h*, using a field discharge resistance of 800 ohms.

    i. Should a field discharge resistance be high or low for maximum safety?

    k. If the field discharge resistance of 80 ohms were used, what percentage of the kinetic energy of the current is consumed in the field discharge resistance? If 800 ohms were used?

    l. What is the rate at which the field current starts to die down at the instant the field switch is opened if a field discharge resistance of 80 ohms were used? If a field discharge resistance of 800 ohms were used?

15. Assume the field coils described in Prob. 14 were connected in parallel instead of series and connected to a line of 50 volts potential, what would be the new field circuit resistance and self-induction?

CHAPTER IV

Armature Windings

Classification of Armature Windings. The windings of direct-current armatures may be classified (1) with respect to the core or frame upon which the winding is placed or (2) with respect to the arrangement of the conductors on the core and their connection to the commutator. Under the first classification is found the *Gramme-ring* type, the *disk* type, and the *drum* type of armature and windings.

The Gramme-ring winding was an early type which found general use for many years. It consisted of an iron core having the shape of a hollow cylinder (or ring) upon which the winding was placed, as illustrated in Fig. 1. The iron core was laminated and without slots on the early machines. This construction required a large air gap, and there was a tendency for the winding to slip on the core. Later forms of Gramme-ring armatures were built with slots. The

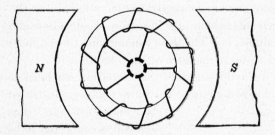

Fig. 1. Gramme-Ring Armature with Commutator.

Gramme-ring winding was difficult to construct and to insulate (generally a hand operation). It was equally difficult to repair. The part of the conductors on the inside of the ring was ineffective, merely serving as a return path for the outer active conductors. These disadvantages caused this type of armature winding to be superseded by the drum type. Today the Gramme-ring type will be found only in museum exhibits. However, the construction of the core, the arrangement of the winding, and the connection to the commutator of the Gramme ring are easy to represent diagrammatically and easy to visualize.

Hence this type of winding is often used in discussing the principles of direct-current machines.

The disk type of armature is a modification of the Gramme-ring type. Its core is a hollow disk instead of a hollow cylinder. As illustrated in Fig. 2, the disk, D, is constructed by tightly rolling a thin strip of sheet iron into a spiral coil. It should be noted that the active parts of the conductors are on the radial sides of the disk instead of on the outside, as was the case in the Gramme ring. Disk-type armatures are museum pieces today.

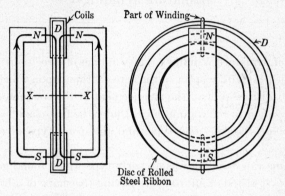

Fig. 2. Dynamo with Disc Armature.

The drum type of armature and winding is illustrated in Figs. 9 and 10, pages 6 and 7. The laminated iron core is cylindrical in shape with parallel slots in the outer surface of the cylinder. All conductors are placed in the slots on the surface of the core and are connected to each other and to the commutator by various arrangements which give rise to a classification known as **series** or **wave, lap** or **multiple,** etc. The theory underlying these different arrangements will be covered in the remainder of this chapter.

In passing, it should be stated that armature windings may be classed as open-circuit and closed-circuit. The former class is illustrated in Fig. 3. This class may have more than two bars, but each coil is connected to bars diametrically opposite which have no electrical connection with each other. Open-circuit armature windings are often used in alternating-current machines but never in present-day direct-current machines. The closed-circuit windings are reentrant, that is, closed upon themselves electrically, so that by starting at any one point in the winding and tracing through the winding in a continuous direction, the path will lead back to the starting point.

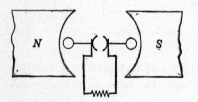

Fig. 3. Generator with Two-Segment Commutator Connected to a Resistance Load.

Slot Pitch and Pole Pitch. The distance from the center of one slot to the center of an adjacent slot measured on the surface of the armature is called the **slot pitch,** or **slot span.** The slot pitch is also equal to the width of a slot plus the width of the top of a tooth.

The distance between the center lines of adjacent poles of a dynamo measured on the surface of the armature is called the **pole pitch,** or **pole span.** This distance is usually expressed in inches, but it may be expressed in slot spans. A pole span is always equal to 180 electrical degrees.

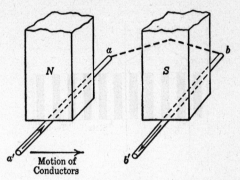

Fig. 4. Two Conductors One Pole-Span Apart.

Fundamental Conceptions and Winding Terms. A conductor cutting the flux emanating from a north pole will have an electromotive force induced in it in a certain direction. Another conductor moving in the same direction but cutting the flux from a south pole will have an emf induced in the reverse direction. For example, consider two conductors placed a pole span apart, as shown in Fig. 4. With the direction of motion and field polarities indicated, the emf's induced in the conductors will have the directions shown by the arrows. In the construction of a dynamo it is desirable to have the emf's of the conductors in any path add to one another so as to give a higher voltage. This result can be obtained in Fig. 4 by connecting the ends a and b in series. Thus, the emf of conductor $a'a$ will be added arithmetically to the emf of conductor bb'. The connected unit $a'abb'$ constitutes a *one-turn coil.*

The coil just considered may be made a part of a drum armature winding by placing it in slots one pole pitch apart, as indicated in the developed view of Fig. 5. That part of the wire of a single turn which lies within a slot is called **an inductor,** or an **active conductor.** Thus, the part between X and Y is an inductor. The inductors constitute that part of the total winding which lies within the iron core and are primarily active in generating emf's and in developing power. For a single-turn coil, the ends a' and b' are connected to the commutator. The ends or leads that connect to the commutator are called the **coil leads.** The connection, aCb, which joins the inductors at the end opposite the commutator is called the **back-end connection,** or **back-end turn.** The number of slot spans inclosed by a back-end connection is called the **back pitch.** In Fig. 5, the back pitch is four slot spans, or four slots.

Armature coils of one turn are frequently used in dynamos having a low and medium voltage rating and in those having a high current rating. For dynamos of high voltage, coils having two or more turns are generally used. A two-turn coil is formed by placing a second coil just like that of Fig. 5 in the same slot and connecting it in series with the first one. This is accomplished by

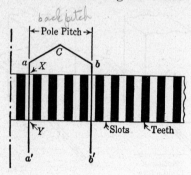

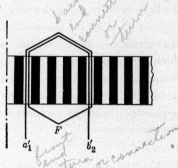

Fig. 5. Coil of One Turn on a Developed Drum Armature. Back Pitch Is Four Slots.

Fig. 6. Coil of Two Turns on a Drum Armature.

connecting the b' end of the first coil to the a' end of the second, as illustrated in Figs. 5 and 6. Coils of three or more turns are formed in a similar manner. The part of the coil which connects the inductors or turns together on the commutator end is called the **front-end connection,** or **front-end turn.** A front-end turn, F, is illustrated in Fig. 6. All of the inductors of a coil which lie in a single slot, taken as a group, are called a **coil edge.** The complete coil shown in Fig. 6

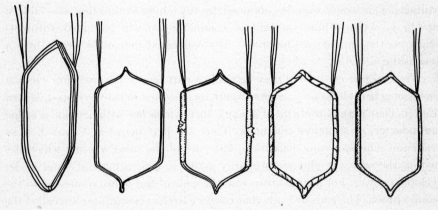

Fig. 7. Process of Making a Three-Coil Winding Element.

constitutes a **winding element.** A winding element may consist of more than one coil. Thus, several coils may be taped together to form a winding element, or coil group. The process of making a winding element consisting of three coils is shown in Fig. 7.

Lap Winding and Wave Windings. There are two types of drum windings known as **lap winding** and **wave winding.** The lap winding is also known as a **multiple winding,** and the wave winding is sometimes called a **series winding.** Both of these windings are made from the simple coil element explained in the previous article and illustrated in Fig. 5. *The two types of windings are distinguished primarily by the way in which the coil leads are connected to the commutator.* This difference will be illustrated by the use of diagrams of the developed surface of a drum armature. A developed diagram is made by unrolling the periphery of the armature and commutator into a plane.

The simplex lap winding is formed by taking the leads of the simple coil of Fig. 5 and connecting them to adjacent commutator bars. Thus, in the developed diagram of Fig. 8, the coil A is placed in slots 1 and 5 (one pole pitch apart) and the leads are connected to adjacent commutator bars 1 and 2. As a next step in the winding, a second coil B is placed in slots 2 and 6, and its leads are connected to commutator bars 2 and 3. It should be noted that the beginning lead of coil B is connected to the end lead of coil A so that the coils are in series between bars 1 and 3. It is observed that the placement of coil B caused it to appear to "lap" over coil A; this fact has given rise to the term **lap winding.** More coils can now be placed on the armature in the same manner as coil B until the right-hand lead of the last coil connects to commutator bar 1 and closes the winding. The number of slot spans included between the coil leads which connect to the same commutator bars is called the **front pitch.** In Fig. 8, the front pitch is three slot spans, or three slots. The back pitch is four slots, in accordance with a previous definition. The number of bars advanced from one end of a coil to the other is called the **commutator pitch.** The commutator pitch for the coils shown in Fig. 8 is one bar.

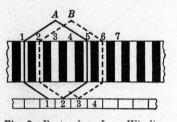

Fig. 8. Part of a Lap Winding Showing Two Coils.

The simplex wave winding is formed by taking the leads of the simple coil of Fig. 5 and connecting them to commutator bars approximately two pole pitches apart. Thus, in the developed diagram of Fig. 9, the coil A is placed in slots 1 and 5 (one pole pitch apart), and the leads are connected to commutator bars 1 and 10. The next coil B is placed in slots 10 and 14, and its leads connect to commutator bars 10 and 19. The simple one-turn coil and its lead have the form of a wave; this has given rise to the term **wave winding.** The commutator pitch for this winding is nine bars, as contrasted with a value of one bar for the simplex lap winding just cited. Following the definitions for pitches, the back pitch is four slots and the front pitch five slots.

Lap Winding. The simplex lap winding can be visualized and its characteristics understood better through the actual construction and calculation of a typical developed diagram. An example will be worked out for a simplex lap winding on a four-pole dynamo having 21 slots with coils of one turn each, and one coil (two coil sides) per slot. The diagram will start with the parallel guide

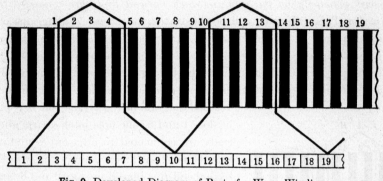

Fig. 9. Developed Diagram of Part of a Wave Winding.

lines C, D, E, F, and G of Fig. 10 serving as the limits of the commutator, armature core, and end turns. Twenty-one equidistant points may be measured off to locate the slots. A full vertical line will be used to represent each slot, and also one coil side in each slot. The armature circumference is cut through the middle of a tooth, and this cut is represented by the line AB. The distance between the two lines AB should be divided into as many parts as there are poles, four in this case. These divisions represent pole spans, and are equal to 21/4, or $5\frac{1}{4}$ slots each. The center of each pole span will be represented by a circle to show the location of the pole faces. Pole faces are usually rectangular in form, but circles will be used here because they will not be confused with other lines on the diagram. The number of commutator bars is equal to the number of coils. In this example there is one coil per slot; hence the number of slots, coils, and commutator bars is the same, or 21. The 21 bars can be represented by drawing vertical lines (for insulation) between the parallel lines C and D. A brush having a width of one bar will be placed on the commutator bar nearest to the center of the first pole face. This bar will be called No. 1 and the others will be numbered consecutively to the right. In practice, brushes usually cover from one and one half to three bars. At distances equal to one pole span (five and a quarter bars) place additional brushes. Connect the positive terminal of a battery to brush No. 1 and leave the negative terminal free for connection to another brush. Beginning at commutator bar No. 1, draw a full line representing a coil lead to an inductor to the left which is midway between the poles. This would be the inductor in slot No. 1. The other side of this coil should be an inductor in a slot approximately one pole pitch or in this case five slots distant. Thus, the inductor in slot No. 1 should connect to the one in slot $1 + 5 = 6$. The inductor of this first coil which lies in slot No. 6 will be shown dotted to indicate that it will lie in the bottom of the slot, since another coil side to be placed later will lie above it. This placement of coils is a logical one and makes for a convenient mechanical arrangement. The coil edge just placed in the bottom of slot No. 6 will connect through a coil lead back to commutator bar No. 2. This corresponds to a back pitch of five slots, a front pitch of four slots, and a commutator pitch of one bar. Using these coil pitches,

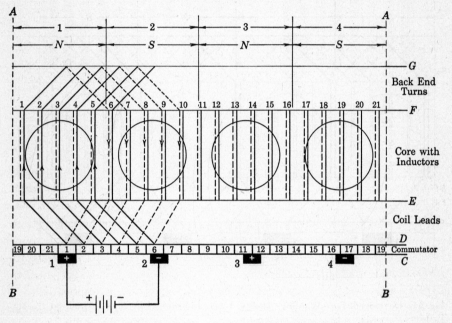

Fig. 10. Construction of a Developed Lap Winding Diagram.

we may continue the procedure of placing additional coils until the winding closes on bar No. 1. The current from a battery is considered to flow from the positive brush to the negative. This fact establishes the direction of current flow from brush No. 1, and arrows may be placed on the inductors to show the direction of current. A study of the direction of current will show that it will be necessary to take the current out at brush No. 2 and thus connect the negative terminal of the battery to this point. If this procedure were not followed, the current would continue on through the winding and would pass through the upper coil edges under pole No. 2 in a direction opposite to that in the lower coil edges. The effect of an opposite direction of current in the upper and lower coil edges of the same slot would be a complete neutralization.

In a motor, this condition would produce zero torque. In a generator, it would mean zero terminal electromotive force. A similar process of reasoning applied to Fig. 11 will show that it is necessary to have brushes at positions No. 3 and No. 4. Between brushes No. 1 and No. 2 there is one electrical circuit or path. Similar paths exist between brushes No. 2 and No. 3, No. 3 and No. 4, and between No. 4 and No. 1. Thus, there are *four paths* for the current in this winding of *four poles*. A further study of the complete winding in Fig. 11 will show that the current must flow into the brushes No. 1 and No. 3 and out at the other two. Brushes No. 1 and No. 3 are connected electrically externally

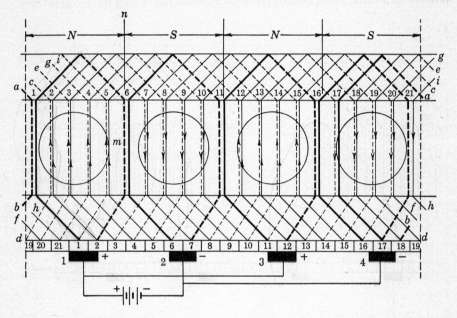

Fig. 11. Developed Lap Winding. Heavy Lines Indicate Coils Short Circuited by the Brushes.

to the commutator, and the same is true of No. 2 and No. 4. Figure 11 illustrates that each path in the winding is made by advancing the winding through one pole span. This figure also shows that the current from the positive terminal of the battery divides into four parts, one quarter of the total entering the winding at each of the paths connected to bars 1, 2, 11 and 12. The four paths are in parallel. Therefore, in the simplex *lap winding*, there will be as many *parallel paths as there are poles*. There must be as many brushes as there are poles. The presence of the parallel (or multiple) paths in a lap winding has given rise to the term **multiple-wound armature,** and the winding is sometimes called a **multiple winding.**

A summary of the developments of the last two articles leads to the following definition of a lap winding. *A simplex lap winding is one in which the coil*

sides are placed in slots approximately one pole pitch apart, the coil leads are con-
nected to adjacent commutator segments, and the number of paths is equal to the
number of poles.

Wave Winding. The characteristic features of the wave winding can be understood easily through the construction of a diagram of a simplex wave winding.
An example similar to the one of the preceding article will be assumed. A
machine having 4 poles, 21 slots, 1 turn per coil, and 1 coil per slot will be
chosen. The developed diagram of Fig. 12 will be constructed by following the
same procedure as that used for the lap winding. First, the parallel lines repre-

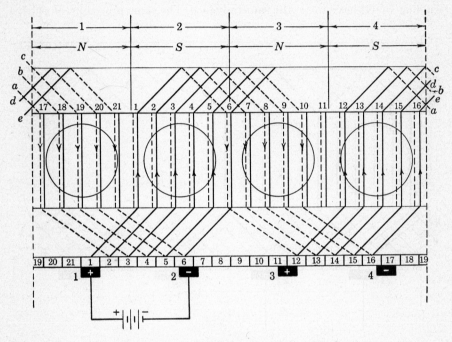

Fig. 12. Construction of a Developed Wave Winding.

senting the limits of the commutator, coil leads, armature core, and back-end
turns are drawn. The slots and commutator bars (21 in number) and the 4 pole
spans are laid out. Beginning with the commutator bar No. 1 which is approximately under the center of the first pole in Fig. 12, a coil lead is drawn to an
inductor in a slot (No. 1) which is practically midway between the poles. The
coil, of which this inductor is a part, should have its center practically over
the center of a pole. This coil is formed by connecting the inductor in slot
No. 1 to the inductor in slot No. 6 (approximately a pole span distant) giving
a back pitch of five slots. From the inductor in slot 6, the coil lead connects
to bar 12, which is practically two pole spans from bar 1. This gives a commutator pitch of 12 − 1, or 11 bars, which is slightly more than two pole

spans, or $2 \times 21/4 = 10\frac{1}{2}$ bars. A fraction of a bar is impossible so that 10 or 11 bars are the nearest to two pole spans. (The use of 10 bars is considered on page 55.) From bar 12 a coil lead connects to an inductor in slot 12, making the front pitch six slots. With the inductor 12 used as one edge, another coil is drawn so that its back-end turn a on the right is completed by the back-end turn a shown on the left. The end turn a should be connected to an inductor which is connected to a bar found by adding the commutator pitch of 11 bars to bar 12. This gives bar No. 23, which is the same as bar No. 2. The armature has been traversed by the winding once and two coils in series have advanced the winding just one bar on the commutator, whereas a single coil in the lap winding would have made the same advance. The same procedure of placing

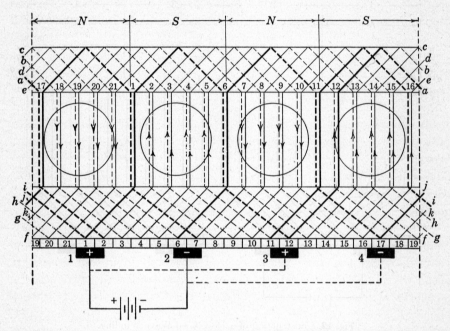

Fig. 13. Developed Progressive Wave Winding. Heavy Lines Indicate Coils Short Circuited by the Brushes.

coils may be followed until the winding closes upon itself on bar 1, as illustrated in Fig. 13. Current from the positive side of the battery (Fig. 13) may be traced from commutator bar 2 through the winding, following the direction indicated by the arrows. When bar 6 is reached, the current should be led out to the negative side of the battery. If this is not done, the current in additional inductors would be in an opposite direction to that of the present inductors. This latter condition would produce a complete neutralization of the effect of current under all poles. Therefore brush No. 2 should be connected to the negative terminal of the battery. The winding represented by the inductors between brushes 1 and 2 (Fig. 12) is one circuit or path through the armature. A study of this figure will show that *one half of the bars and inductors* have been used by this circuit. A continuation of this winding will give the completed diagram of Fig. 13. A study of this completed diagram will show that beginning at brush 2 and leading to the right, the winding will fill *the other half of the slots and bars* and close on bar 1. This second half of the winding gives a second circuit or path between brushes 1 and 2. The fact that only two paths exist in this winding would not be changed by adding more poles, since the only effect would be to place more coils in series before arriving at brush 2. Therefore the simplex wave winding has only *two paths* in parallel, regardless of *the number of poles.* The simple addition of coils in series in each of the two paths, as the number of poles of a wave winding is increased, has given rise to the term **series winding,** and the armature has been termed **series wound.**

A study of the complete wave winding of Fig. 13 shows that the distribution of currents indicated will exist when brushes 1 and 2 only are used. These two brushes are all that are necessary, although brushes 3 and 4 may be used if desired. Brush 3 is at the same potential as brush 1, since it is connected directly to 1 by a single coil lying in slots 1 and 6. This coil does not have any emf induced in it because its inductors lie midway between magnetic poles. It serves merely as a connection between brushes. Thus, if in addition to brushes 1 and 2, 3 and 4 are also to be used, they should be connected, as shown by the dotted lines, in parallel with 1 and 2 respectively. It is also evident that brushes 3 and 4 could be used exclusively, and brushes 1 and 2 omitted.

The number of brushes used with wave windings depends on the engineering considerations involved. On some railway motors where it is desired to have the brushes accessible either from above or below, only two brushes are used. On small low-capacity machines, two brushes are usually sufficient. On machines of medium and large size, the use of the same number of brushes as poles will usually give the required brush surface area with a shorter commutator, and hence a lower cost for the dynamo.

Summarizing, we may give the following definition for the wave winding. *A simplex wave winding is one in which the coil sides are placed in slots approximately one pole pitch apart, the coil leads are connected to commutator bars approximately two pole pitches apart, and the number of paths in the armature is always two.*

Comparison of the Lap and Wave Windings. A comparison of the four-pole lap winding and the four-pole wave winding reveals that one half of all the inductors of the wave winding are in series between brushes, while only one fourth of the total number of inductors of the lap winding are in series. Thus, one half as much voltage will be induced in the lap winding for the same number of inductors, poles, and rpm. The number of parallel paths in the lap winding is double that in the wave winding. Hence the current output of the lap winding will be double that of the wave. Therefore the power output of the two is the same. If, on the other hand, a comparison of two four-pole machines of the same rpm is made on the basis of the same output voltage and current rating, the wave winding, which has half of its total inductors in series, has only two paths in parallel, while the lap winding has only one fourth of its total conductors in series, and therefore has four parallel paths. For the same terminal voltage the wave winding requires only one half as many total inductors on the armature as the lap winding. However, since each inductor of the wave winding carries one half of the total output current while the inductors of the lap winding carry only one fourth of the output current, the inductors of the wave winding must have twice the cross section of those used in the lap winding. Since it is necessary to insulate each inductor and there are more inductors of smaller cross section in the lap winding, the slot factor (that is, the ratio of the space occupied by the copper in a slot to the space occupied by insulation) is greater in the wave winding.

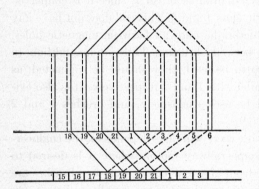

Fig. 14. Part of a Developed Retrogressive Lap Winding.

In the general case, the simplex lap winding has $1/p$ of the total number of inductors in series between brushes for a p-pole dynamo. Each inductor will carry $1/p$ of the total current output. The lap winding has as many brushes as poles.

The simplex wave winding has one half of its total number of inductors in series in each of two paths between brushes. Each inductor must carry one half of the total current output, regardless of the number of poles. The wave winding requires only two brushes, regardless of the number of poles, although it can use as many sets of brushes as poles.

A brush on a lap-wound machine short-circuits one coil during commutation, whereas with only two brushes on a wave-wound machine, one brush will short-circuit as many coils in series as there are pairs of poles. With as many brushes as poles, a coil will be short-circuited by two brushes in series.

Progressive and Retrogressive Windings. In Fig. 10, the first coil to the left began at bar 1, passed through inductors 1 and 6, and led back to bar 2. Thus, the coil leads progressed from bar 1 to bar 2. The next coil advances or progresses from bar 2 to bar 3. The winding progresses (to the right) from bar to bar and is called a **progressive winding**. Obviously, the second lead of the first coil in Fig. 10 could have come back to bar 21 and the second coil could begin at bar 21 and lead to bar 20, etc. This procedure is shown in Fig. 14. For these connections, the winding would step back (to the left) each time, or retrogress; such a winding is known as a **retrogressive winding**.

The wave winding may be either progressive or retrogressive. The wave winding shown in Fig. 12 is progressive, since, starting with bar 1, and passing through two coils, the winding leads to bar 2, which is an advance to the right. A retrogressive winding would result for this dynamo if a commutator pitch of 10 instead of 11 were used. (It should be remembered that the double pole pitch is $2 \times 21/4$, or $10\frac{1}{2}$ bars, and either 10 or 11 could be used.) Using a commutator pitch of 10, the coils advance from bar 1 to 11 and from 11 to

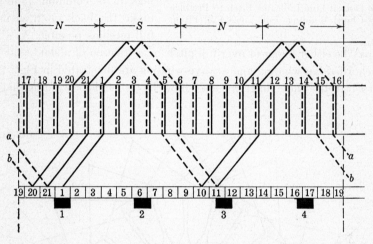

Fig. 15. Part of a Developed Retrogressive Wave Winding.

21, which is to the left of 1, and the winding becomes retrogressive. This retrogressive wave winding is illustrated in Fig. 15.

There is no special advantage in using either the progressive or retrogressive winding other than in the amount of copper required in the leads. For a lap winding, the progressive type will use less copper in the leads.

Chorded Windings. A *chorded* winding is one in which the coil span or back pitch is less than one pole span. Such a winding is illustrated by the dotted line of Fig. 16. The chorded winding has the obvious advantage that it reduces the length and amount of copper in a coil. If the coil is shortened or chorded enough so that it does not encircle all of the flux per pole, the generated emf is reduced. Chorded windings were commonly used on all dynamos before the adoption of the interpole. On these early machines, many of which are still in use, the chorded winding served to improve commutation for reasons which will be covered in a later chapter. *Dynamos with interpoles should have approximately full-pitch windings.* Lap windings are nearly always designed to have fractional slots per pole, such as an integer plus one half slot. The winding is then chorded to the extent of one half slot short of full pole pitch. Occasionally a winding may not lend itself to one half slot chording. In such cases it may be made full pitch or one slot short of a pole span. In the design of wave windings it is common practice to make the back pitch as near to full pitch as possible. As a result they may be either under or over full pitch by a fraction of a slot.

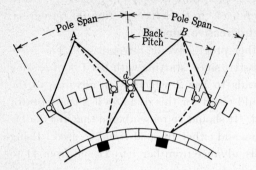

Fig. 16. Dotted Line Indicates Pitch to Produce a Short-Chord Winding, Full Lines Full Pitch.

A chorded lap winding and a wave winding are illustrated in Figs. 17 and 19, respectively. These diagrams also show the use of clock-winding diagrams,

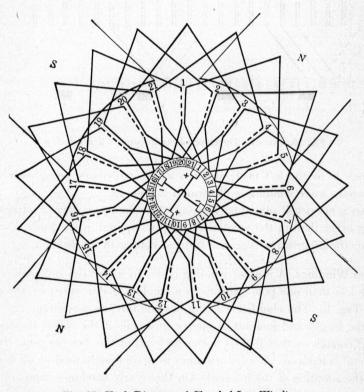

Fig. 17. Clock Diagram of Chorded Lap Winding.

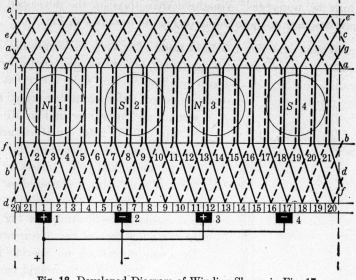

Fig. 18. Developed Diagram of Winding Shown in Fig. 17.

Fig. 19. Clock Diagram of Chorded Wave Winding.

which may be more easily visualized than those of the developed type. A developed diagram of the winding of Fig. 17 is shown in Fig. 18.

Random-Wound and Form-Wound Coils. The coils for armature windings are manufactured in various ways. Small armatures are usually wound by turning the armature axis end over end in a machine while wire is fed into the slots one turn at a time. Armatures produced in this manner are called **random-wound,** and appear as in Fig. 10, page 7.

The coils for large armatures are wound on forms and then placed on the machine. If the individual coil consists of several turns of small wire, it is wound on a simple O-shaped form and then pulled into shape and insulated, as illustrated in Fig. 7. Coils having a few turns of heavy wire are formed by hand operations on special jigs and winding forms. A form-wound coil of this

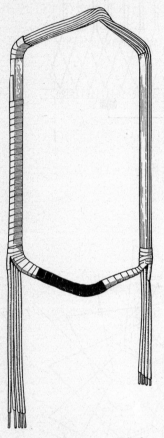

Fig. 20. Form-Wound Coil.

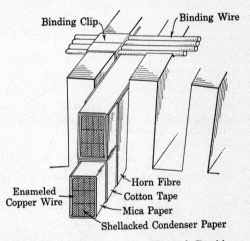

Binding Clip

Binding Wire

Enameled
Copper Wire

Horn Fibre

Cotton Tape

Mica Paper

Shellacked Condenser Paper

Fig. 21. Cross-Section of a Typical Double-Layer Winding Showing Upper and Lower Coil Edges in Each Slot.

type is shown in Fig. 20. All form-wound coils are assembled on the armature after the manner illustrated in Fig. 22.

The common practice in armature windings is to place two winding-element edges in one slot. This arrangement is called a **double-layer winding,** and is shown in Figs. 21 and 22. Figure 21 also illustrates one method of insulating inductors, coils, winding elements, and slots.

Multiplex Windings. Multiplex windings have two or more times as many paths in parallel for the same number of poles as the simplex windings. These windings really consist of two or more simplex windings placed on the same armature. For example, if an armature had 100 slots and 100 bars, a simplex lap winding could be placed on the armature by using 50 alternate slots and 50 commutator bars. This winding would close on itself. A second simplex lap winding exactly like the first could be placed in the remaining 50 slots and commutator bars. If the brushes used on this machine cover two or more bars, both simplex windings are in parallel and the armature will have two times as many parallel paths as the usual simplex winding. Accordingly, this winding is called a **duplex winding.** Each of the individual (simplex) circuits closed on

ig. **22.** Assembling Form-Wound Coils on Armature Core

itself once so that the duplex winding, as a unit, closed or reentered on itself twice; this fact gives rise to the term **doubly reentrant** duplex winding. The use of 99 slots on the armature of the previous example would have reduced the reentrancy to one. Thus, the first simplex winding filling alternate slots and commutator bars would not have closed on itself but would have returned to a bar adjacent to the initial one. The second simplex winding beginning where the first one left off will return to the starting point (bar) for the first winding and thus close or reenter once for the whole or duplex winding. This gives a **singly reentrant** duplex winding.

Triplex and higher multiple windings can be made by placing three or more simplex windings on the same armature. Both lap and wave windings may be multiplex. Multiplex windings have more paths in parallel, and hence are adapted for machines having a large current output at a low terminal voltage. In practice, multiplex machines are *rarely* used because the designer finds more satisfactory methods of producing the armature with a large current capacity.

Calculations for Lap Windings. The formulas given in this article and the following one are based on the assumption that the number of slots and commutator bars are equal. Let B denote the number of commutator bars or segments, S the number of slots, Y_b the back pitch, Y_f the front pitch, p

the number of poles, and cp the commutator pitch. Then, for interpole machines,

$$Y_b = \frac{S}{p}, \quad \text{approximately.} \tag{1}$$

In the case of noninterpole machines (now seldom used in machines above 1 horsepower) this formula becomes $Y_b = 0.90\ S/p$. Again, for both interpole and noninterpole machines,

$$cp = Y_b - Y_f = +1, \quad \text{or} \quad -1 \tag{2*}$$

for progressive or retrogressive lap, respectively. A simplex lap winding can be placed on an armature with any number of slots.

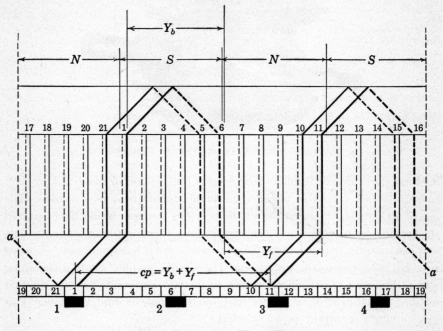

Fig. 23. Pitches for a Wave Winding.

Calculation of Wave Winding. The back pitch of wave windings is calculated in the same manner as for lap windings. The front pitch should be approximately equal to the back pitch. The commutator pitch must be exactly equal to the sum of the back and front pitches, so that the commutator bars for the coils will keep in step with the coil positions. Hence we have

$$cp = Y_b + Y_f. \tag{3}$$

The commutator pitch is approximately equal to two pole spans, as shown in Fig. 23, and when stepped off on the commutator as many times as there

* For calculating duplex lap winding $cp = Y_b - Y_f = \pm 2$.

are pairs of poles the winding should return to a commutator bar adjacent to the starting one. In Fig. 23, this would be either bar 21 or 2. If pitches as illustrated in Fig. 23 are used, bar 21 is encountered. If Y_f in the figure had been 6 instead of 5, the winding would have returned to bar 2. In general, if the bar preceding the starting one is reached, the winding is retrogressive, and if the first bar beyond the initial one is reached, the winding is progressive. These statements may be expressed algebraically as follows:

$$\left\{ \begin{array}{l} \text{Commutator bar} \\ \text{used for start} \end{array} \right\} + \left\{ \text{total advance} \right\} = \left\{ \begin{array}{l} \text{bar desired for type} \\ \text{of windings} \end{array} \right\}$$

$$1 + \frac{p}{2}(Y_b + Y_f) = B \qquad \text{retrogressive winding} \qquad (4)$$

or, $\qquad\qquad\qquad\qquad = B + 2 \qquad \text{progressive winding.} \qquad (5)$

Solving for commutator pitch, we find, for simplex wave winding,

$$cp = (Y_b + Y_f) = \frac{B \pm 1}{p/2}. \qquad (6)*$$

An example will illustrate the use of these formulas. For a dynamo having 6 poles, 122 slots, 122 bars, interpoles, and a wave winding, we may write

$$Y_b = \frac{122}{6} = 20\tfrac{1}{3}.$$

A back pitch of fractional number of slots is impossible, so that either 20 or 21 should be used. The use of 20 slots will save copper in the end connections and will be used although 21 slots would serve as far as the armature connections are concerned. By equation 6 we find

$$cp = (Y_b + Y_f) = \frac{B \pm 1}{p/2} = \frac{122 \pm 1}{3} = 41, \qquad \text{or} \qquad 40\tfrac{1}{3}.$$

A fractional commutator pitch is impossible, so that 41 should be chosen, which yields a progressive winding. Hence we have

$$Y_f = cp - Y_b = 41 - 20 = 21 \text{ slots.}$$

Dummy Coils. A dummy coil is an idle or unused coil which is placed on a wave-wound armature for mechanical balance. Its use results from certain combinations of numbers of slots and commutator segments which may not permit possible windings. For example, assume that the armature of the preceding example had 123 slots and bars instead of 122. The back pitch would have been $123/6 = 20\tfrac{1}{2}$, or 20 slots. The commutator pitch would have been

$$cp = (Y_b + Y_f) = \frac{123 \pm 1}{3} = 41\tfrac{1}{3}, \qquad \text{or} \qquad 40\tfrac{2}{3}.$$

Neither of these fractional pitches can be used. Hence a simplex wave winding could not be constructed using 123 commutator bars for a 6-pole machine.

* For a duplex wave winding $cp = (B \pm 2)/(p/2)$.

Thus, a commutator having 122 commutator bars should be used, and 122 active coils should be connected to them. The 123rd or dummy coil would be placed in the slots for mechanical balance, but its leads would be taped (insulated) and it would not form any part of the electrical circuit.

Figure 24 shows a winding with a dummy coil. Such windings are called **forced windings.** Windings employing dummy coils are used when it is desired

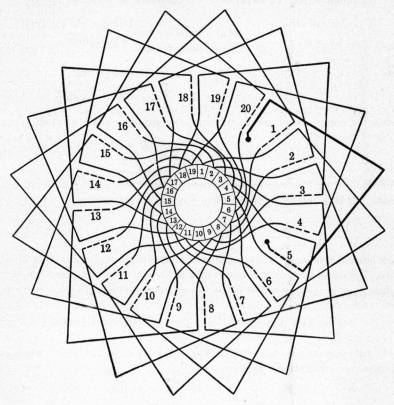

Fig. 24. Winding with a Dummy Coil.

to use punching dies or certain laminations on hand instead of incurring the expense of providing laminations having the required number of slots.

Dummy coils are never necessary on simplex lap windings.

Winding Calculations for Slots Containing More Than Two Coil Sides. The rules and formulas of the two preceding articles can be readily adapted for use on armatures having two or more coils per slot. To do this, it should be remembered that the number of commutator bars must be equal to the number of active coils. Slots with two or more coils may be visualized as divided by planes which separate the slot into two or more individual subslots, with only one coil in each subslot. The new subslots formed are really half-slots or third-slots; and they may be handled much like the full slots of the preceding considerations. For example, consider an 8-pole simplex wave winding which has 3 coils per slot and which is placed on a core having 123 slots. Each coil will be considered to occupy one third of a slot. There will be $3 \times 123 = 369$ third-slots and coils. Hence we have

$$Y_b = \frac{369}{8} = 46\frac{1}{8} \text{ third-slots.}$$

A whole number of slots should be used for back pitch to avoid the use of different lengths of back turns; hence the nearest number will be 45 third-slots, or 15 full slots.

$$cp = \frac{B \pm 1}{p/2} = \frac{369 \pm 1}{4} = 92\frac{1}{2}, \quad \text{or} \quad 92 \text{ bars.}$$

The commutator pitch must be in whole bars, so that 92 is used. This gives a retrogressive winding, and we have

$$Y_f = cp - Y_b = 92 - 45 = 47 \text{ third-slots.}$$

The front pitch does not need to be a whole number of slots, as it has nothing to do with the shape and size of the coils. The coil leads can be accommodated to the required pitch during assembly.

Symbolic Winding Diagrams. Armature-winding diagrams may be reduced to simple symbolic circuits for the purpose of visualizing their internal paths and resistance, and their connections to brushes and external circuits. A symbolic diagram for a six-pole lap winding is given in Fig. 25. Each coil of the winding

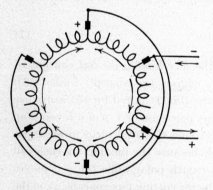

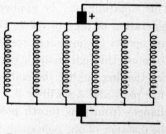

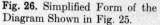

Fig. 25. Symbolic Diagram of a Six-Pole Lap Winding Showing Parallel Paths.

Fig. 26. Simplified Form of the Diagram Shown in Fig. 25.

is indicated as a coil, and the commutator bars are not shown. It will be noted that the positive brushes and negative brushes are connected in parallel respectively, giving six paths in parallel for the six-pole machine. Accordingly, this diagram can be further reduced to the simple parallel circuit of Fig. 26.

A symbolic diagram for a six-pole simplex wave winding is given in Fig. 27. Brushes of the same polarity are connected by one or several armature coils in parallel, depending upon the number of commutator bars spanned by a brush. The coils functioning in this manner are inactive in so far as they are

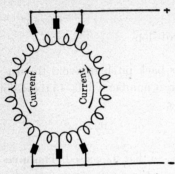

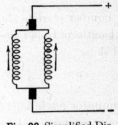

Fig. 27. Symbolic Diagram of a Six-Pole Simplex Wave Winding.

Fig. 28. Simplified Diagram of Fig. 27.

not contributing to the generated emf between positive and negative brushes. These principles may be understood by studying the winding diagram of the four-pole machine shown in Fig. 13. The six-pole machine represented by Fig. 27 has only two paths in parallel and its circuit may be further simplified to the symbolic form shown in Fig. 28.

Electromotive Force Induced in Windings. The calculation of the emf induced in an armature winding between the positive and negative brushes follows from the fundamental voltage equation 30, page 362, if incremental values of flux and time are used.

$$E = N \frac{\Delta\phi}{\Delta t} 10^{-8}. \tag{7}$$

This equation may be applied to either the *flux linking the coil* concept of generation of an emf, or to the *conductors cutting flux* concept. Under both concepts it is convenient to assume Δt as the time required for the armature to rotate through an angle equivalent to one pole span or $1/p$ of a revolution. For the flux linking the coil concept, N becomes the total turns in an armature path and $\Delta\phi$ will be 2 × flux per pole because the flux linking each coil changes from plus (north pole) to minus (south pole) while the coil moves the distance of one pole span. For the conductor cutting flux concept, N is the effective number of inductors per armature path and $\Delta\phi$ is the flux per pole. It is apparent that both concepts give the same result because in one case the number of turns is one-half the number of inductors and the change in flux is two times the flux per pole, while in the other case the number of inductors is double the number of turns and the flux is that of one pole only. The increment of time Δt is the same for both concepts.

The conductor cutting flux concept is the more natural one to use in d-c machines and is illustrated by the following example.

Example. Assume an eight-pole, wave-wound dynamo having 400,000 maxwells per pole and rotating at 600 rpm. The armature has 123 slots and there are 3 coils per slot, each having 2 turns.

The solution of the problem requires the determination of (1) the effective number of inductors in each armature path, and (2) the time required for each inductor to cut the flux per pole, given as 400,000 lines. The total number of inductors on the armature is 123 (slots) × 3 (coils per slot) × 2 (turns per coil) × 2 (inductors per turn) = 1476 inductors. A wave winding has only two paths in parallel; therefore the number of effective inductors in series per path is

$$\frac{\text{Number of inductors}}{\text{Number of paths}} = \frac{1476}{2} = 738 = Z_a.$$

Each inductor cuts all of the flux per pole ($\Delta\phi$) during the time required for it to move the distance of one pole span (Δt). The time for one revolution is 1/600 of a minute, or $1/600 \times 60 = 1/10$ second. The time to pass one pole $= 1/p$ of the time for one revolution $= 1/8 \times 1/10 = 1/80$ second $= \Delta t$. Substituting these values in the general equation, we find

$$E = Z_a \frac{\Delta\phi\ 10^{-8}}{\Delta t} = \frac{738 \times 400,000 \times 10^{-8}}{1/80} = 236 \text{ volts.}$$

The solution for a lap winding would have been identical except for the number of paths in the armature, eight instead of two. This would have given one fourth as many inductors in each path, and hence one fourth the generated emf.

A special formula may be deduced from the general one (equation 7) for application to d-c dynamos.

Let Z be the total number of inductors on the armature

ϕ the flux in maxwells per pole

n the speed in rpm

p the number of poles

a the number of parallel paths through the armature.

Then from equation (7)

$$N = \frac{Z}{a} \text{ (inductors in series per path)}$$

$$\Delta\phi = \phi \text{ (the flux per pole)}$$

$$\Delta t = \frac{1}{p} \times \text{time of one revolution}$$

$$= \frac{1}{p} \times \frac{1}{\frac{n}{60}} = \frac{60}{pn}$$

and the generated emf is

$$E = \frac{Z\phi np\ 10^{-8}}{a\ 60} \text{ volts} \tag{8}$$

If ϕ is expressed in webers instead of maxwells, equation 8 becomes

$$E = \frac{Z\phi_{\text{webers}} \, np}{a \, 60} \text{ volts.} \tag{9}$$

Determination of Type of Winding. A common problem in the design of a dynamo is the determination of the type of winding (lap or wave), and number of coils when various factors of rating and mechanical construction are given.

Example. Find a winding that will produce 225 volts on an 8-pole dynamo rotating at 600 rpm, with 400,000 maxwells per pole and 123 slots on the armature core.

We have
$$E = Z_a \frac{\Delta\phi \, 10^{-8}}{\Delta t}$$

whence
$$225 = Z_a \frac{400,000 \, 10^{-8}}{1/80}$$

or $Z_a = 703$ inductors in series per path.

The winding can be found by trial. Assume a simplex wave winding with three coils per slot. Then we may write

$$\text{Total inductors necessary} = 2 \times 703 = 1406$$

$$\text{Inductors per slot} = \frac{1406}{123} = 11.4.$$

For three coils per slot, there would be $3 \times 2 = 6$ coil edges per slot. This gives $11.4/6 = 1.9$ inductors per coil edge. The inductors per coil edge must be an integer, so that the nearest whole number 2 would be chosen. A slight adjustment of either the speed or the flux could be made to give the required emf.

If a simplex lap winding had been assumed, the total number of inductors would be $703 \times 8 = 5624$. Hence we have

$$\text{Inductors per slot} = \frac{5624}{123} = 45.7$$

$$\text{Inductors per coil edge} = \frac{45.7}{6} = 7.6.$$

Thus, eight inductors per coil edge or eight turns per coil would be necessary for a simplex lap winding.

The above computations are based on the induced voltage which in the generator is the terminal voltage *plus* the armature resistance drop, while in the motor it is the terminal voltage minus the armature resistance drop.

Equalizing Connections. It is natural to assume that the emf's induced in the different parallel paths of lap windings are exactly equal, but this assumption is seldom true. A study of the developed winding of Fig. 18 shows that the flux from the adjacent poles 1 and 2 produces the emf in the path between brushes 1 and 2, and the flux from poles 2 and 3 the emf between brushes 2 and 3, etc. If the flux through the armature from pole 1 to 2 is not the same as from 3 to 2, the voltage induced in the two paths will not be the same. In like manner, the emf's induced in the other paths may differ. Since all of these paths are in parallel (Fig. 32), the unequal induced voltages will cause circulating currents in the windings and through the brushes. Such circulating currents will cause unnecessary heating of the coils and brushes and will tend to produce poor commutation.

Unequal fluxes from the poles of a dynamo are due to unequal reluctances in the magnetic circuit. Thus, the armature core may be closer to some poles than others, due to wear of bearings, springing of the armature shaft, or inaccuracies in alignment of poles or armature during assembly of the machine. It is also evident that impurities of material, blowholes, etc., may alter the reluctance of some parts of a magnetic circuit and thus produce unequal fluxes from the poles. A small change in the length of the air gap causes a relatively large change in the reluctance of the magnetic circuit. Any of the above factors might cause an unbalance in flux sufficient to unbalance the induced emf's by 4 per cent. If one half the paths have an emf 4 per cent below and one half 4 per cent above the average, a current will flow in the winding which will cause a voltage drop of 4 per cent. The voltages of the two sets of paths would be equalized through the agency of those drops. A 100-kilowatt dynamo has a resistance drop (RI) due to a full-load current of about 4 per cent. Thus, the above assumption of flux unbalance would cause a circulating current equal to full load to flow when the machine was running idle. Any load whatever placed on such a machine would cause it to exceed its safe operating temperature.

Objectionable circulating currents due to unequal fluxes on lap-wound armatures can be remedied by the use of equalizing or cross connections. Equalizing connections consist of heavy copper conductors which connect points on the armature winding two poles apart and which normally should be at the same potential. These connections may be made to copper rings on the pulley end of the armature, as illustrated in Fig. 29, or they may be made on the commutator end, as illustrated in Fig. 30. Past practice used the equalizer rings connected to the back-end turns of the coils. It was considered that the use of from three to six rings (three to six points in each path) was sufficient to reduce the unbalance in voltage to satisfactory proportions. Recent practice has tended toward placing the connections on the commutator end and to placing an equalizer connection on every coil. The appearance of these front-connected equalizers, as illustrated in Fig. 31,

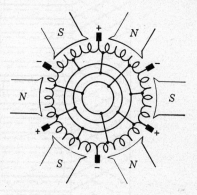

Fig. 29. Equalizing Connections.

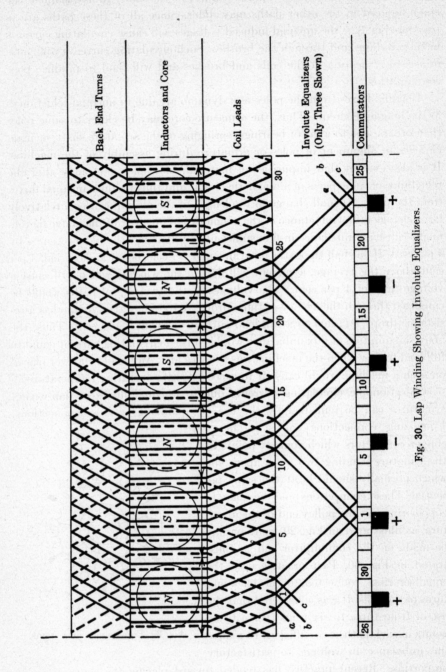

Fig. 30. Lap Winding Showing Involute Equalizers.

Back End Turns

Inductors and Core

Coil Leads

Involute Equalizers
(Only Three Shown)

Commutators

has given rise to the term **involute equalizers.** The circuits of the involute equalizers are clearly shown in the developed diagram of Fig. 30.

Theory of Armature Equalizing Connections. It was originally assumed that the use of equalizers would provide a low-resistance path for the circulating currents thus keeping them from passing through the brushes and from interfering with good commutation. Their adoption did produce this very beneficial effect. In addition, the use of equalizing connections produces an electromagnetic action which counteracts the very cause of circulating currents. In other words, the induced circulating currents oppose the differences in flux which produce

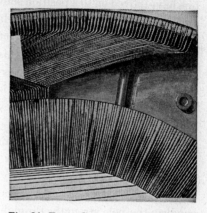

Fig. 31. Front-Connected or Involuted Equalizers.

them. This action may be understood by consideration of a four-pole machine having poles of such strength that two armature paths have emf's equal to each other, but higher than the two equal emf's of the other two paths, as illustrated in Fig. 32. The paths having the higher emf's are at the instant under poles of greater strength. The unbalanced emf of 2 volts will cause a current to flow in a direction from the higher to the lower potential. The direction of this unbalanced emf is shown in Fig. 33 for two of the poles on a dynamo

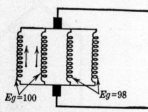

$Eg=100$ $Eg=98$

Fig. 32. Symbolic Diagram of a Four-Pole Lap Winding Having Unequal Induced Voltages in Half of the Parallel Paths.

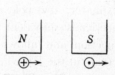

Fig. 33. Position of Coil Sides when Induced Voltage Is a Maximum.

having the greatest field strength. The circulating current which flows through the coils and equalizers is not commutated; hence it is an alternating current. An alternating current rises to a maximum, falls to zero, reverses, builds up to a maximum in the negative direction, and then falls to zero, etc. The maximum value of an alternating current does not occur at the same time as the maximum value of the emf which induces it, and it may fall behind (in time) the emf if the circuit contains inductance (page 385). Thus, if the unbalanced emf reaches its maximum value in the position of Fig. 33, the current is then being accelerated and may not reach its maximum until the particular inductors have moved on to a position shown in Fig. 34. In this position, the magnetomotive force of the coil is in the direction of the arrow, which is opposite to the direction of the mmf of the south pole. There-

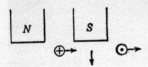

Fig. 34. Position of Coil Sides when Current Through Equalizing Connections Is a Maximum Because of High Inductance and Negligible Resistance.

fore, this delayed current tends to demagnetize the poles which are too strong. Since the circulating current is being forced against the direction of the induced voltage in the paths having only 98 volts, it will be reversed relatively with respect to the other pair of poles. Thus, it will tend to strengthen the flux from the weaker poles. Therefore, the tendency of the currents flowing in the armature windings due to the equalizer connections is to equalize the pole strengths through the agency of magnetic reactions from the armature. The circulating currents due to magnetic unbalance are small when equalizers are used.

In the wave winding, there are only two paths through the armature, and the inductors comprising each path are distributed uniformly around the armature. Thus, unequal fluxes from the poles cannot produce any unbalanced emf in the armature paths, and equalizer connections are never needed.

Frog-Leg Windings. Frog-leg windings consist of a lap and wave winding placed on the same armature, in the same slots, and connected to the same commutator bars. Each coil of the wave winding connects commutator bars which are approximately two pole spans apart. This connection is equivalent to an equalizing connection and allows the unbalanced currents in the lap winding to flow in the wave winding. This arrangement permits the equalizing connections to contribute toward the output of the machine. The windings are called **frog-leg windings** because of the peculiar appearance of the lap-wound coil and wave-wound coil, which are taped together and placed in the same slots. The number of turns on the lap and wave windings must be chosen

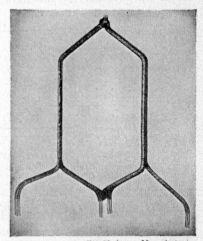

Courtesy Allis-Chalmers Manufacturing Company

Fig. 35. Frog-Leg Winding Element.

so that both windings induce the same voltage between brushes. A frog-leg winding element is shown in Fig. 35.

Lap Winding *vs.* **Wave Winding.** The wave winding has many advantages over the lap winding. Since it has only two paths through the armature, it has fewer inductors than the lap winding. The smaller number of inductors means fewer total turns and fewer turns per coil. It also frequently leads to fewer coils to form, fewer coils to place on the armature, and fewer coils to connect to the commutator. These reductions result in a saving in labor and some saving in materials. The inductors of the wave winding carry a larger current and have a larger cross section than those of corresponding lap winding. The copper inductors of larger cross section cost less per pound than the smaller ones required for lap windings. All inductors and coils must be carefully insulated. The fewer inductors of the wave winding require less space for the insulation material for the individual inductors, so that the space factor (ratio of space occupied by copper in a slot to the total space available in a slot) is higher than for lap windings. The reduction in the space required for insulation aids in the heat transfer from the copper, so that the winding should operate at a lower temperature. The wave winding never requires equalizer connections; the lap winding does. The wave winding requires only one pair of brushes, which is an advantage in some cases.

The wave winding has certain limitations. If the current output of a machine is very large the cross section of the conductor for a simplex wave winding, which has only two parallel paths, becomes too large to be formed, placed in slots, and connected to the commutator bars satisfactorily. Also the eddy current losses in the large conductor become excessive. On this account some designers have deemed it advisable to give serious consideration to using lap windings when the armature current at rated load exceeds about 400 amperes. Furthermore, in machines of a sufficiently low voltage rating in comparison with the amount of pole flux and number of poles, the required number of turns per coil is less than one. Since it is impossible to have less than one turn per coil, the designer is forced to employ a lap winding. For machines of a given voltage rating the required number of conductors in series between brushes decreases when the size of the machine increases. Ultimately this means a reduction of the number of coils, and consequently a smaller number of commutator bars. The voltage per bar therefore increases and poor commutation becomes probable. In some instances this factor becomes of such importance as to require the use of a lap winding.

The pronounced advantage of the wave winding cause it to be used in over 90 per cent of all machines built. In general, it is used in all machines up to and including 75 horsepower capacity. It is also used in all high-voltage machines up to several hundred horsepower. The lap winding is used only when one or more of the foregoing limitations preclude the use of a wave winding. This occurs mostly on large-capacity dynamos having a relatively low voltage and high current output.

PROBLEMS

The first 31 problems are listed in the table below. Supply the answers denoted by the question marks. State where dummy coils are required and whether winding is progressive or retrogressive.

PROBLEM	TYPE OF WINDING	POLES	SLOTS	COILS PER SLOT	TURNS PER COIL	INTERPOLES	PITCHES	FLUX PER POLE	RPM	EMF	COIL RESISTANCE (OHMS)	ARMATURE RESISTANCE (OHMS)
1.	s. lap	6	73	1			?					
2.	s. wave	6	73	1			?					
3.	s. wave	6	71	1			?					
4.	s. wave	6	71	1		I	?					
5.	s. wave	6	71	2		I	?					
6.	s. wave	6	71	3		I	?					
7.	s. lap	6	71	2		I	?					
8.	s. lap	4	47	2	4		?					
9.	s. wave	4	47	2	4		?					
10.	d. lap	6	123	2	1	I	?					
11.	d. lap	8	141	2	2	I	?				.0012	?
12.	d. wave	10	123	3	1		?				?	.24
13.	s. wave	10	161	3	2	I	?	1.5×10^6	500	?	?	.36
14.	s. wave	4	47	1	5			0.6×10^6	1500	?		
15.	s. lap	4	47	3	4	1	?					
16.	s. lap	4	47	3	4	I		0.8×10^6	900	?		
17.	s. wave	4	47	3	2		?	2.7×10^6	?	550		
18.	s. wave	4	47	3	2			1.4×10^6	1000	?	?	0.4
19.	s. wave	6	97	2	3	I	?	?	800	110	6×10^{-4}	?
20.	s. lap	6	97	2	3	I	?	?	1600	110	6×10^{-4}	?
21.	d. wave	10	112	2	4	I	?	0.8×10^6	?	220		
22.	s. wave	8	147	3	2	I	?	1.2×10^6	?	440		
23.	s. wave	8	146	3	2	I	?					
24.	?	4	63	1	?		?	2×10^6	475	120		
25.	?	8	167	3	?	I	?	1.75×10^6	375	220		
26.	?	4	97	2	?			0.49×10^6	1200	230		
27.	?	8	137	3	?	I	?	3×10^6	600	240		
28.	?	8	123	2	?	I	?	1.2×10^6	400	120		
29.	?	8	123	3	?	I		1.2×10^6	400	240		
30.	?	8	163	2	?	I		1.6×10^6	640	220		
31.	s. lap	8	83	?	?			2×10^6	720	240		

32. A 10-pole, simplex lap-wound generator is built for 110 volts and 600 amp capacity. It has an armature resistance of 0.0072 ohm and is wound in 163 slots, 2 coils per slot, and 3 turns per coil.

  a. Find the resistance per coil and resistance per turn.

  b. Find the average emf generated per coil when the armature induced emf is 114.32 volts.

c. If the coils of this generator were reconnected to form a simplex wave-wound generator, find the new voltage and current ratings, and new armature resistance.

d. Find the kilowatt rating before and after the change in coil connections.

e. Compare the armature I^2R heating at full load before and after change.

f. Based upon rated voltage for the respective connections, calculate the percentage armature IR drop before and after the change in connections.

33. The armature in Prob. 8 is wound with No. 12 AWG wire and the coils have a mean length per turn of 24 in. Calculate the armature resistance at 20 C.

34. If the full-load current in Prob. 19 is 150 amp, what would be the flux per pole if the terminal potential of the generator were 110 volts? *Hint:* Induced emf must be greater than the terminal potential by the armature resistance drop.

35. If the armature coils of Prob. 9 have a mean length per turn of 20 in. and the dynamo has an armature resistance of 0.395 at 20 C when the armature is contacted at the positive and negative brush positions without short-circuiting any coils, find the gauge size of wire used in the armature.

36. If the dynamo in Prob. 19 were to be operated as a motor at full-load current of 150 amp on a line of 110 volts, what flux per pole would be needed? *Hint:* Induced emf in a motor is less than the terminal voltage by the amount of the armature resistance drop.

37. A 10-pole simplex wave generator has a full-load current rating of 200 amp and a full-load terminal potential of 1200 volts. It has 157 slots, 3 coils per slot, and 2 turns per coil, and an armature resistance of 0.24 ohm.

a. The above generator is to be reconnected to form a simplex lap-wound generator operating at the same speed and same flux per pole. What would be the emf and terminal potential after the change in connection?

b. After changing to lap winding, find the new current and kilowatt rating.

c. After changing to lap, find the new armature resistance.

d. What is the per cent IR drop in the armature before and after change in connections based upon emf as 100 per cent?

e. If the mean length per turn of the armature coil is 64 in., what is the circular mil cross section of the strap copper used, assuming the temperature is the standard hot temperature of 75° C when the resistance was taken?

CHAPTER V

Armature Reaction

Armature Fields. The inductors on the armature of a loaded dynamo carry a current proportional to the load. The current flowing in these inductors produces magnetomotive forces and fields in the surrounding region. These fields produced by the load current in the armature inductors react with any other fields which may be present and constitute what is termed **armature reaction.** The nature and effect of the armature fields may be understood from the following considerations.

A straight conductor carrying a current produces a magnetic field in the direction indicated by the application of Ampere's right-hand rule. The lines of flux around the conductor will be circles, as shown in Fig. 1, if the wire is alone, straight, and in a medium of uniform permeability. The addition of a second conductor parallel to the first and carrying an equal current in the same direction will modify the field distribution, as shown in Fig. 2. The resulting

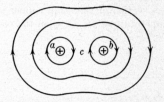

Fig. 1. Magnetic Field About a Straight Conductor Carrying a Current.

Fig. 2. Magnetic Field About Two Parallel Conductors in Proximity Carrying Currents in the Same Direction.

field has two groups of magnetic lines: (1) those which link one conductor only, and (2) those which link both conductors. This configuration follows because the fields surrounding conductors a and b neutralize each other at one central point c. At other points between the conductors the neutralization is not perfect, and in other parts of the surrounding region the fields assist each other. The same method of analysis may be carried further by taking a group of eight conductors, as shown in Fig. 3. Here some lines of flux link with one conductor only and the remainder link with two or more conductors. This group of parallel conductors may be referred to as a *band or belt of conductors.*

The armature of a dynamo has two or more belts of inductors on its surface. The inductors under each pole span carry current in the same direction and constitute a current belt, as was shown in Fig. 12, page 51. Direct-current machines usually have two layers per slot, and more than one inductor per winding element, but this does not appreciably change the type of fields produced. However, the presence of iron in the armature core, the armature teeth, and the pole faces does influence the direction of the flux paths.

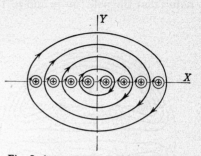

Fig. 3. Approximate Field About a Belt of Conductors Carrying Currents in the Same Direction.

The flux distribution in a bipolar dynamo due to current in the armature inductors alone is illustrated in Fig. 4. This schematic diagram assumes that the air gap is uniform and that the brushes are connected (via commutator and leads) to inductors lying half way between the pole tips (mechanical neutral). The general direction of the magnetic field due to the current in the armature inductors is along the line of the brush position or brush axis. This direction is at right angles to the center line through the field poles. The flux lines represented by *c* and *d* are small in number as compared to those entering the pole faces, because of the high reluctance of the path through air in passing from the armature to the field yoke.

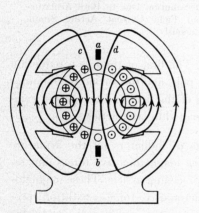

Fig. 4. Approximate Field Distribution in a Dynamo Due to Current in the Armature Alone.

The distribution of the flux in a bipolar dynamo due to the coils on the main field poles is shown in Fig. 5. This figure likewise assumes a uniform width of air gap and a uniform reluctance of the gap except for the local irregularities due to the slots on the armature. This results in an approximately uniform distribution of flux under the pole faces. A study of this flux distribution and the contrasting distribution due to the armature alone will indicate the probable resultant flux distribution under load. The resultant distribution of flux is indicated in Fig. 6. The flux between the field poles has been skewed by the combination of field current and armature current acting simultaneously. At the upper pole tip *k* and at the lower pole tip *l*, the field, due to the armature inductors, is in the same direction as the main field; hence it tends to concentrate the flux at these points. In a similar manner, the flux density is greatly reduced at the pole tips m and n. This shift in the density of the flux under the

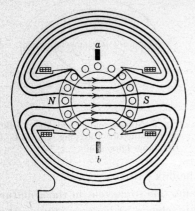

Fig. 5. General Distribution of the Flux in a Dynamo Due to the Field Mmf Acting Alone.

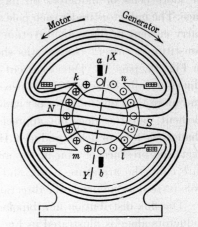

Fig. 6. Combined or Resultant Field Distribution Due to Both Armature and Field Current Acting Simultaneously.

pole faces produces two unfavorable results. The first of these is a reduction in the total or effective flux issuing from each pole, and the second is commutation difficulties which arise from the shifting of the field and the axis of commutation. Both of these difficulties will be treated in later articles.

Definition of Armature Reaction. The belts of inductors on the armature carrying current in a given direction produce magnetomotive forces and resultant magnetic fields, as explained in the preceding article. These magnetomotive forces and fields react with the magnetomotive force (excitation) produced by the winding on the field poles. This reaction causes a *change in flux paths* and *in the magnitude of the resultant flux* entering the armature. These reactions lead to two definitions of *armature reaction*. Thus, in the minds of some engineers, armature reaction may be considered as the *magnetomotive force* produced by the current flowing in the armature inductors. This conception pictures armature reaction as a *cause*. In the minds of other engineers, armature reaction is considered as the resultant *distortion of the flux* and the *change in magnitude of the flux* in the magnetic circuit. This conception visualizes armature reaction as an *effect*.

Cross-Magnetizing Armature Reaction. It has been shown that the load current in the armature inductors tends to produce a field through the armature coil which is at right angles or crosswise to that due to the field winding alone.

This crosswise action has been aptly termed **cross-magnetizing armature re-action.** Cross magnetization produces two detrimental effects. One effect, distortion of the main field, has been explained previously. The other effect of the cross-magnetizing armature reaction is a demagnetizing effect on the field accompanied by a possible reduction in the field flux. The reason for this second effect is not so obvious, since it follows from a consideration of the magnetization curve of the iron and the magnetomotive forces acting at the pole tips.

The cross-magnetizing ampere-turns which lie between the pole tips of adjacent poles act through a path of high reluctance and have little effect upon the flux of the field poles. But those cross-magnetizing ampere-turns due to the inductors lying directly under the pole faces are quite effective and are the ones to be considered. These inductors together with the path of the flux which they produce are shown in Fig. 7. This figure shows that the mmf produced by

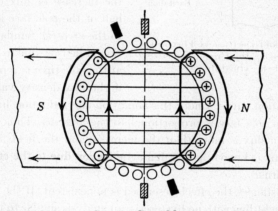

Fig. 7. Inductors Causing Cross-Magnetization in the Pole Faces.

the inductors opposes the flux of the north pole at the upper tip and assists it at the lower tip. The total mmf of these inductors in ampere-turns is equal to the number of inductors under a pole face multiplied by the armature current per inductor. Half of this mmf is considered to act at each pole tip. Therefore the cross-magnetizing ampere-turns producing magnetization or demagnetization per pole tip are

$$\text{Inductors under one half the pole face} \times \frac{\text{armature current}}{\text{paths}}. \qquad (1)$$

The effect of this mmf on the pole tips will be shown by referring to the magnetization curve in Fig. 8. In this figure, Ob represents the ampere-turns of excitation due to the field winding alone for the armature teeth, air gap, and pole face. The flux density over the pole face produced by this mmf is bf. The total flux from the pole would then be proportional to the rectangular area *aefgca*, the dimension of the pole perpendicular to the paper being the constant of proportionality. The actual distribution of mmf produced by the conductors under the pole face is shown in Fig. 9. At point *b*, which corresponds to the center of the pole face, the mmf of the armature inductors is zero, but it increases on either side of the center, aiding the mmf of the pole to the right of the center *b* and decreasing it to the left. The increase in density at the pole tip *c* due to the cross-magnetizing turns is represented by *gj* (Fig. 8), and the increase of flux over the right half of the pole face is proportional to the area *fjg*. Similarly, the reduction in density due to the same mmf at the pole tip *a* is represented by *ed* if the flux density variation follows the magnetization curve.

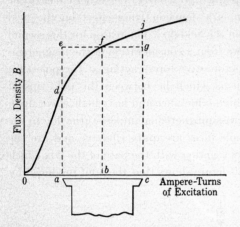

Fig. 8. Increase and Decrease of Flux in the Pole Face Caused by the Cross-Magnetizing Ampere-Turns of the Armature.

Under this condition the reduction in flux over the left half of the pole face is proportional to the area *def*. Thus it is seen that the decrease in flux is more than the increase, and the field flux as a whole is reduced. This is known as the **demagnetization due to the cross-magnetizing ampere-turns.**

In some instances the effect described is nonexistent. If the magnetization curve is a straight line with no hysteresis, an analysis similar to that illustrated in Fig. 8 shows no change in flux. Even in the practical case of operation on the so-called straight-line portion of the magnetization curve, the demagnetization is of negligible proportions. If hysteresis effects are considered, the demagnetizing mmf *ba*, Fig. 8, will cause a reduction of flux density from *e* to some value higher than *d*. It is conceivable that for some type of magnetic material this effect might be of such proportions as to cause not only no demagnetization but might even result in increased magnetization.

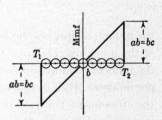

Fig. 9. Distribution of the Mmf Produced by the Inductors Under the Pole Face.

The usual result of cross-magnetizing armature reaction is to cause enough demagnetization to reduce the full-load generated voltage from its no-load value by about 2 to 5 per cent.

The demagnetizing effect of cross-magnetizing armature reaction can be completely neutralized by means of the compensating winding to be explained later in this chapter. It may also be reduced by increasing the reluctance of the air gap at the pole tips, where the armature reaction tends to be most effective. Two methods of increasing the pole-tip reluctance are illustrated in Figs. 10 and 11. In Fig. 10, the air gap under the pole tips is made greater than at the center of the shoe. This may be done by chamfering the pole tips, or it may be accomplished by using a greater radius of curvature for the pole face than for the armature. In Fig. 11, the pole core and shoe is made up of iron punchings which have only one pole shoe tip. If every other punching is reversed as

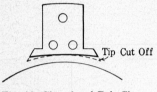 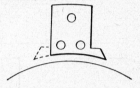

Fig. 10. Chamfered Pole Shoe.   **Fig. 11.** Special Pole-Core Lamination.

assembled, there will be only one half as much cross section of iron under the pole tips as under the pole core.

The foregoing discussion was confined to the cross-magnetizing ampere-turns that produced magnetization and demagnetization per *pole tip*. In connection with the quantitative theory of interpoles it is important to be able to calculate the cross-magnetizing ampere-turns per brush position. When the brushes are placed on the mechanical neutral, the cross-magnetizing armature reaction is the total mmf produced along the brush axis. Reference to Fig. 7 shows that the number of cross-magnetizing turns acting along the brush axis, when the brushes are on the mechanical neutral, is numerically equal to the number of inductors per pole span. Since there are two brushes along the brush axis, the turns *per brush position* are one half the number of inductors per pole span. It will be shown in the next chapter that this statement is also applicable to a machine of more than two poles. Expressed as an equation

Cross-mag. ampere turns per brush position =

$$\text{inductors in } \tfrac{1}{2} \text{ pole span} \times \frac{Ia}{\text{paths}}. \quad (2)$$

Cross Magnetization and Field-Flux Distribution. The phenomenon discussed in the preceding article can be readily visualized by a study of diagrams illustrating flux and magnetomotive force distributions on a dynamo. Parts 1 and 2 of Fig. 12 show the flux and mmf distributions due to the main field and to the armature acting individually. The flux diagram is governed by the distribution of both the mmf and the reluctance of the magnetic path. Thus, in part 2, the flux produced by the armature alone actually drops in magnitude midway between the poles where the mmf is a maximum. Part 3 of Fig. 12

clearly illustrates the distortion, shifting, and reduction of the resulting flux due to cross-magnetizing armature reaction.

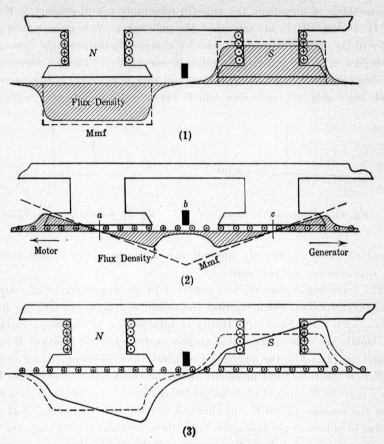

Fig. 12. (1) Magnetomotive Force and Flux Distribution Due to Field Alone. (2) Same Due to Armature Alone. (3) Combined Distribution of Fluxes.

Cross Magnetization and Flashover. *Flashover* is a complete short-circuit from brush to brush across the face of the commutator of a direct-current dynamo. The path of this short-circuit passes through the commutator segments and then arcs across the insulation between the bars. Flashover is a rather serious occurrence since it always involves the "shut down" of the machine. It may also open circuit breakers which feed other machines, and the heavy arc formed may damage the brushes and melt holes in the commutator surface.

Flashover may be due to several causes,* but is produced primarily by a severe transient armature reaction resulting from a sudden and heavy over-load upon the machine. Any load upon the armature will cause a strong cross-magnetizing armature reaction at the pole tips which tends to concentrate

*See chapter on Commutation.

the flux at some pole tips, as shown in part 3 of Fig. 12. The coils cutting flux at these tips have induced in them an abnormally high voltage, which causes an increase in voltage between adjacent commutator bars connected to these coils. If the machine is operating as a motor, this causes a greater proportion of line voltage to be absorbed in voltage drop across these bars. In some cases, the voltage is sufficiently high to cause arcing between two or three of these bars. When this occurs, it is nearly the same as short-circuiting these bars and, as a result, the line voltage is then distributed across the remaining bars, raising the average voltage per bar. Simultaneously, there is a tendency for the high flux density at the pole tips to move a little closer toward the center of the pole face. Then two or three more segments arc over and the action becomes cumulative and progressive. Finally, the arc is carried from brush to brush and a short circuit on the line is established.

Flashover can be prevented by eliminating the primary cause: cross-magnetizing armature reaction at the pole tips. This desirable result can be accomplished by the use of compensating windings in the pole faces.

The Compensating Winding. A single conductor carrying a current sets up a field, as shown in Fig. 13. If a second conductor carrying an equal and opposite current is brought parallel to the first, as shown in Fig. 14, the mmf's of the two oppose and tend to prevent any flux being set up. This principle is used in winding noninductive resistors and it suggests a method of neutralizing the mmf of armature reaction. Remembering that the effect of armature reaction on the poles is due to those inductors under the pole faces, it would be logical to place a like set of conductors in the pole face. If these pole-face conductors

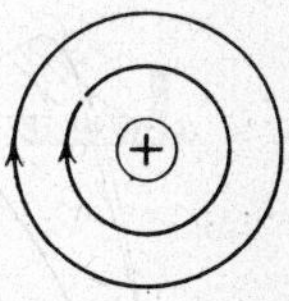

Fig. 13. Field Caused by Current in a Single Conductor.

were made to carry a current equal to that in the armature inductors but opposite in direction, pairs of conductors in pole face and armature like those in Fig. 14 would exist. The mmf's of the inductors on the armature which are under a pole face would then be neutralized and the effect of the armature reaction on the pole face would be eliminated. This is the principle of the compensating winding. In the actual design of compensating windings, no attempt is made to use the same current and number of conductors, since the desired result may be attained by making the ampere-turns of a distributed winding on the pole face equal to those produced by the armature inductors directly under the pole face.

Fig. 14. Opposition of Mmf's Due to Currents in Opposite Directions in Two Conductors in Proximity.

In general, the compensating winding is placed in slots in the pole face, as shown in Fig. 15. It is connected in series with the armature. To neutralize the effect of the armature mmf on the pole face, it is apparent from the preceding discussion that the *number of conductors in each pole face times the armature line current must equal the number of armature conductors under each pole face times*

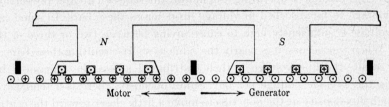

Motor ←   → Generator

Fig. 15. Compensating or Pole-Face Winding.

the armature current per path. To illustrate, assume the dynamo in Fig. 15 is wave wound and has an armature line current of 50 amperes. Since there are four conductors in each pole face and eight armature conductors under each pole face, the condition for compensation states that:

$$4 \times 50 = 8 \times \frac{50}{2}.$$

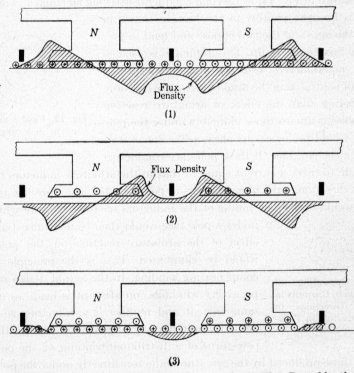

Fig. 16. Parts (1), (2), and (3) Show Respectively the Flux Caused by the Armature Current Acting Alone, the Compensating Winding Alone, and the Combination of the Two.

Since the line current appears on both sides of the equation it is apparent that if a machine is compensated at one line current it will be compensated at all values of line current. Hence compensation is independent of the value of the line current.

Example. A lap-wound dynamo has 10 poles, 860 armature conductors, and is rated at 1000 amperes. The pole face covers 70 per cent of a pole span. Calculate the number of conductors in the pole face to give full compensation.

$$\text{Conductors per pole} = \frac{860}{10} = 86.$$

$$\text{Conductors under a pole face} = 0.7 \times 86 = 60.2.$$

Let the compensating winding consist of Z_c conductors in each pole face.

$$Z_c\, 1000 = 60.2 \times \frac{1000}{10}$$

$$Z_c = 6.02. \qquad \text{Use 6 conductors.}$$

In general, the compensating winding is placed in slots in the pole faces, as shown, and is connected in series with the armature.

The distribution of the flux caused by the armature current acting alone, the compensating winding alone, and the combination of the two, is shown in parts 1, 2, and 3, respectively, of Fig. 16. These diagrams show that distortion of the flux and flashover will be prevented by a compensating winding and that the flux distribution over the pole face will be determined by the main field alone.

Another important reason for using a compensating winding is to aid commutation in machines designed to meet certain overload requirements. More will be said about this use in the next chapter.

Two pole cores containing slots for compensating windings are shown in Figs. 17 and 18. A complete compensating winding on a dynamo is shown in

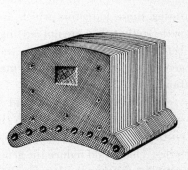

Fig. 17. Pole Core Slotted for Rectangular Compensating-Winding Conductors.

Fig. 18. Pole Core for Round Compensating-Winding Conductors.

Fig. 19. The compensating winding adds considerably to the cost of a machine and the additional expense is not justified except where the service conditions

Courtesy Allis-Chalmers Mfg. Co.

Fig. 19. Dynamo with Compensating Winding.

are unusually severe. Therefore overcompensation is never employed. Undercompensation to the extent of two thirds of full compensation is sometimes employed.

Dynamo Neutrals. The preceding discussion leads to the definition of two dynamo neutrals. In Fig. 5, the brushes are placed so that they are commutating those inductors which are moving in a direction parallel to the flux paths so that they are not cutting any flux. The brushes on the line ab half way between the pole tips are in the geometric neutral between the poles. This geometric neutral is called the **mechanical neutral,** and is fixed by the construction of the machine.

Under the condition of load (Fig. 6), the field flux has been distorted and some of the inductors close to the brush (a) on the right-hand side would be cutting flux in an opposite direction from the others with which they are in series. This would reduce the generated emf at the brushes which could be overcome by shifting the brushes to the line XY, so that the conductors, being commutated, would be moving parallel to the resultant field. This line XY

represents the **magnetic neutral** of the machine. *It might also be described as the position on the armature where no flux enters or leaves the armature.* It is evident that the position of the magnetic neutral is determined by the symmetry of the construction of the dynamo, by the current flowing in the armature, and by the excitation of the magnetic field. At no load, the magnetic neutral and the mechanical neutral will usually coincide. In fact, the mechanical neutral is used as the most convenient method of finding the magnetic neutral at no load.

Demagnetizing Armature Reaction. Most of the present-day dynamos are designed so that the brushes may be set in a position on the commutator corresponding to the mechanical neutral of the armature. A few exceptions are certain classes of generators used to excite alternating-current generator fields, most automobile generators, farm lighting generators, and some aircraft generators. All of the earlier machines, some of which are still in use plus the exceptions just noted rely upon a shifting of the brushes to care for the field distortion due to cross-magnetizing armature reaction, and also to care for certain commutation difficulties. Whenever the brushes are properly shifted on such machines, a new form of armature reaction takes place. Thus, Fig. 20

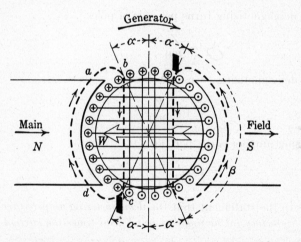

Fig. 20. Division of Armature Conductors Into Belts Producing Cross-Magnetization and Demagnetization.

shows a bipolar dynamo with the brushes shifted clockwise from the mechanical neutral by the angle α. Here the inductors on the armature may be paired together on horizontal lines to form turns which will produce the cross-magnetizing action previously discussed. It will be evident at once that there remains a group of inductors in the angle 2α near each brush which cannot be connected horizontally. These two groups may be connected vertically to form another solenoid or electromagnet. Applying Ampere's right-hand rule to this vertical band or group, we see that there exists a field directed to the left, as shown by the wide-faced arrow. This field is directly opposed to that produced by the main field; hence it is a demagnetizing reaction. This reaction which results from the brush shift is termed the **demagnetizing armature reaction.** The magnetomotive force of this reaction may be easily expressed in ampere-turns. Thus, in Fig. 20, there are four turns. If these turns bear a current of 10 amperes, they represent $4 \times 10 = 40$ demagnetizing ampere-turns. But those ampere-turns are acting on two poles, so that those effective per pole are only one half this number, or 20.

To derive the expression for the demagnetizing ampere-turns per pole for the general case, let Z be the number of conductors on the armature, α be the displacement of the brushes from the mechanical neutral in mechanical degrees, and a the number of paths through the armature. All of the conductors producing demagnetizing action per pair of poles are in the angle 4α degrees.

Number of inductors on the armature per degree $= Z/360$

Number of inductors producing demagnetizing action per pair of poles

$$= 4\alpha \cdot \frac{Z}{360}$$

Number of demagnetizing turns per pair of poles

$$= \tfrac{1}{2} \cdot 4\alpha \cdot \frac{Z}{360}$$

Number of demagnetizing turns *per pole*

$$= \tfrac{1}{2} \cdot \tfrac{1}{2} \cdot 4\alpha \cdot \frac{Z}{360}$$

Demagnetizing ampere-turns per pole

$$= \tfrac{1}{2} \cdot \tfrac{1}{2} \cdot 4\alpha \cdot \frac{Z}{360} \frac{I_a}{a} = \frac{\alpha}{360} Z \frac{I_a}{a}. \tag{3}$$

which leads to the statement that the *demagnetizing ampere-turns per pole are equal to the inductors in the angle of brush lead times the current per armature path.*

Since demagnetizing armature reaction is produced by the shifting of brushes from mechanical neutral, any construction which eliminates the need of brush shift will eliminate demagnetizing armature reaction itself. Such a construction is to be found in the interpole dynamo described in the following chapter. However, it should be noted that the prevention of demagnetizing armature reaction is merely an incidental result of the use of the interpole.

Flux Distribution When Brushes Are Shifted. The mmf due to the armature is shifted with respect to the field when the brushes are shifted from the mechani-

cal neutral. This produces a nonsymmetric distribution of flux due to the armature alone, as shown in part 2 of Fig. 21. The combination of the normal field
mmf and the shifted armature mmf produces the resultant-flux distribution
illustrated in part 3. Here the distortion of the flux is greater than before the

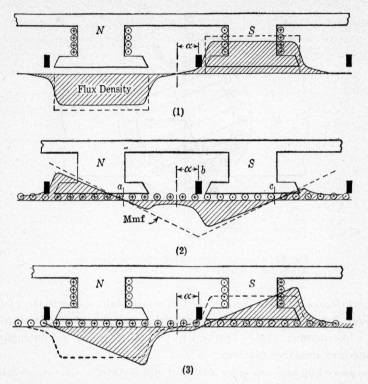

Fig. 21. Parts (1), (2), and (3), Respectively Show the Distribution of
the Mmf and Flux for the Field Alone, Armature Alone, and the Combination of These when Brushes Are Shifted.

brushes were shifted. In addition, the resultant flux (area) is much reduced
over the no-load value and over the full value with brushes on the neutral.
This greater reduction follows because demagnetizing armature reaction has
been added to the normal demagnetization due to cross-magnetization.

Components of Armature Reaction. The two forms of armature reaction just
described (cross-magnetizing and demagnetizing) are often referred to as the
components of armature reaction. This conception can be visualized from the
analysis of Fig. 22. Here it is assumed that the brushes of a bipolar dynamo
have been shifted off the geometric neutral by the angle α. The two belts of
inductors between the brushes may be connected together to form a solenoid
coil, as indicated by the parallel lines. Ampere's right-hand rule applied to
this grouping will show a field directed along the line OA. Now let the line OA

represent the magnetomotive force of the current in the armature inductors both in direction and magnitude. Also, let OF represent the magnetomotive force due to the field coils. The vector OA may be resolved into two com-

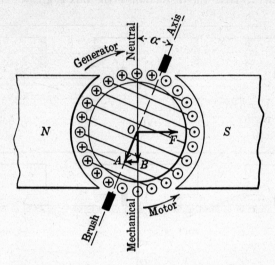

Fig. 22. Diagram Illustrating the Components of Armature Reaction.

ponents, OB and AB. The component OB acts at right angles to the main field OF; hence it is termed the **cross-magnetizing component of armature reaction.** In like manner, AB is opposed to OF and is called the **demagnetizing component of armature reaction.**

The preceding analysis gives a helpful and qualitative picture of armature reaction but the student should recognize that the concept is not rigidly correct, since it shows demagnetizing armature reaction to be proportional to sine of the angle α, whereas such reaction is really directly proportional to the angle itself, as previously demonstrated.

PROBLEMS

1. A simplex wave winding on a 4-pole generator consists of 95 coils each of which is made up of 3 turns. The full-load armature current is 24 amp. The diameter of the armature is 6.5 in., length of active conductor 4 in., and it runs at 1150 rpm. The pole face covers 70 per cent of the pole span. Calculate the cross-magnetizing ampere-turns per pole tip at full load. If this machine is reconnected in lap, calculate the cross-magnetizing ampere-turns per pole tip if the armature current output is 24 amp.

2. A simplex lap winding on a 6-pole generator is placed in 95 slots. There are 4 coils per slot and 2 turns per coil. The rated armature current output is 600 amp and the pole face covers 70 per cent of a pole span. Calculate the cross-magnetizing ampere-turns per pole tip at rated armature current.

3. Calculate the cross-magnetizing ampere-turns per pole tip for the machine of Prob. 2 if it is reconnected in wave and the armature current output is 200 amp.

4. Calculate the cross-magnetizing ampere-turns per brush position for the machine of Prob. 1 if the brushes are on the mechanical neutral and the armature current output is 24 amp.

5. If the machine of Prob. 1 is reconnected in lap, what will be the cross-magnetizing ampere-turns per brush position for an armature current output of 24 amp when the brushes are on the mechanical neutral? What will be the cross-magnetizing ampere-turns per brush position for the rated armature current output for the lap winding connection? Compare with the results in Prob. 4.

6. Calculate the cross-magnetizing ampere-turns per brush position for the machine in Prob. 2 if the brushes are on the mechanical neutral and the armature current output is 600 amp. If this machine is reconnected in wave, what will be the cross-magnetizing ampere-turns per brush position if the armature current output is 200 amp?

7. How many conductors should be placed in each pole face for a compensating winding for the machine in Prob. 1? What is the direction of current in the compensating winding?

8. If the machine of Prob. 1 is reconnected in lap, find the number of conductors to be placed in each pole face for the compensating winding. How does this number compare with that found in Prob. 7?

9. How many conductors should be placed in each pole face for a compensating winding for the machine in Prob. 2?

10. If the brushes on the machine in Prob. 1 are shifted 16 electrical degrees from the mechanical neutral, calculate the demagnetizing ampere-turns per pole at full load. How many cross-magnetizing ampere-turns per brush position are there under these conditions?

11. If the machine of Prob. 1 is reconnected in lap, what will be the demagnetizing ampere-turns per pole for an armature current output of 24 amp if the brushes are shifted 16 electrical degrees from the mechanical neutral?

12. If the brushes on the machine in Prob. 2 are shifted 6 mechanical degrees from the mechanical neutral, calculate the demagnetizing ampere-turns per pole at full load. How many cross-magnetizing ampere-turns per brush position are there under these conditions? Repeat the calculations if the machine is reconnected for wave and the armature current output is 200 amp.

CHAPTER VI

Reactance Voltage and Commutating Poles

EMF of Self-Induction. A direct current passing through a coil of wire wound on an iron core will set up a magnetic field, as shown in Fig. 1. This electromagnet possesses self-inductance and will oppose any change of current through it. Thus, if the circuit to the coil be broken, a spark or perhaps a long arc will occur at the point of the break. The break of the electric circuit tends to reduce the current to zero. The reduction of the current, in turn, reduces the mmf of the coil and the number of lines of flux. This reduction (or change) in the lines of flux threading the coil induces an emf in the coil. In accordance with Lenz's law, the direction of this emf will be such as to oppose the change which produces it. Thus, this emf will be in the same direction as the original voltage which caused the current flow. It will add to this voltage and cause a much higher voltage across the gap where the circuit is broken. This higher voltage is the cause of the spark or arc. The induced emf due to the current change is known as the **emf of self-inductance** and it always acts against the change which produces it. The average emf of self-inductance follows the equation $e = -L\,di/dt$ (page 386), and it is directly proportional to the permeability of the magnetic circuit, the rate of change of current, and the square of the number of turns.

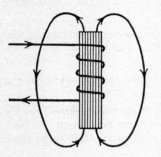

Fig. 1. Coil on an Iron Core Showing Directions of Current and Flux.

Reactance Voltage. Each coil on the armature of a dynamo has one or more turns, and these turns lie in slots which are surrounded by iron on three sides. Thus, each coil may be likened to the electromagnet described in the previous article, and possesses the same properties of self-inductance and opposition to current change. Direct current flowing in the ar-

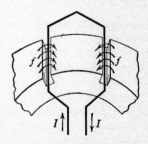

Fig. 2. Flux Linking an Armature Coil Caused by Current in the Coil.

90

mature coil sets up lines of flux, as shown in Fig. 2. A change in this current will produce a flux change and an induced emf of self-inductance reacting against this change. It should be noted that the induced emf results from *an inherent property of the coil itself and that it may be produced by a current change when the armature is stationary or in motion and regardless of the position of the coil.*

The armature of a dynamo in operation is revolving, and the coils are moving at considerable speed. Direct current is led to or from the coils by the brushes and commutator. The current in each coil must reverse during the time that the commutator bars to which the coil is connected pass under a brush. This reversal requires a change of current from its full magnitude in one direction to the same magnitude in the opposite direction. Reference to Figs. 11, page 50, and 13, page 52, will show how this current changes in the lap and wave winding, respectively. During the reversal, a coil or several coils in series are short-circuited by a brush. The reversing current induces an emf of self-induction which opposes the current change. This *emf of self-inductance* is called **reactance voltage.** It slows down the reversal of current and tends to produce a spark or arc as the trailing bar leaves the brush. Reactance voltage always has been a detriment to good commutation and is one of two important limiting factors in the design of a direct-current dynamo. The magnitude of the reactance voltage depends directly upon the square of the number of turns in the coil, the current flowing in each inductor, the reluctance of the magnetic circuit of the slot, and the speed of rotation.

It is *impossible to prevent* the existence of reactance voltage because it is due to an inherent property of the coil circuit. However, methods have been developed for counteracting or neutralizing reactance voltage through the use of an opposing voltage. The coils on the armature are in motion during the period of commutation and their inductors can be made to cut a flux by this movement and thereby generate a counter emf. This counter emf is a rotational emf and is called **the commutating emf.** Commutating emf's may be produced by the proper shift of the brushes on noninterpole machines or by the use of interpoles.

Neutralizing Reactance Voltage by Brush Shift. The brushes on a dynamo without interpoles may be shifted from what corresponds to the mechanical neutral position for the inductors for two reasons. The first is to make allowance for the flux distortion due to armature reaction and the second to neutralize the reactance voltage of the coil undergoing commutation.

An analysis of the proper brush shift for a generator can be made in Fig. 3. Assuming the indicated polarity of the field poles, a clockwise rotation, and a brush setting on the mechanical neutral, the emf generated in the armature inductors will have a direction as indicated by the inner circle of symbols. Since the machine is a generator, the current will flow in the same direction as the induced electromotive force and may be represented in direction by the outer circle of inductors. Now applying Ampere's right-hand rule, we see that the current in the armature inductors under the pole face will tend to set up a cross field, as indicated. At the leading pole tips, the direction of this field is opposite to that produced by the field-coil winding, while at the trailing tips the two fields will have the same direction across the air gap. This will cause a concentrated flux at the trailing pole tips and will cause the field flux issuing from the poles to shift in the clockwise direction. If the conductors undergoing commutation are to lie in the magnetic neutral, the brushes should be shifted from the mechanical neutral to a new position *ab*. With the brushes shifted to this position, an inductor *X* in the magnetic neutral will have induced in it a reactance voltage "in" as indicated, due to the self-induction of the coil undergoing commutation. But at the magnetic neutral, the inductor is not cutting any flux; hence there is no electromotive force induced to counteract this reactance voltage. If the brushes were shifted counterclockwise from the magnetic neutral (*ab*), the electromotive force induced due to the rotation would be "in" (as shown by the inner circle of signs) and in the same direction as the reactance

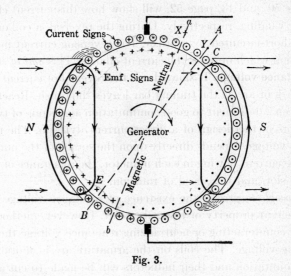

Fig. 3.

voltage, so that such a shift would make commutation worse. But if the brushes are shifted clockwise from the magnetic neutral to a position *AB*, the flux will be cut by the conductors under the brush at position *Y* in a direction opposite to the cutting of flux by these same conductors before reaching the magnetic neutral *AB*. In this way a commutating emf due to rotation will oppose and tend to neutralize the reactance voltage. Hence, *in a generator, the brushes should be shifted forward in the direction of rotation* in order to secure the best operating conditions.

A similar analysis for the proper brush shift for a motor can be obtained from Fig. 4. Here the field polarity and direction of rotation has been shown the same as for the preceding case. For the same direction of rotation, the generated or *counter emf* in the armature inductors must have the same direction as in the preceding case and is illustrated by the symbols of the inner circle. The direction of current through the armature inductors for this direction of rotation will now be opposite that of the previous case (generator), and will be opposite to the direction of the counter emf (apply Ampere's right-hand rule). The reversed current through the armature inductors will tend to set up a field as indicated. This field opposes the field produced by the field-pole windings at the trailing pole tips and aids at the leading pole tips. Such a combination causes the flux to concentrate at the leading pole tips of the motor. Thus, the resultant field has been shifted against the direction of rotation and the brushes must be shifted backward to bring the inductors undergoing commutation into the magnetic neutral position. With the inductors undergoing commutation in a magnetic neutral, the reactance voltage of the coil (position X) will not be neutralized. A brush shift clockwise from the

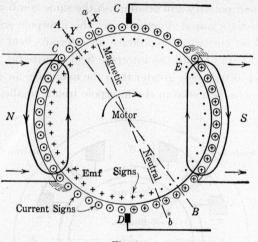

Fig. 4.

magnetic neutral will induce an emf of rotation in the same direction as the reactance voltage and make sparking of the brushes worse. A brush shift counterclockwise will induce a commutating emf of rotation in the same direction as the counter emf (inner circle of signs); hence it will tend to neutralize the reactance voltage. Thus, *in the case of a motor, the brushes should be shifted backward* (against the direction of rotation) in order to secure the best commutating conditions under load.

Commutating Poles. Commutating poles, also called **interpoles,** are small narrow poles placed midway between the main field poles on a dynamo, as illustrated in Fig. 5. The field winding on the interpole consists of a few turns of large cross section, and is connected in series with the load current of the armature.

A preceding article has shown how satisfactory commutation may be obtained by shifting the brushes of the generator forward as in Fig. 3. This shift placed the inductor undergoing commutation in a weak field flux near the south pole. This same result could have been obtained by keeping the inductor in the mechanical neutral position (brush position) and moving a piece of the south pole (near C) counterclockwise to a position above this inductor. Such a piece of the south pole having the proper strength would counteract the flux at that point due to armature reaction and also induce an emf to oppose the reactance voltage. Similar reasoning will show that for the motor of Fig. 4 the inductors undergoing commutation could remain in the mechanical neutral position if a piece of the north pole near C were moved into the mechanical neutral position. It should be noted also that the strength of the section of a pole which should be moved to the mechanical neutral position will depend upon the magnitude of the armature reaction and, in turn, upon the load current of the machine.

Obviously, an interpole placed at the mechanical neutral and having the proper strength and polarity will accomplish the same result as the section of the main pole just suggested. Furthermore, the interpole winding, being in series with the load current, will produce an interpole field directly proportional to the load current until the interpole field approaches saturation. The interpole air gap is often made greater than the main pole air gap. This makes the drop in magnetic potential in the interpole iron a smaller fraction of the

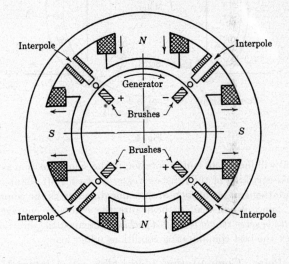

Fig. 5. Positions of Interpoles on a Dynamo.

total drop of magnetic potential for the complete interpole magnetic circuit. On this account the greater interpole air gap contributes toward increasing the linearity between interpole mmf and interpole flux. In this way the interpole action is entirely automatic and may give ideal commutation at all loads within the limits of the rating of the machine.

Since the interpole permits commutation to take place at the mechanical neutral position for the inductors, the dynamo may be operated equally well in either direction and also either as a motor or as a generator. This is true because for a reversal of direction of rotation of a generator the generated emf and armature current reverse, thus reversing the polarity of the interpole field. And in the case of a motor operating in the same direction as a generator, the armature current will reverse, and hence reverse the polarity of the interpole field as required.

Magnetomotive Force Required for Interpoles. The general theory of the interpole is relatively simple and was known to electrical scientists as far back as 1890. But all applications of the principle previous to about 1900 resulted in failures to improve commutation. In fact, the commutation actually became worse when the interpole was added. The reason for this was the fact that the early experimenter merely saw the need of an interpole mmf sufficiently strong to counteract the cross-magnetizing armature reaction for brush position. Hence the interpole mmf was made of sufficient strength to balance the armature reaction. But this balance did nothing toward neutralizing the reactance voltage, and the presence of the interpole produced a low reluctance flux path

at this point which actually increased the flux linkages, and hence the reactance voltage. Since the year 1905, interpole windings have been given enough ampere-turns to neutralize cross-magnetizing ampere-turns at the brush positions, plus enough more to send a small flux into the armature.

The importance of the armature reaction to be counteracted by the interpole field and the method of computing its value can be illustrated readily, as follows. If the bipolar dynamo of Fig. 6 be assumed to be acting as a generator and to be rotating clockwise, the inductor band under the north pole will be carrying a current "in" and the

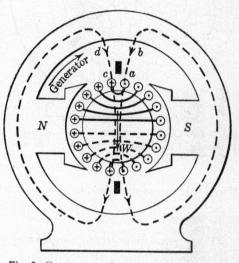

Fig. 6. Currents in the Armature Conductors Producing Cross-Magnetization at the Brush Positions of a Dynamo.

band under the south pole an outbound current. The inductors of these two current bands may be connected or tied together as indicated so as to produce a form of solenoid wound on a cylinder. Only inductors carrying current in opposite directions can be paired. Such a solenoid will tend to set up a field through the cylinder in the direction indicated by the arrow. This field is directed at the two brush positions.

In a similar manner, the four-pole dynamo of Fig. 7 may be considered with its belts of inductors as indicated by the curved lines. (Incidentally, these curved lines indicate the general direction of the normal flux paths through this armature.) Here, also, the inductor groupings will produce a cross-magnetizing field as shown by the arrows and directed *along the line* of the brush or interpole position. The mmf in ampere-turns per brush position is readily calculated. Reference to Fig. 6 will show that all inductors tied together by full lines produce a mmf at the upper brush position, while those tied by the dotted lines may be considered to act toward the lower brush. There are five turns effective at each brush position, and, if the current per path (inductor) is 10 amperes, the cross-magnetizing ampere-turns per brush (or interpole) position are $5 \times 10 = 50$. In a similar way, the multipolar dynamo of Fig. 7 has four turns per brush position and for a like current of 10 amperes would have $4 \times 10 = 40$ cross-magnetizing ampere-turns per brush position. What has been termed the **brush position** is really the proper position for the interpole. Therefore, for the general case, the *cross-magnetizing ampere-turns per interpole position* are one half the inductors per pole span times the current per inductor.

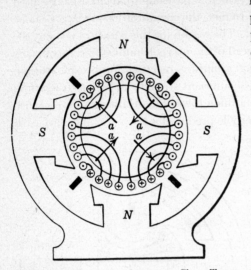

Fig. 7. Grouping of Conductors to Show Turns Producing Cross-Magnetization in a Multipolar Dynamo.

Cross-mag. ampere-turns per interpole position

$$= \text{inductors in } \tfrac{1}{2} \text{ pole span} \times \frac{I_a}{\text{paths}}. \quad (1)$$

These cross-magnetizing ampere-turns produce a cross flux midway between the pole tips, and they must be counteracted by the interpole field. In addition, the interpole field must be powerful enough to send some flux into the armature which will produce the rotational commutating emf to counteract the reactance voltage. Since there is some leakage of flux from the interpole to the main poles and some other undeterminable factors, it is customary for the designer to place on the interpole field approximately *one and one-fourth times as many ampere-turns as the cross-magnetizing ampere-turns per interpole position*. In the few cases where the machine has a compensating winding, the number obtained by the above rule is reduced by the number of ampere-turns per pole tip in the compensating winding.

The number of ampere-turns provided by the above rule is approximate and allows a liberal factor of safety. The proper adjustment for the interpole field has been obtained in two ways. The first method placed an adjustable shunt around the interpole and determined the proper resistance by experiment. This method of adjustment was satisfactory for conditions of steady load, but under sudden changes in load the self-inductance of the interpole winding opposed changes of current through it, so that the current variations passed through the noninductive shunts. Thus, under changing loads, the interpole flux is too small or too great for good commutation, and sparking occurs. The modern method of adjustment of the interpole flux is affected by a variation of the reluctance of the magnetic circuit of the interpole. This variation in reluctance is accomplished by making the interpole core too short and then filling the gap between the interpole and the yoke with magnetic and nonmagnetic shims. The proper balance of these two types of metallic shims is determined by testing the dynamo under load. Some of the later practice employs only magnetic shims to adjust the interpole air gap until the correct amount of interpole flux is secured.

The addition of the interpole improves the commutation of the direct-current dynamo so greatly that the use of the interpole has become practically universal on all machines above 1 kilowatt in size. Exceptions to its use are found in some of the generators used as exciters. Exciters are direct-current generators used to energize fields of other direct-current machines or alternating-current generators. When used to supply excitation for alternating-current generators it is sometimes desired to have the direct-current generator increase or decrease its voltage very rapidly. The omission of interpoles decreases the inductance of the total armature circuit and thereby aids in increasing the speed of response of the dynamo in changing to different terminal voltages. Again, in machines which supply relatively small load currents of comparatively steady value the flux distortion due to armature reaction and the reactance voltage are of relatively small magnitude, and satisfactory operation can be obtained without the use of interpoles.

In passing, it should be recalled that the interpole *does not neutralize or prevent* the cross-magnetizing armature reaction at the pole tips and the resulting flux distortion in the pole faces of a dynamo. But the use of the interpole *does prevent demagnetizing armature reaction* because the brushes remain on the mechanical neutral for all loads.

There are instances where only a single interpole is used. The coil edges of a given coil used on an interpole machine are separated by very nearly a full pole span or 180 degrees. During commutation either a single coil or several coils in series are short-circuited by the brushes. It is necessary simply to induce an emf in the single coil or the series circuit of the several coils in series of the proper sign and value to secure good commutation. This can be done by causing only one coil edge of the single or one coil edge of one coil of the several in series to cut the interpole flux. Hence it is sufficient to have only one interpole in a wave winding. In a lap winding one interpole for every pair of main poles is required. These relations may be understood from a study of Figs. 11 and 13, pages 50 and 52. For a two-pole machine it is plain that only one interpole is necessary. If the smallest required number of interpoles is used the strength of the interpoles must be correspondingly increased.

Flux Distribution on a Machine with Interpoles. The important part played by the interpole in the operation of a dynamo may be clearly visualized by a

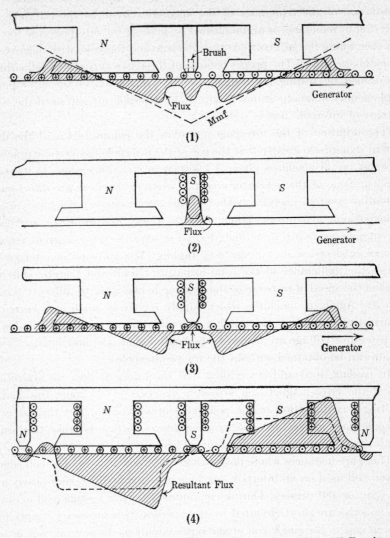

Fig. 8. Part (1) Shows Flux Distribution For the Armature Alone, (2) For the Interpole Alone (3) For the Interpole and Armature and (4) For the Field Armature, and Interpole Acting Simultaneously.

study of flux distribution diagrams. Part 1 of Fig. 8 shows how the flux due to the armature mmf alone has been increased beneath the interpole. Part 2 of this figure depicts the strong reversed flux under the interpole due to the interpole mmf. The combined fields of part 3 show the reversed flux under the interpole which generates the commutating emf to neutralize reactance voltage. The diagram of part 4 is of interest in showing that while the flux from the field poles is badly distorted, yet the interpole has provided the necessary reversed flux for satisfactory commutation. The ideal resultant flux distribution for a dynamo under load, as produced by the combined action of armature, interpoles, field, and compensating winding, is shown in Fig. 9.

Direct-current machines are sometimes used in applications where they are subject to heavy overload for short intervals of time. In some of these machines the cross-magnetizing ampere-turns per brush position becomes very large. As a result the interpole is required to produce a large number of ampere-turns to neutralize this cross-magnetization and then, in addition, must produce enough more ampere-turns to cause adequate flux for inducing the commutating emf. On this account there is a large drop in magnetic potential between various parts of the interpole core and other parts of the magnetic

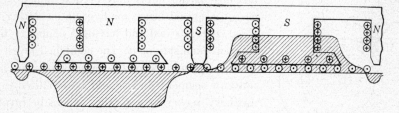

Fig. 9. Resultant Flux Distribution Caused by Combined Actions of Armature, Interpoles Field, and Compensating Windings.

circuit. This large drop in magnetic potential causes a large amount of leakage flux, that is, flux from the interpole which is not cut by the coils undergoing commutation. This leakage flux may amount to several times the value of the useful flux at overloads. In addition to not being useful, the leakage flux saturates the interpole core and thus destroys the proportionality between commutating pole mmf and flux. At overloads where this condition obtains, commutation becomes poor. In these instances the interpole alone is inadequate. The remedy is to neutralize or partially neutralize the cross-magnetizing ampere-turns of the armature by the addition of a compensating winding as discussed is the previous chapter. Through this arrangement fewer ampere-turns are required on the interpole, the drop in magnetic potential across the interpole air gap is reduced, and the leakage flux from the interpole is greatly reduced. Thus the useful interpole flux is made more nearly proportional to the load current. The factors outlined above attain such importance in machines designed to meet heavy overload requirements that they are just as important as field distortion and demagnetization in deciding whether a machine is to be compensated.

Experimental Determination of Flux Distribution. The actual flux distribution around the armature of a dynamo depends upon the interaction of the various magnetomotive forces present and the reluctance of the various parts of the magnetic circuit. The flux distribution curve is a map or curve which shows the flux density at all points around the periphery of the armature. This curve can be determined experimentally in a simple manner by determining the emf that is generated in a coil as it moves around the periphery of the armature. The magnitude of the emf that is produced in such a coil is equal to $N \, d\phi/dt$. If very short increments (arcs) along the periphery of the armature are considered, the average $e = N(\Delta\phi/\Delta t)$, where $\Delta\phi$ is equal to the flux density $B \times$ the small area on the armature represented by the arc. The number N is a constant for the inductors of a coil, and Δt is also constant for a machine operating at a constant speed. Hence the emf produced will be proportional to flux density and therefore gives a point on the flux distribution curve.

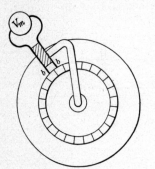

For a machine having a full-pitch winding, the flux distribution curve may be determined by the use of a special brush made of an insulating material such as wood and having a copper or brass strip on each side of it. The combined brush and insulator should be of the same width as a commutator segment and should be mounted on an auxiliary rocker arm so that it can be revolved from point to point about the commutator (Fig. 10). A low-reading voltmeter connected to the copper brushes will give a reading proportional to the flux density being cut by the coils that pass through the position corresponding to the brush position.

Fig. 10. Device for Determining the Flux Distribution For a Dynamo with a Full-Pitch Winding.

If the generator is loaded, the voltage between bars indicated by the voltmeter will be less than the induced emf by the amount of the **IR** drop in the coil. This drop can be calculated and added to the voltmeter reading to obtain the true induced emf. The flux distribution for no-load condition may be determined by raising all of the brushes from the commutator and replacing one brush with the special brush. The rocker arm of the machine may be used for revolving the special brush about the armature.

PROBLEMS

1. A 4-pole, wave-wound generator rated at 80 amp has 65 coils in 65 slots. Each coil has 2 turns. The diameter of the armature is 9 in. and the length of active conductor is 8 in. The armature runs at 1150 rpm, the thickness of insulation between commutator segments is 30 mils, the thickness of each commutator segment is 3/16 in., and a brush spans 2 segments on the commutator. The equivalent flux surrounding the armature inductors is 12 lines per ampere per inductor per inch of active conductor.

(This equivalent flux takes into account the flux which links the end connections). Calculate the average reactance voltage per coil.

2. *a.* Calculate the number of turns for each interpole for the machine of Prob. 1, page 88, when no compensating winding is used.

b. How many turns should be placed on the interpole if the machine is to be completely, that is 100 per cent, compensated?*

3. *a.* Calculate the number of turns for each interpole for the machine of Prob. 2, page 88, if a compensating winding is used.

b. Also make the calculation if the machine is uncompensated.*

4. If the machine of Prob. 2, page 88, is reconnected in wave, calculate the number of turns for each interpole if a compensating winding is employed. Also make the calculation if no compensating winding is used.*

5. If the machine of Prob. 1, page 88, is reconnected in lap, calculate the number of turns for each interpole when no compensating winding is employed. Also make the calculation if a compensating winding is used.*

* Note: The number of ampere-turns for the interpole should be calculated as one and one-fourth times the cross-magnetizing ampere-turns per interpole position. When compensating windings are called for, assume 100 per cent or full compensation, which means that the compensating winding neutralizes all of the mmf produced by only the armature conductors which are under the pole faces.

CHAPTER VII

Dynamo Voltage Characteristics

Dynamo Characteristics. The magnetization curve of Chap. III is a good example of a dynamo characteristic. This curve shows how the generated emf of a dynamo varies with the field excitation when other important factors are held constant. All dynamo characteristics follow this same principle of showing how a certain variable factor changes while another factor passes through a controlled set of values. In addition to the magnetization curve, there are three other important characteristics of dynamos. These characteristics show (1) how the terminal voltage varies with load, (2) how the speed varies with load, and (3) how the torque varies with load. This chapter will deal with the first of these characteristics.

The type of voltage characteristic which should be possessed by a dynamo when used as a generator is determined by the service requirement, namely, the type of distribution system and the load which it must supply. The voltage characteristic to be expected from a given dynamo is determined by the connection and type of winding used on its field. Both of these general considerations will be treated in the following articles.

Electric Distribution Systems. The two classes of electric distribution which have been adopted are termed the **constant-current system** and the **constant-potential system.** In the constant-current system, the various loads are connected in series and the same current exists in all of them, as shown in Fig. 1. The voltage of a dynamo supplying current to this system must vary to accommodate the changes in load as units are added or taken out of the circuit. The series system inherently tends to be of high potential and

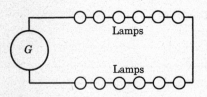

Fig. 1. Constant-Current System of Distribution.

relatively low current. A break or open circuit anywhere in the system causes an interruption of service for every load. The danger to human life of high potentials and the inconvenience of interruption of service make the constant-current system unsuited for use in the home or the factory. The constant-current system was first applied for street lighting in connection with the electric arc light. The system is still used in America for many street-lighting systems, which use both the arc and the incandescent lamp.

A series system called the **Thury system** has been used in some parts of Europe. The system uses a series generator regulated to give constant current and high voltage, feeding through transmission lines to motors placed in series. These motors operated other generators for low-voltage distribution. The generators for the system were operated in series to produce the high voltage (about 50,000 volts) for the transmission of power over long distances.

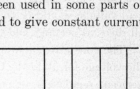

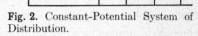

Fig. 2. Constant-Potential System of Distribution.

The constant-potential system was first used by Thomas A. Edison in 1881 and has been widely adopted since that date. In this system, the loads are connected in parallel across the supply lines, as indicated in Fig. 2. Each load on this system is designed for the same voltage and takes a current that depends upon the power required. The individual loads are entirely independent of each other; hence the generators which supply them should give a constant voltage and a variable current. It is very important to have a practically constant voltage to assure satisfactory operation of all kinds of present-day loads on this type of distribution system. The light output, the efficiency, and the life of incandescent lamps are very sensitive to changes in applied voltage. The thermal output of heating appliances varies as the square of the applied potential. Also, the power output and speed of electric motors are greatly influenced by the potential of the supply line.

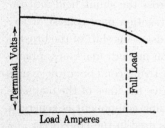

Fig. 3. External Characteristic of a Separately Excited Generator.

External Characteristic. The terminal voltage of a dynamo (generator) tends to change when the machine is loaded. This change in voltage can be depicted by a curve called the **external characteristic,** which is obtained by plotting the terminal voltage as ordinates and the load current as abscissas. An example of an external characteristic which is typical of a separately excited generator is given in Fig. 3. The external characteristic shows the change or regulation of the voltage of the generator from no load to full load and is sometimes called the **regulation curve.**

The term **voltage regulation** is applied specifically to the change in voltage between no load and full load and is expressed in per cent of full-load voltage. Thus,

$$\text{Per cent voltage regulation} = \frac{\text{no-load voltage} - \text{full-load voltage}}{\text{full-load voltage}} \times 100.$$

The full-load voltage should be the rated value for the dynamo and the no-load voltage should be that which is obtained when the load is removed, with all rheostat settings and the speed kept constant.

The constant-potential system of distribution requires good regulation of the voltage for all loads. Generators supplying this system should have a zero per cent regulation, or perhaps a rising voltage with load to compensate for the potential drop in the distribution lines.

Fundamental Equation of a Dynamo. The generated voltage of a dynamo is represented by the equation $E = BlvN10^{-8}$ volts (29, page 362). The product Blv is the flux cut per second, and this factor is directly proportional to the flux per pole ϕ, and the revolutions per minute n. Therefore $Blv = K_1'\phi n$, and since N is proportional to the conductors Z_a we have

$$E = K_1 \phi n Z_a. \tag{1}$$

For any given dynamo, the number of conductors Z_a in series (per armature path) is constant and does not change with load.

When the speed n varies, equation 1 shows that the generated emf is directly proportional to speed if the other factors remain constant. In the case of a generator, the machine speed is determined by the regulation of the prime mover.

The flux per pole depends on the mmf of the field, the reluctance of the magnetic circuit, and the effect of armature reaction. The mmf of the field consists of that produced by the shunt field and the series field (if one exists). The former depends on the voltage impressed across the shunt field and the latter depends upon the load current. Armature reaction may consist of two components. The demagnetizing component depends on the shift of the brushes from mechanical neutral; hence it does not exist on modern machines, practically all of which have interpoles. The cross-magnetizing component decreases the flux per pole when the machine is operated above the knee of the magnetization curve. The net effect of the cross-magnetizing component is generally small and is zero when a compensating winding* is used in the pole faces.

The terminal voltage of a dynamo under load differs from the generated voltage by the amount of the fall of potential in the armature series circuit. The resistance drop is due to the *total* resistance encountered by the load current as it flows between the positive and negative terminals of the machine. This total resistance includes that of the brushes, the brush contact, the armature, and, if they exist, the series field, the interpole field, and the compensating windings.

* See page 81.

It follows from these considerations that the terminal potential of a dynamo is always equal to the generated voltage minus the fall of potential in the armature series circuit. This may be expressed by the equation

$$V = E - I_aR_a \tag{2}$$

where the dynamo is operating as a generator. For motor action the sign of the IR drop becomes minus (since the direction of I changes), and the appropriate equation is

$$V = E + I_aR_a. \tag{3}$$

The two equations 1 and 2 just developed may be combined into a single equation which is appropriately called the **fundamental equation of a dynamo**:

$$V = K_1\phi nZ_a - I_aR_a. \tag{4}$$

This equation contains all of the factors which govern the important characteristics of dynamos. As it stands, the equation shows directly the factors which control the external characteristics of generators. A change in the sign of the resistance drop in the armature circuit and a rearrangement of the equation make it directly applicable to a study of the speed characteristics of motors.

Equations 2, 3, and 4 assume that the total drop in the armature circuit is proportional to the armature current. This is not exactly true. The drop across the brushes and contact between the brushes and commutator (see page 325) is nearly constant for all values of current. In recognition of this fact the ASA Standardization Rules state that the total drop (at positive and negative brushes) of 2 volts shall be assumed as the standard drop in determining brush-contact loss for carbon and graphite brushes with pigtails (brush shunts) attached. A total drop of 3 volts shall be assumed where pigtails are not attached. In view of these rules, the total voltage drop for the armature circuit is $(I_aR_a' + 2)$ in the usual case where brush shunts are employed. It should be clear that R_a' for this case should be the total resistance of the armature circuit copper only. Hence to be somewhat more precise and in accordance with the ASA Standardization Rules, the drop $(I_aR_a' + 2)$ should be used instead of I_aR_a in the previous equations. Because this somewhat more accurate expression is conventional and, in itself, is to some degree an approximation, and since its use in many of the succeeding equations underlying graphical solutions increases the complication to the point where it is apt to mask the results sought, the approximate forms as shown in equations 2, 3, and 4 will be used. In many, though not in all, cases the constant drop of 2 volts may be added or subtracted from the final result obtained by neglecting contact drop and a more accurate figure obtained. When this can be done is left to the acumen of the student.

Several succeeding articles are to deal with the external characteristics of dynamos operating as generators. As an approach to these studies, it is well to note from the preceding discussion and the fundamental equation of the dynamo that the three major factors which affect the terminal voltage of a generator under load are (1) armature (series) resistance drop, (2) change of flux per pole, and (3) change in speed.

Algebraic Determination of the External Characteristic. The determination or calculation of the external characteristic of a dynamo by the algebraic method is generally very tedious and difficult. The reason for this statement can be understood from a study of the fundamental equation of a dynamo, $V = K_1\phi n Z_a - I_a R_a$, which contains all of the factors for determining the external characteristic. In this equation K_1 is a constant depending on units and dimensions, and may be determined for a given machine, n is fixed by the prime mover and may be obtained from its regulation curve, Z_a is constant, R_a is known, and I_a is given by the load desired.

The flux per pole ϕ is a variable and follows, not a straight line, but the trend of the magnetization curve for the dynamo under consideration. The magnetization curve may be calculated if the machine has not been built, or determined experimentally if the machine has been built. If the straight analytical method is to be followed, it will be necessary to express the magnetization curve in algebraic form. One algebraic form requires the use of Froehlich's equation, and it will be recalled that this equation is difficult to handle and does not fit the magnetization curve perfectly. Assuming for the moment that the equation of magnetization curve is satisfactory, the flux ϕ will be expressed as a function of the net excitation. The net excitation is the algebraic sum of the shunt field mmf, series field mmf, and armature demagnetizing mmf. If the machine is self-excited (as is generally the case), the shunt-field current, and hence the mmf, depends on the terminal voltage impressed across it. Since the terminal voltage is the unknown which is being sought, the attempt at direct calculation fails. A trial value of terminal voltage might be assumed and a calculation made, but if the solution gave a different value of terminal voltage, another trial solution would have to be made, etc.

The difficulties in the algebraic determination of the external characteristic are not present in certain graphical forms of solution; hence such graphical methods are generally used.

Basis of Graphical Determination of External Characteristics. The principles given in the preceding articles form the basis for the graphical solutions. The following three specific equations and two definitions are desirable as aids to a graphical solution:

$$\text{Net excitation} = \text{shunt excitation}$$
$$\pm \text{ series excitation} - \text{demagnetization} \qquad (5)$$
$$V = E - I_a R_a \qquad (6)$$
$$E = (K_1 \phi Z_a) n = \text{constant} \times \text{speed}. \qquad (7)$$

1. The magnetization curve always shows generated voltage E and net excitation.

2. The excitation line, field-resistance line, or field characteristic shows how the shunt-field ampere-turns per pole vary with armature-terminal potential. Since the resistance of the field circuit is constant for constant temperature, the excitation line is a straight line.

External Characteristic of a Separately Excited Generator. The field excitation of a separately excited dynamo is independent of the load, as may be observed from Fig. 12, page 30. This observation applied to the fundamental equation shows that for constant speed and constant field-excitation potential, the terminal voltage will drop due to demagnetizing armature reaction and the resistance drop in the armature. Thus, the external characteristic and the factors affecting it appear as in Fig. 4. If the brushes are set on the mechanical neutral, the demagnetizing armature reaction becomes zero. The demagnetizing effect of cross-magnetizing armature reaction is small in magnitude, and its effect on the flux ϕ will be neglected in the graphical solution which follows.

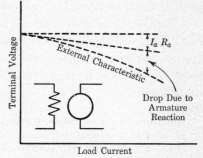

Fig. 4. External Characteristic of a Separately-Excited Generator and Factors Causing the Voltage Drop.

The graphical method of solution of the external characteristic will be applied first to the separately excited generator having the brushes set on the mechanical neutral. With constant speed and excitation F, the generator will always be operating at the same point on the magnetization curve, corresponding to F in Fig. 5. This gives a generated voltage of E_1. The terminal voltage $V = E_1 - I_a R_a$, is a straight line determined by any two points. The

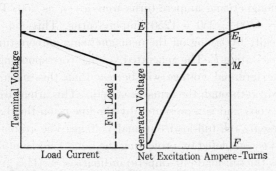

Fig. 5. Construction of External Characteristic of a Separately-Excited Generator without Armature Reaction.

voltage E_1 is the no-load voltage and will serve as one point. Due to full-load armature current, the I_aR_a drop may be calculated and laid off to the scale of volts from E_1 to M. A line projected horizontally from point M until it intersects the vertical through full-load current on the graph will determine the other point. Since the I_aR_a drop depends directly on the load, E_1M could be divided into n equal parts. From E_1 to the first division would represent the I_aR_a drop due to $1/n$ of full load and the voltage corresponding to this point as read on the axis of ordinates by projecting the point parallel to the axis of excitation would be the terminal voltage at $1/n$ load. Thus, the divisions along line E_1M could be labeled in terms of load or armature amperes.

A shift of the brushes from the mechanical neutral will produce armature reaction and will change the net excitation of the dynamo with load. The construction applying to all separately excited generators can be illustrated more clearly by means of a specific case. A generator with the following constants will be used:

Armature circuit resistance: 0.2 ohm.
Shunt-field resistance: 100 ohms.
Shunt-field rheostat setting: 20 ohms.
Shunt-field turns per pole: 1500.
Shunt-field excitation potential (separate source): 120 volts constant.
Full-load armature current: 40 amperes.
Magnetization curve: given in Fig. 6.

The brushes are shifted from the neutral so as to cause a demagnetizing armature reaction mmf of 250 ampere-turns per pole at full load. In general, the demagnetizing ampere-turns are calculated from equation 3, page 86. Note that this same effect could be produced by a differential series field instead of shifting brushes from the neutral.

The shunt-field current is $120/120 = 1$ ampere, and the ampere-turns per pole are $1500 \times 1 = 1500$. The value of this separate-field excitation is constant, so that the excitation line is vertical, as shown by line FA in Fig. 6. At full load the demagnetizing ampere-turns were given as 250. Therefore, the net excitation $= 1500 - 250 = 1250$ ampere-turns. This net excitation is obtained graphically by laying off the demagnetizing ampere-turns Fg to the left of the field excitation F. The generated voltage corresponding to this excitation is gb. The terminal voltage will be less than this generated voltage, due to the I_aR_a drop through the armature circuit. This armature-circuit drop is $40 \times 0.2 = 8$ volts and is represented by the line bc on the diagram. Thus, the line gc represents the full-load terminal voltage. The graphical construction for this load is completed by projecting the point c horizontally to the left until it intersects the full-load (40-ampere) ordinate at X. This gives one point on the external characteristic.

It should be noted that the I_aR_a drop bc and demagnetizing ampere-turns

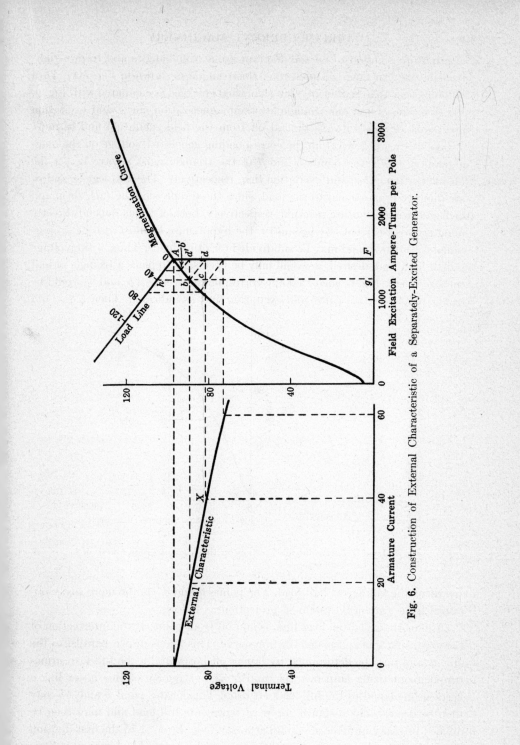

Fig. 6. Construction of External Characteristic of a Separately-Excited Generator.

of armature reaction cd on the diagram are at right angles and form a right triangle bcd. An enlarged picture of this triangle is shown in Fig. 7(1). To a different scale than that in 7(1) but somewhat enlarged as compared with Fig. 6, Fig. 7(2) shows how the triangle fits the magnetization curve and excitation line. Since dc must always be laid off from the field excitation and bc must always be drawn down from the corresponding generated voltage on the magnetization curve, the points b and d of the triangle must always lie on the magnetization curve and excitation line, respectively. The two legs bc and cd are directly proportional to the load, since these represent the I_aR_a drop and demagnetizing armature reaction, respectively, both of which depend directly upon the load current. By geometry, the hypotenuse bd must also be proportional to the load, and may be subdivided for other loads. Thus, if the voltage at half load were desired, it would only be necessary to place a triangle of half the size of bcd, Fig. 6, such that the corresponding vertices b' and d' would be on the magnetization curve and excitation line, as indicated. Then Fd' would

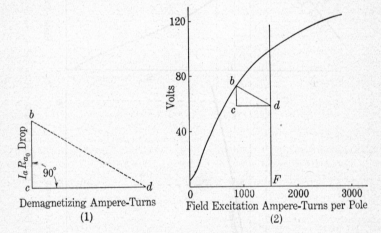

Fig. 7. Load Triangle and its Position on the Magnetization Curve of a Separately Excited Generator.

represent the voltage at half load. The points d and d' can be more easily obtained by a graphical system of projection as follows.

A line Ah, called the **load line**, is laid off from point A, the intersection of the excitation line and magnetization curve. This line is drawn parallel to the line db and may be determined by laying off horizontally the full-load armature-demagnetizing ampere-turns, and at the extremity of this latter line a vertical line equal to the full-load IR drop. This locates point h and Ah may then be drawn. The distance $Ah = bd$ represents full load and may then be divided into any number of equal parts, say four. From A to the first division would then represent $\frac{1}{4}$ load, to the second $\frac{1}{2}$ load, etc. The terminal voltage for any load may then be determined by projecting vertically to the magnetization curve, thence parallel to the load line hA until intersection with the excitation line FA is made. A horizontal line through this intersection will locate the corresponding point on the external characteristic.

Effect of Change in Speed on External Characteristic. The effect of a change in speed on the external characteristic can readily be obtained by a slight modification of the method outlined in the previous article. Assuming an increase of speed of 40 per cent, the magnetization curve for the new speed must be calculated. Each ordinate of the magnetization curve corresponding to the first speed must be multiplied by 1.4 to obtain the corresponding ordinates of the new magnetization curve, Fig. 8. The I_aR_a drop and demagnetizing ampere-turns at full-load current are not affected by the change in speed. The load line and the load triangles will be the same in the two cases for the same current loads. The total drop AP from no load to full load is made up of two parts.

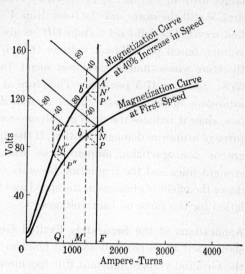

Fig. 8. Construction for Determination of Effect of Speed on the External Characteristic of Separately-Excited Generator.

The first is AN, due to the demagnetization of armature reaction, while the second is NP, due to the resistance drop. The latter is affected only by the current and will be the same at different speeds. The drop in voltage due to the demagnetization will not be the same, which may be shown as follows:

$$AN = FA - Mb, \qquad A'N' = FA' - Mb'.$$

But $\qquad FA' = 1.4\,FA$, and $Mb' = 1.4\,Mb$

Therefore,

$$A'N' = 1.4\,FA - 1.4\,Mb = 1.4\,(FA - Mb) = 1.4\,AN.$$

The drop due to the demagnetization has therefore increased 40 per cent, but the total drop $A'P'$ has not increased 40 per cent. The per cent regulation at the first speed is

$$\frac{AP}{FP} = \frac{97 - 82.5}{82.5} = 17.6 \text{ per cent.}$$

At the second speed it is

$$\frac{A'P'}{FP'} = \frac{136 - 118}{118} = 15.25 \text{ per cent.}$$

The regulation has been improved while the no-load voltage has been increased 40 per cent. If the no-load voltage is held constant by increasing the field resistance, operation would be at point A'' on a new magnetization curve for the higher speed. Because the machine now operates at a lower degree of saturation, the same number of ampere-turns of demagnetization cause a much larger drop in voltage, as is shown by comparing $A''N''$ with AN. The I_aR_a drop is still the same and the total drop $A''P''$ is therefore greater than at the first speed. The full-load voltage QP'' is also less and the percentage change in voltage based on full-load voltage OP'' is much greater. The regulation is therefore worse than at the lower speed. In this case, the regulation is $(97 - 65.8)/(65.8) = 47.5$ per cent. Therefore *it is apparent that a high degree of saturation of the magnetic circuit is desirable in order to secure good regulation,* since it reduces the drop in voltage caused by a given number of ampere-turns of armature demagnetization. If the machine has interpoles, so that there are no demagnetizing ampere-turns, the load triangles reduce to vertical straight lines and the regulation becomes better. The use of the interpole reduces the effect of changes in the speed and the degree of saturation upon regulation for the same no-load voltages.

Applications of the Separately Excited Generator. The foregoing discussion shows that the separately excited machine has an inherent tendency to hold the terminal voltage constant if it has interpoles and an armature winding of low resistance. It would be suitable for power installations demanding such service.

The separately excited generator has one outstanding advantage over self-excited machines. It can operate with perfect stability on any part of the magnetization curve, particularly at very low excitations. It offers a wide variation in voltage through the control of its field excitation. This advantage leads to the frequent use of the separately excited machine in experimental laboratories and in commercial testing laboratories. Separate excitation is also sometimes used commercially for low-voltage high-current machines.

The disadvantage of separate excitation lies in the inconvenience and in the cost of providing the source for the separate excitation. Many forms of self-excitation provide an equally good or better external-voltage characteristic.

Armature Characteristic. The terminal voltage of a shunt generator decreases with load due to the demagnetizing action of the armature and due to the resistance drop in the armature circuit. This decrease in potential can be offset by the proper increase in field current as the load comes on. A curve which shows the field current necessary to maintain a constant terminal voltage with the increase of armature current is called an **armature characteristic.** Such a curve is shown in Fig. 9. It may be determined experimentally or by graphical construction. The armature characteristic gives the data needed for compounding a generator.

The armature characteristic may be obtained from the graphical construction shown in Fig. 10. Since the armature characteristic is obtained for a constant terminal voltage, the base of the load triangle must always be at the same height OV above the horizontal axis, where OV is the constant terminal voltage at which the characteristic is desired. The no-load excitation is ON. To determine the excitation for full-load current, the full-load triangle as shown in Fig. 7(1) is drawn with its base on the line VA, Fig. 10. It is then moved along VA until its vertex b falls on the magnetization curve. The distance $Vd = Od_1$ then

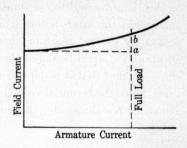

Fig. 9. Armature Characteristic.

gives the excitation since it was shown previously that for equilibrium vertices b and d must always be on the magnetization curve and field-excitation lines respectively. The excitation for half load can be found by fitting, in a similar manner, a triangle of half the linear dimensions. These results are most easily accomplished through the following graphical procedure. At M in Fig. 11 erect a vertical line. Lay off, to the voltage scale used, a distance Mb' which is equal to the full-load armature circuit resistance drop. Also from M lay off Md', to the excitation scale, a distance equal to the

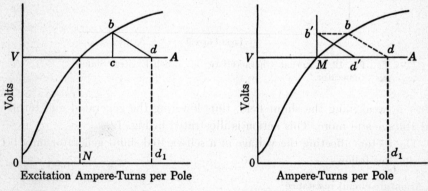

Fig. 10. Construction to Secure a Point on the Armature Characteristic Corresponding to Full Load Current.

Fig. 11. Construction to Secure a Point on the Armature Characteristic for Any Load Current.

full-load demagnetizing ampere-turns per pole. Draw line $b'd'$. The triangle $Mb'd'$ is the full-load triangle. Now project point b' horizontally to the magnetization curve at b. At b draw a line parallel to $b'd'$. The intersection with the line VA at point d determines the excitation. For half load, a point halfway between M and b' is used and the procedure outlined repeated. Other fractions of Mb' may be chosen to obtain values of excitation for corresponding fractions of full-load current.

External Characteristic of a Self-Excited Shunt Generator. The diagram of connections for the self-excited shunt generator is given in Fig. 12. Reference to this diagram and to the fundamental equation of the dynamo (equation 4) shows that the same factors which serve to lower the terminal voltage of the separately excited machine should be equally effective on this machine. In addition, it should be noted that the excitation of the shunt field is no longer constant, and that it is dependent upon the terminal voltage of the generator itself. Since the terminal voltage is being lowered by armature resistance drop, armature reactions, etc., it is evident that these drops have a cumulative

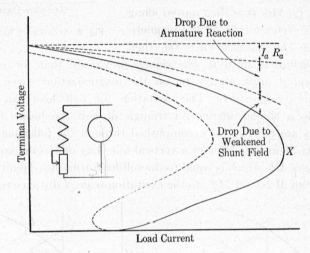

Fig. 12. External Characteristic of a Self-Excited Shunt Generator.

effect in weakening the shunt field, thus lowering the generated and terminal voltage still more. This action is illustrated in Fig. 12.

The factors affecting the voltage of a self-excited shunt generator may be classified as follows:

1. Armature-circuit resistance
2. Reduction of flux per pole
   a. Demagnetizing armature reaction
   b. Demagnetization due to cross-magnetization
   c. Reduction of field current due to reduced voltage caused by 1, 2a, 2b, and 3
3. Speed changes due to load (characteristic of prime mover).

In addition to these, there are several minor factors, such as changes of resistance of armature and field due to temperature changes, hysteresis effects, and changes in permeability due to temperature changes. The effect of these

minor factors depends upon both the ambient temperature and the load, and
hence will be neglected in all graphical solutions.

The external characteristic of this generator can be understood by referring
to the magnetization curve and the field-resistance line, as shown in Fig. 13.

The terminal voltage at no load (A) is approximately equal to the generated voltage, since the only variation from the latter
is caused by the I_aR_a due to the small
shunt-field current flowing through the armature. This current will be neglected for
the time being, and a method for taking it
into account will be explained later. When
a load is placed on the generator, the demagnetization due to armature reaction
will reduce the excitation which is effective
in producing the generated voltage. The

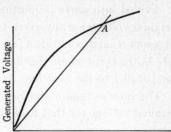

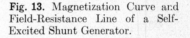

Field Excitation Ampere-Turns per Pole

Fig. 13. Magnetization Curve and
Field-Resistance Line of a Self-
Excited Shunt Generator.

terminal voltage will be less than the generated voltage. The terminal voltage will be less than the generated voltage due to the armature-circuit
resistance drop. The demagnetizing ampere-turns and the voltage drop due
to armature circuit resistance are related to each other on the diagram at
right angles, since the I_aR_a drop must be drawn vertically downward and the
demagnetization must be subtracted horizontally. This relation is the same
as explained for Fig. 7(1), page 110. Since the generated voltage must lie
on the magnetization curve and the I_aR_a drop subtracts from it to produce the terminal voltage, point b of Fig. 7(1) must lie on the magnetization curve. This terminal voltage determines the field excitation which is found
on the excitation line corresponding to the terminal voltage. The generated
voltage is determined by the net excitation, which is less than the field excitation by the demagnetizing ampere-turns represented by dc in Fig. 7(1). Therefore point d must be on the field-resistance line with dc extending to the left to
give the net excitation, and Fig. 7(1) must fit into Fig. 14 with d on the field
resistance line, b on the magnetization curve, and bc extending vertically downward as shown. For the load for which bc and cd are drawn, Om would be the
field excitation, On the net excitation, and nb the corresponding generated
voltage. Subtracting the I_aR_a drop bc from this leaves $nc = OV_1$ as the terminal voltage. Terminal voltages for other loads are determined by fitting triangles, like bcd drawn for the different loads, in between the field resistance
line and the magnetization curve. These triangles can be located by a geo-
metrical system of construction similar to that outlined in a preceding article.

The graphical construction begins with the load line AL which may be
drawn parallel to line bd or it may be laid out without the presence of line bd.
In the latter case, lay off horizontally to the left of A a length representing the

demagnetizing ampere-turns at full load. At the point thus determined, erect a perpendicular and measure upward a length proportional to full-load $I_a R_a$ drop. Let the point thus determined be L. Then the line AL is the load line and its magnitude is proportional to the full-load current. The line AL may be divided into parts proportional to 1/4 load, 1/2 load, 3/4 load, etc. The terminal voltage for any given load can be determined by drawing a line from the proportional point on AL (assume 1/2 load) parallel to the excitation line OA. At the point where this line cuts the magnetization curve b' draw a second line parallel to the load line AL.

The intersection of the latter line with the excitation line (d') shows the terminal voltage for that load. The two points b' and d' establish the position

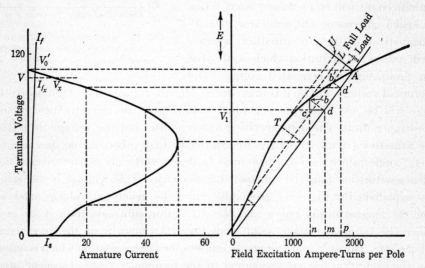

Fig. 14. Construction of External Characteristic of a Self-Excited Shunt Generator.

of the load triangle, but the triangle does not need to be completed since pd' represents the voltage desired.

The construction just given shows the relation between armature current and terminal voltage. Usually it is desired to know the relation between the load current and the terminal voltage. Since the load current is the armature current minus the field current, it is necessary to calculate the field current for one assumed potential, and then to draw the line OI_f to represent the field current. The field current is equal to the armature current at voltage V_o'. Therefore the no-load voltage is V_o'. At any voltage V_x, the load current is the armature current minus the field current, or $I_{f_x} V_x$ in Fig. 14.

It is of interest to note that, if the self-excited shunt generator does not have any demagnetizing armature reaction, the load triangle reduces to a vertical line, the load line AL likewise becomes a vertical line, and the graphical construction is simplified.

The self-excited shunt generator has a more rapid decrease of terminal voltage than the separately excited machine, and it will not sustain so large a short-circuit current as the separately excited generator. From Fig. 14, it can be seen that the largest armature current a self-excited shunt generator can produce is that corresponding to the intersection of AL with the tangent TU to the magnetization curve drawn parallel to OA. The maximum current is determined by the maximum distance between the excitation line and the magnetization curve. As the load resistance is decreased after the point of maximum current is

Excitation Ampere-Turns per Pole

Fig. 15. Magnetization Curve and Field-Resistance Line Which Permit a Self-Excited Shunt Generator to Deliver Only a Small Current.

reached both the terminal voltage and the load current fall in value, as shown by the external characteristic. The point of maximum current is called the **breakdown point.** It is obvious that, for a large maximum current and a small change in terminal voltage, it is desirable for the generator to operate well above the knee of the magnetization curve. A generator with a magnetization curve and a field-resistance line as shown in Fig. 15 could deliver only a very small current and its voltage regulation would be very poor.

The effect of a change in the speed of the generator upon its regulation at a fixed no-load voltage is illustrated in Fig. 16. A higher speed of the generator causes the machine to operate on a steeper portion of the magnetization curve (full lines in figure), makes the regulation much poorer, and reduces the maximum current output. At a lower generator speed (dotted lines), the machine operates above the knee of the magnetization curve, the regulation is improved, and the maximum current output has been increased. Hence the voltage regulation of a generator can be improved for a given no-load voltage by a reduction in speed.

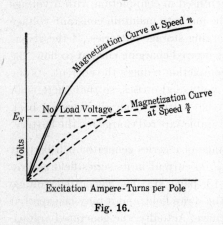

Excitation Ampere-Turns per Pole

Fig. 16.

The self-excited shunt generator can sustain only a small short-circuit current under a steady-state condition. This is true because, under short circuit, the terminal voltage of the machine is zero, the potential across the shunt field is zero, and the shunt-field current is zero. The loss of field excitation is primarily responsible for the low short-circuit current. The short-circuit current under a steady-state condition will be less than the voltage of residual magnetism divided by the armature-circuit resistance because of the demagnetizing effect of armature reaction. The short-circuit current I_s in Fig. 14 is obtained by using that portion of the magnetization curve to the left of the origin, which would be obtained by a reversed excitation. The load triangle is then fitted in as usual with its base resting on the axis of abscissas. It is unsafe to place a sudden short circuit upon a self-excited shunt generator because a large transient current will exist until the steady-state condition is reached. The large transient current results because the field flux ϕ does not fall to zero immediately but dies out rather slowly. The field flux, while dying, is effective in generating an emf which will produce a large short-circuit current.

An inspection of the external characteristic of the self-excited dynamo shows that two different terminal voltages are possible for the same armature current over a considerable range of the curve. The particular voltage which exists for the given armature current depends on the resistance of the load.

Application of the Self-Excited Shunt Generator. The self-excited shunt generator has a greater voltage variation than the same machine operated separately excited, yet it tends to maintain constant terminal potential when properly designed. A self-excited shunt generator, having a relatively small voltage drop from no load to full load, is suitable for constant potential systems when the distance of transmission is not sufficiently long to require an increase of generator voltage to compensate for the line drop when the load increases. It is suitable as a source of excitation for alternator fields where the voltage can be controlled manually. When used in conjunction with a voltage regulator described on page 149, it can be made to maintain constant voltage automatically. It is also suitable for charging storage batteries. If the generator emf is initially adjusted to cause the desired charging current to flow, the rise in battery emf as the charge nears completion reduces the current. As the charging current falls off, the generator voltage also rises, so that there is an automatic regulation, which prevents the battery from discharging back through the source, and which gives a desirable tapered charge for the battery.

The Series Generator. The no-load voltage of a series generator will be that due to residual magnetism, since there is no current in its series field and no excitation (see circuit diagram of Fig. 13, page 31). The generated voltage depends upon the load current through the series field, and it may be expected to follow the trend of a magnetization curve. Actually, the generated voltage is proportional to the net excitation which consists of the ampere-turns of the series field less the demagnetizing ampere-turns. The terminal voltage, in turn, is equal to the generated voltage minus the resistance drop in the armature and the series field. Beginning at no load, the terminal voltage of a series generator rises quite rapidly and is almost proportional to the load. As the saturation of the magnetic circuit is approached, the generated voltage rises at a slower and slower rate while the armature circuit resistance drops and armature reaction gradually reduces the terminal potential back toward zero. The external characteristic can be determined by the use of the saturation curve, the data concerning the armature reaction, and the resistance of the field and the armature.

The saturation curve of a series generator is shown in Fig. 17. It is obtained by measuring the armature potential when the series field is disconnected and separately excited. A wave-wound generator will be assumed to have a full-load current of 30 amperes, 50 field turns per pole, 50 volts of $I(R_a + R_s)$ drop at full load, and 50 demagnetizing turns per pole on the armature. At full-load current, the demagnetizing ampere-turns equal $(30/2) \times 50$; or 750 AT/pole. These are laid off as FD, giving a net excitation of OD and a generated voltage

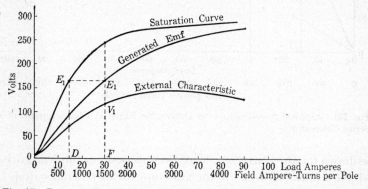

Fig. 17. Construction of External Characteristic of a Series Generator.

of DE_1. This is the generated voltage FE_1 at 30 amperes load and it is projected horizontally to the 30-ampere ordinate to give a point on the generated emf curve. The series-resistance drop of 50 volts is deducted from the generated voltage at this load to give the net terminal voltage FV_1. The complete external characteristic is obtained by a continuation of this procedure. The construction of Fig. 17 has been made clearer by the assumption of an excessive number of demagnetizing ampere-turns and an exaggerated resistance drop.

The external characteristic of a series generator can be determined by a simple graphical construction. Since both the gross ampere-turns and the demagnetizing ampere-turns are proportional to the load, the net excitation which is their difference is directly proportional to the load current. We can therefore employ the load triangle in a manner similar to that previously used. Now, however, the excitation line becomes the Y-axis since the series generator has zero shunt field excitation. Therefore one vertex of the load triangle must fall on the Y-axis while the other, as before, must lie on the magnetization curve. To fit these load triangles to the magnetization curve and

Y-axis (excitation line) the following construction is convenient. Lay off the net excitation OD in ampere-turns, as shown in Fig. 18. The net excitation OD

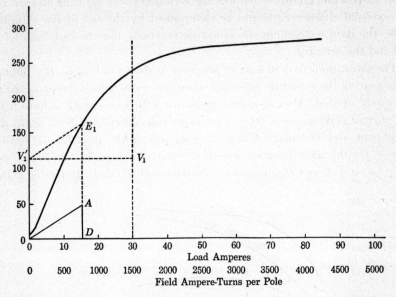

Fig. 18. Graphical Construction to Determine External Characteristic of a Series Generator.

may be drawn for any convenient load. For this example full-load current will be used. Now draw AD equal to the armature circuit resistance drop $I(R_a + R_s)$. Draw OA which completes the load triangle for full-load current. To find the terminal voltage project DA to the intersection E_1 with the magnetization curve. Then draw a line from E_1 parallel to OA. The intersection on the Y-axis at V_1' is the terminal voltage for the load current represented by the triangle. A point on the external characteristic is then located by projecting V_1' horizontally until it intersects this load current at V_1. To find other points the load line OA may be divided into fractional parts of full load and the system of projection illustrated by the dotted lines repeated for each load.

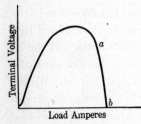

Fig. 19. External Characteristic of a Series Generator for a Constant-Current Output between a and b.

Applications of the Series Generator. The foregoing discussion shows that by employing a high value of armature reaction, the external characteristic of the series generator can be made to bend over quickly and then rapidly approach zero voltage for only a small change of load current, as shown in Fig. 19. This gives a nearly constant current with a variable voltage within the range a to *b.* This principle was formerly applied in the design of series generators for constant-current systems, but has generally been superseded by other methods for obtaining the same result.

The series dynamo has had little application as a generator. It was used in Europe in the Thury system for transmission of power, and in America it has been used as a booster on electric railway systems (see page 283).

The Cumulative-Compound Generator. The cumulative-compound generator (Fig. 14, page 31) combines the characteristics of the self-excited shunt and the series generator. The shunt field determines the voltage at no load, while under load the series field adds and superposes upon the shunt characteristic the rising characteristic of the series generator. The voltage of a compound generator may drop under load, always being slightly above that of the shunt machine, or it may rise considerably above the corresponding shunt characteristic, depending on the relative strength of the series and shunt fields. When the terminal voltage of a cumulative-compound generator is less at full load that at no load, it is said to be **undercompounded.** If the full-load voltage is higher than the no-load voltage, it is **overcompounded,** and, if the terminal voltage is the same at no load and full load, the generator is said to be **flat-compounded.**

The generated voltage of a compound generator will depend on the net or effective excitation of any given load. The ampere-turns due to the series field increase directly with the load current, the shunt-field excitation depends on the terminal voltage and is approximately constant, and the demagnetizing ampere-turns (for noninterpole machines) vary directly with the load current. The net excitation equals the sum of the shunt and series ampere-turns minus any demagnetizing ampere-turns. The terminal voltage can be found by subtracting the armature-circuit drop from the generated voltage. These steps may be performed graphically, as explained in the following article.

External Characteristic of a Cumulative-Compound Generator. The magnetization curve of a compound generator is given in Fig. 20. The excitation line OA is constructed in the same manner as for the self-excited shunt generator. Assuming the long-shunt connection of part (2), Fig. 14, page 31, the same current flows through the series field and the armature. The external characteristic will be plotted for the armature current and the small correction due to the shunt-field current may be made later if desired.

The no-load voltage is given by point A, the intersection of the excitation line and the magnetization curve. To be precise, it should be noted that the actual no-load voltage would be less than that indicated by A by the amount of the RI drop due to the small shunt-field current through the armature and the series field. In like manner, the no-load voltage would be increased by the ampere-turns added by the shunt-field current flowing through the series-

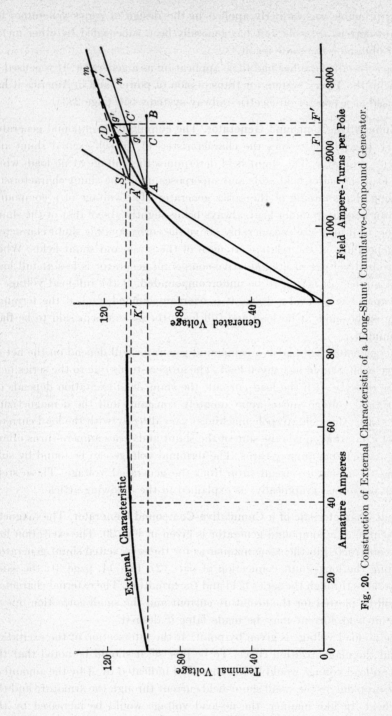

Fig. 20. Construction of External Characteristic of a Long-Shunt Cumulative-Compound Generator.

field turns. These factors are compensating in action and very small in magnitude, so that their resultant effect will always be negligible.

At full load, the series field produces a number of ampere-turns which add to the excitation due to the shunt field. Let the line AB represent the series ampere-turns, and add it by extension to the right of point A (Fig. 20). The full-load demagnetizing armature reaction may be represented by the line BC, which should be subtracted from point B. Then AC represents the net additional ampere-turns due to the load. The corresponding generated voltage might be thought to be represented by FD. This is not the case, since the shunt-field excitation increases with the rise in terminal voltage due to the increased excitation AC. The new terminal voltage is equal to the generated voltage minus the $I_a(R_a + R_s)$ drop, where R_a and R_s represent the armature-circuit and series-field resistance, respectively. Let this $R_{a_o}I_a$ drop be represented graphically by the line gC. This gives a load triangle ACg. A simple method of determining the generated voltage and the terminal voltage for this load consists in sliding the load triangle upward, so as to keep the point A on the excitation line and the line AC horizontal until point g lies on the magnetization curve. This gives a new position $A'C'g'$ for the triangle, where $F'g'$ represents the generated voltage, since g' is on the magnetization curve. The corresponding terminal voltage is the generated voltage minus the $R_{a_o}I_a$ drop of Cg or its equivalent $C'g'$, which gives a net value of $F'C'$. This voltage of $F'C'$ impressed across the shunt field gives the shunt-field excitation indicated by the abscissa of A'. The points A', g', and C' give all of the desired information for this condition of load on the machine. The task of fitting a load triangle into a new position can be performed graphically in a simple manner by drawing a line through point g parallel to the excitation line OA. The intersection g' gives the generated voltage $F'g'$, and any other desired information can be readily obtained.

The construction of the load triangle ACg for full load offers a simple method of determining the terminal voltage for other loads and other points on the external characteristic. Each side of the load triangle is proportional to the armature current, since

$$AC = AB - CB = I_aN_s - I_aN_d = I_a(N_s - N_d)$$

where N_s and N_d are the series-field and demagnetizing turns, respectively. Line gC is proportional to the armature current because $gC = I_a(R_a + R_s)$. Hence the hypotenuse Ag must be proportional to the armature current, and may be extended as An to serve as a load line corresponding to line AL for the self-excited generator. The line An may be divided into parts proportional to fractions of full load. Thus line An may represent two times full load. The generated voltage for this double load may be found by constructing the line mn parallel to the excitation line and intersecting the magnetization curve at some point m. A line Sm drawn parallel to An through the intersection at m will intersect the excitation line at S, which is the terminal voltage for this load. Terminal voltages should be projected horizontally to the left to the corresponding current abscissa in order to determine the complete external characteristic.

Effect of Series Turns, Saturation, and Speed on Compounding. The degree of compounding of a generator depends upon the saturation of the magnetic circuit, as well as upon the relative ratio of the series ampere-turns to shunt ampere-turns on the field. An overcompounded dynamo will produce a rise in voltage as the load is increased, so that the full-load voltage is higher than the no-load value. If the machine is carried past full load, the rise in voltage becomes less rapid and ultimately begins to fall, because of the saturation of the magnetic circuit. From Fig. 20, it can be seen that the maximum terminal voltage will occur at that load which makes the hypotenuse of the load triangle tangent to the magnetization curve. After this point is reached, the saturation of the magnetic circuit increases the reluctance to such an extent that the increase of ampere-turns due to the series field is unable to offset the $I_a(R_a + R_s)$ drop.

If a small number of ampere-turns is placed on the series field, the line AC will be shortened, and, for approximately the same $I_a(R_a + R_s)$ drop, the load line Ag will become steeper. The load line may have such a slope that it will be tangent only to some part of the magnetization curve below point A. The generator will then be undercompounded, and the terminal voltage will always decrease as the load is applied. It is possible for a compound generator to have some rise in voltage as a light load is applied and still be termed undercompounded, provided that the terminal voltage at rated full load falls below that at no load.

The compounding of a generator may be increased by operating the machine at a speed in excess of its rating, but at its rated no-load voltage. To obtain the same no-load voltage at the higher speed it is necessary to decrease the shunt field excitation by increasing the field resistance. This causes the dynamo to operate at a lower point on the magnetization curve where the reluctance of the magnetic circuit is less, and consequently the effect of a given number of ampere-turns in producing flux is increased. The compounding is increased for two reasons. First, the addition of a given number of ampere-turns caused by a certain load current in the series field produces a greater increment of flux than when the machine was operating higher on the magnetization curve. Second, the increment of flux produced is cut at a higher speed and the generated voltage per unit flux is increased. Hence the compounding is increased because of both the increase of flux per ampere-turn and the increase of generated voltage per unit flux.

The compounding of a generator may be changed (1) by changing the number of turns on the series field, (2) by varying the resistance of a shunt placed in parallel with the series field, and (3) within narrow limits, by varying the speed at which the machine is operated for the same no-load voltage.

Flat-Compounding a Generator. By definition, a flat-compounded generator has the same voltage at no load and at full load. Its series field must provide enough ampere-turns at full load to offset the drop in voltage due to several causes. The armature characteristic curve of Fig. 9 shows the number of amperes of field current required to maintain a constant voltage under load. From this curve, the additional field current ab which is necessary to give the same voltage at full load, may be obtained. This additional current multiplied by the number of turns on the shunt field gives the number of ampere-turns which should be provided by a series field having a negligible resistance. These ampere-turns, divided by the current through the series field, give the number of series turns which should be placed on each pole in order to flat-compound the machine. The current through the series field is the armature current for a long-shunt connection, while it is the load current for a short-shunt connection. Calculations based on this method are a little low, since they do not take into account the small $R_s I$ drop in the series field.

External Characteristic of a Short-Shunt Compound Generator. The external characteristic for a short-shunt compound generator can be determined very closely by a slight modification of the method employed for the long-shunt connection. In this modification, the resistance of the armature between the junctions of the shunt field (Fig. 14, page 31) is used for calculating the resistance drop for the vertical leg of the load-triangle. The external characteristic obtained by the use of this load-triangle and its load line will apply to the terminal volts across the junctions of the shunt field. The actual line-terminal voltage will be less than this by the amount of the drop in the series field. Therefore the terminal voltage characteristic is obtained from the above curve by subtracting the resistance drops due to the load current flowing through the series field. It is rarely necessary to use these refinements for the graphical solution, since the external characteristic calculated for a long-shunt machine is sufficiently accurate to serve for the short-shunt machine.

The Differential-Compound Generator. The differential-compound generator has its series field reversed from that of the cumulative-compound generator. The mmf of the series field is demagnetizing and acts exactly like additional ampere-turns of armature demagnetization, and may be included with them. If dc in Fig. 14 includes the series ampere-turns and bc the armature-circuit and series-field resistance drops, the procedure outlined for obtaining the external characteristic of the self-excited shunt generator would be that required to obtain the external characteristic of the differential-compound generator. Therefore the external characteristic of a differential-compound generator is similar to that of the self-excited shunt machine but more drooping, as shown in Fig. 21. The full line applies to the self-excited and the dotted line to the separately excited shunt field.

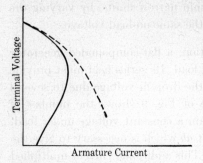

Fig. 21. External Characteristic of a Differential-Compound Generator.

Application of Compound Generators. The cumulative-compound generator is used more than any other type of generator, since it can be designed to have a wide variety of characteristics which range from a falling to a rising voltage. The rise of voltage from no load to full load is used to maintain constant voltage at the end of a transmission line by compensating for the line drop. Such generators are used to supply lighting and heavy-power loads requiring constant-potential service, such as electric railways and various motor drives as found in industrial plants. Among these, one of the more important is the steel industry where large amounts of direct-current power are used by motors driving rolling mills. The compounding can be made to compensate partially for a drop in speed of the prime mover driving the generator. All modern compound generators are equipped with interpoles.

The differential-compound generator has a very limited field of application. It is used on some wind-electric generator plants because of its current limiting characteristic at high speeds. It was once used for automobile generators but has been superseded for this purpose by the shunt generator with voltage and current regulators. Some direct-current welding generators are differential compound.

Dual Excitation. This is a combination of separate excitation and self-excitation to produce an external characteristic similar to the dotted line of Fig. 21 with much less field excitation and field copper. In Fig. 22, the line MP_1 represents the separate excitation. Another set of shunt-field coils is placed on the same poles and is connected self-excited, as in Fig. 23, which produces an additional excitation and a resultant excitation line MP_2. The resistance of the self-excited field is made so that MP_2 is nearly parallel to the lower portion of the magnetization curve. The field yoke is made entirely of laminations in order that change in excitation may follow promptly change in load. The cross-sectional areas of the various parts of the magnetic circuit may be so proportioned that they reach saturation at about the same excitation. This gives a sharper knee to the magnetization curve than is shown in previous diagrams,

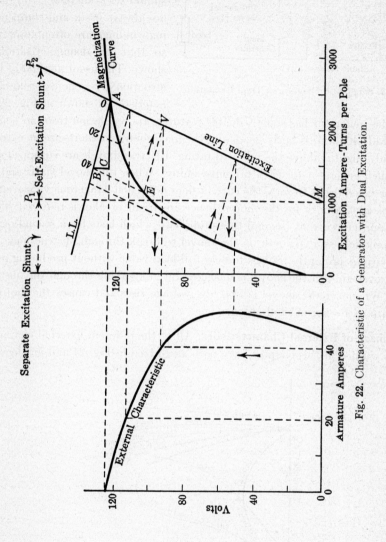

Fig. 22. Characteristic of a Generator with Dual Excitation.

where the armature teeth are arranged to become saturated before the armature and pole cores. A differential series field should be used which has an exci-

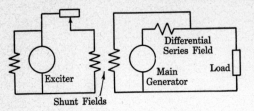

Fig. 23. Schematic Diagram of Dual Excitation.

tation at full load (*AC* in Fig. 22) a little less than the separate shunt excitation (*OM*). Interpoles are always used, and compensating windings are often employed, so that no demagnetization is shown. The usual method of construction gives the external characteristic as shown in Fig. 22.

This generator has some valuable features. Its regulation from no load to full load (40 amp) is fairly good, and the maximum and short-circuit currents are only slightly above the full-load rating. Electric shovels are equipped with one such generator for each principal motor. When the shovel stalls and the motor speed drops to zero, the current does not reach dangerous values either for the generator or for the motor; hence no circuit breaker is required. There is a transient current (several times full load) which lasts for a second or two and produces an extra jerk on the shovel to break through obstructions. The line current promptly returns to near full-load value without producing much heat, even though the shovel is unsuccessful in breaking through the obstruction. Whenever the shovel is free, the voltage rises and causes the motor to operate at its normal full speed.

Summary of External Characteristics. All of the different external characteristics studied in this chapter have been assembled in Fig. 24 and arranged on

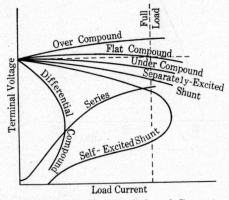

Fig. 24. External Characteristics of Generators.

a common voltage and load current scale for direct comparison. A good review of the chapter may be made by giving an explanation of the trend and the difference of all these curves, without referring to the preceding pages.

PROBLEMS

The following table and Fig. 25 should be used to secure any required data not given in the statement of the problems for this chapter.

TABLE I. TWENTY–HORSEPOWER MOTOR

Armature Data

Line potential	230
Full-load armature current	72.5
Armature resistance 25 C	0.110
Armature resistance 75 C	0.133
Type of winding	Simplex wave
Number of slots	45
Number of coils per slot	3
Turns per coil	2
Back pitch (slots)	11
Full-load speed	1150

Shunt Field Data

Number of poles	4
Turns per coil	2000
Cold resistance (total for all poles)	164
Hot resistance (total for all poles)	199
Mean length of turn (inches)	18.98
Connection	Long-shunt

Series Field Data

Number of poles	4
Turns per pole	$3\frac{1}{2}$
Cold resistance (all poles)	0.0041
Hot resistance (all poles)	0.00568
Mean length of turn (in.)	24 in.
Size of wire	0.229 sq.

Interpole Data

Number of poles	2
Turns per pole	52
Cold resistance (all poles)	0.0175
Hot resistance (all poles)	0.0212
Mean length of turn	15.2 in.
Size of wire	0.258 sq.

Commutator Data

Diameter	7 in.
Thickness of mica	0.025 in.
Size of brush	1/2 in. $\times$ 1 in.
Number of studs	4
Number of brushes per stud	2
Current density in brushes	36.2 amps per sq in.
Bars contact of brush on commutator	3.06

Core Data

Diameter of armature core (over top of teeth) $10\frac{1}{2}$ in.
Over-all length of armature core   .   .   .   4 in.
Number of ducts   1
Width of each duct   .   .   .   .   .   .   3/8 in.
Diameter inside armature yoke   .   .   . $4\frac{1}{2}$ in.
Depth of slots   .   .   .   .   .   .   1.38 in.
Width of slot .   .   .   .   0.296 in.
Air gap (main pole)   .   .   .   .   .   .   0.125 in.
Air gap (interpole)   .   .   .   .   .   .   3/16 to 7/16
Pole-face arc measured on armature surface   .   5.75 in.
Pole-core material   .   .   .   .   .   .   Lam. S.
Pole-core cross section   .   .   .   .   . $3\frac{1}{2} \times 4$ in.
Inside diameter of field yoke   .   .   .   . $19\frac{5}{8}$ in.
Outside diameter of field yoke .   .   .   . $21\frac{7}{8}$ in.
Field-yoke cross section .   .   .   .   . $7\frac{3}{4} \times 1\frac{1}{8}$ in.
Field-yoke material   .   .   .   .   .   .   Rolled steel
Interpole face .   .   .   . $1\frac{1}{4} \times 3\frac{3}{4}$ in.
Interpole core .   .   .   . $1.7 \times 3\frac{3}{4}$ in.
Core losses (watts) and   }   .   .   .   766
Friction and windage (watts) }

1. The full-load voltage of a certain generator is 220. When the load is removed and the speed kept constant the voltage rises to 240. What is the percentage regulation?

2. *a.* At 25 C calculate the shunt-field excitation in oersteds and also ampere-turns per pole for the machine in Table I when the field is across 240 volts.

    b. For the same impressed voltage what is the percentage change in the shunt excitation from 25 C to 75 C?

    c. What is the percentage change in full-load series excitation from 25 C to 75 C ?

3. For a constant temperature and terminal potential, what is the per cent change in shunt-field excitation from full load to no load in a motor? Answer the same question for series excitation.

4. If the dynamo in Table I is operated in the hot state at constant rated speed as a shunt generator with interpoles and with full-shunt field separately excited from a source of 240 volts, calculate the field-resistance line and the no-load terminal voltage. Also calculate the terminal voltage for full-load armature current. Calculate the per cent voltage regulation.

5. What is the per cent regulation for the generator of Prob. 4 when operated under the conditions of Prob. 4?

6. What is the per cent regulation of the generator of Prob. 4 operated at 50 per cent of rated speed and rated load current?

7. How many ohms resistance in a field rheostat will be necessary when full load is removed to bring the no-load voltage for the generator of Prob. 4 to the full-load value?

8. Determine the full-load voltage for the generator in Prob. 4 if the excitation potential dropped 25 per cent.

9. Assuming the speed constant, what is the theoretical value of the short-circuit current for the generator of Prob. 4? Under these conditions, what is the total *armature-circuit* copper loss? How many times normal is this?

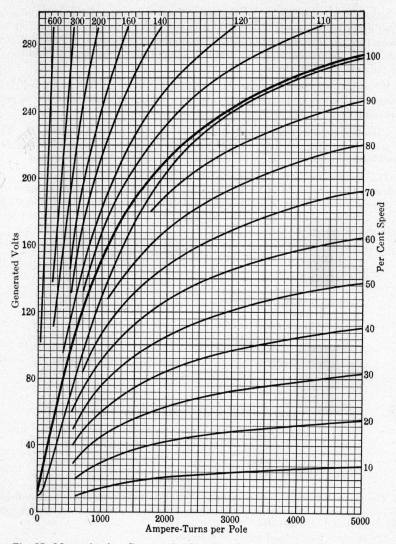

Fig. 25. Magnetization Curves of a Dynamo for Various Speeds. Ascending and Descending Branches for 100 Per Cent Speed Are Shown.

10. Assume that the interpoles of the dynamo in Prob. 4 are omitted and the brushes shifted in the correct direction for good commutation, so that the commutating zone is under a pole tip. The rest of the conditions are the same as those in Prob. 4. Find the full-load terminal voltage. Calculate the voltage regulation.

11. Assume the interpoles of the dynamo in Prob. 4 are omitted and the brushes are shifted in the correct direction for good commutation so that the commutating zone is under a pole tip. The rest of the conditions are the same as those in Prob. 4. Calculate the terminal voltage for 25, 50, 75, 100, and 125 per cent of full-load armature current. Plot the external characteristic.

12. When the dynamo is operated as specified in Prob. 11, find how much field resistance will have to be inserted to reduce the full-load terminal voltage to 80 per cent of its value in Prob. 11.

13. Calculate the short-circuit current for the dynamo as used in Prob. 11. What is the generated voltage at short circuit? Calculate the ratio of the short-circuit current to full-load current. How does this compare with that in Prob. 9? Explain.

14. The dynamo in Table I is operated at 100 per cent speed in the hot state without interpoles and series field and with the brushes shifted for good commutation so that the demagnetizing ampere-turns per pole at full-load current are 700. Calculate points for the armature characteristic at 0, $\frac{1}{4}$, $\frac{1}{2}$, $\frac{3}{4}$, and full-load armature current for a terminal voltage of 240 volts.

TABLE II. DATA ON A 3-KW GENERATOR

Number of shunt field turns per pole	1070
Number of series field turns per pole	18
Number of interpole field turns per pole	58
Armature resistance	0.38 ohm
Shunt field resistance (total)	66.6 ohms
Series field resistance (total)	0.069 ohm
Interpole field resistance (total)	0.0716 ohm
Rated current output	24 amp
Speed	1150 rpm
Rated voltage	125

DATA FOR MAGNETIZATION CURVE

I_f	0	0.18	0.335	0.589	0.74	.89	1.08	1.253	1.402	1.856	2.04
E	5.2	26	42	66	79.9	92.3	107.3	120	130	151	157

I_f	2.2	2.34	2.65	2.88
E	162	166	172	175

15. The generator in Table II is operated with interpoles and without series field with the brushes set on the mechanical neutral. It is separately excited with a constant field current of 1.325 amperes.

    a. Calculate the no-load terminal voltage.

    b. Calculate the terminal voltage when supplying rated current.

    c. How much field current would be required to yield a terminal voltage of 125 when the generator supplies rated current?

16. Assume the brushes of the generator in Table II are shifted so as to produce 171.2 ampere-turns per pole of demagnetizing armature reaction at full load. The generator is operated without interpoles and series field.

    a. How much field current is required to produce 125 volts at the terminals when full-load current is being delivered?

    b. When operating at half-load current?

17. Calculate the terminal voltage for $\frac{1}{4}$, $\frac{1}{2}$, $\frac{3}{4}$, $\frac{4}{4}$, and $\frac{5}{4}$ of full load and plot the external characteristic if the dynamo in Table II is operated without series field and interpoles. It is separately excited with a field current of 1.33 amp and the brushes are shifted so there are 171.2 demagnetizing ampere-turns per pole at full load.

18. The dynamo in Table II is operated with interpoles and without series field with the brushes set on the mechanical neutral. It is separately excited with a field current of 1.33 amp. Determine the terminal voltage for $\frac{1}{4}$, $\frac{1}{2}$, $\frac{3}{4}$, full, and $\frac{5}{4}$ of full load. Plot the external characteristic.

19. The dynamo in Table I is operated self-excited in the cold state with 18.5 ohms added to the field circuit. Interpoles are used but the series field is omitted. Determine points for the external characteristic from no load to short circuit. What is the maximum current delivered? At what terminal voltage does maximum current occur? What is the short-circuit current?

20. The dynamo in Table I is operated as a self-excited shunt generator with interpoles until the hot field resistance is attained. The speed is kept constant at rated value, and no external resistance is placed in the field. Determine points for the external characteristics from no load to that load which gives zero terminal potential. What is the maximum current delivered? What is the short-circuit current?

21. The dynamo in Table I is operated self-excited in the cold state with 18.5 ohms added to the shunt-field circuit. Interpoles and series field are omitted and the brushes are shifted for good commutation so that the full-load demagnetizing armature ampere-turns per pole are 700. Determine points for the external characteristic from no load to short circuit. What is the maximum current delivered? How does this compare with the value obtained in Prob. 19? What is the short-circuit current?

22. The dynamo in Table I is operated in the hot state at rated speed as a self-excited shunt generator without interpoles. The brushes are shifted so that the demagnetizing ampere-turns per pole at full-load current are 737. Determine the external characteristic from no load to short circuit. What is the maximum current and what is the current at short circuit?

23. The dynamo in Table II is operated as a self-excited shunt generator with interpoles. The field resistance is adjusted so that the no-load terminal potential is 125 volts. Determine points for the external characteristic from no load to the point of maximum current which the machine can deliver.

24. The dynamo in Table II is operated as a self-excited shunt generator without interpoles. The brushes are shifted to get good commutation so that there are 171.2 demagnetizing ampere-turns per pole when the armature current is 24 amp. Determine points for the external characteristic. What is the maximum current output? What makes this dynamo unsatisfactory for this condition of operation?

25. A series generator has the same magnetization curve as that given for 100 per cent speed for the dynamo in Table I. The full-load current is 50 amp and there are 60 turns per pole. The armature resistance is 0.14 ohm and the series-field resistance is 0.06 ohm. The brushes are set so that there are 625 demagnetizing ampere-turns per pole at full load. Determine the external characteristic.

26. A series generator has 50 turns per pole, rated armature current of 40 amp, and 380 demagnetizing ampere-turns of armature reaction at rated current. The armature resistance is 0.25 ohm and the series field resistance is .05 ohm. The magnetization curve at rated speed follows:

Ampere-turns of excitation per pole	0	200	400	500	750	1000	1300	1500	1750	2000
Generated emf	5	23.3	40	48.6	68.5	86.8	107.4	117.5	125.6	130.7

Ampere-turns of excitation per pole	2250	2500	3000
Generated emf	134	136.2	140

Determine the terminal voltage when supplying 10, 20, 30, 40, and 50 amp.

27. Determine the external characteristic for the series generator of Prob. 26 when operated at 25 per cent of rated speed if the brushes are given an additional shift so that the demagnetizing ampere-turns per pole of armature reaction at rated current of 40 amp are 1000. What is the short-circuit current?

28. Connect the machine in Table I as a cumulative-compound long-shunt dynamo. Use the hot field resistance with no external (rheostat) resistance and 100 per cent speed. Assuming that interpoles are used, determine the external characteristic from no-load to twice full-load current. What is the maximum voltage, and at what load does it occur?

29. Repeat Prob. 28 when a series field of three times the number of turns given in the table of constants for the machine is used.

30. The machine in Table II is connected long-shunt, cumulative-compound and is operated at rated speed with sufficient resistance in the field to produce 125 volts at no load. Assuming interpoles are used, determine the external characteristic from no-load to one and one-half times full-load current. What is the maximum voltage, and at what load does it occur?

31. Work Prob. 30 if the number of series turns is increased to a total of 54 per pole and the corresponding series field resistance becomes 0.207 ohm if all of the other conditions remain the same.

32. Determine the external characteristic for the dynamo in the table when no interpoles are used and the brushes are shifted to give 737 demagnetizing ampere-turns per pole at full-load current. Use three times the number of series-field turns given by the manufacturer with series field resistance increased accordingly, the hot-state field resistance, long-shunt cumulative-compound connection, and rated speed.

33. Operate the generator in Table II short-shunt, cumulative-compound with three times the series field turns and series field resistance. Assuming interpoles are used, determine the external characteristic from no load to full load if the field resistance is adjusted so that 125 volts are produced at the terminals at no load. Assume the shunt field is connected directly across the armature terminals with the interpole and series fields connected on the line side of the common shunt field and armature connection.

34. Assume the generator in Table II operated long-shunt, cumulative-compound with three times the series field turns and resistance and without interpoles. To secure good commutation the brushes are shifted until there are 171.2 demagnetizing ampere-turns per pole for an armature current of 24 amp. If the field resistance is such that 125 volts are produced at the terminals at no load when the resistance drop caused by field current at no load is neglected, determine the external characteristic from no load to full load.

35. A 230-volt generator has 1970 shunt-field turns per pole and a rated armature current of 37.7 amp. The armature characteristic is given by $I_f = 0.01 I_a + 0.57$. Calculate the number of series field turns per pole to flat compound the generator. Neglect resistance of the required series field.

36. Connect the dynamo in Table II as a long-shunt differential-compound generator and operate it with interpoles. Assuming it operates at rated speed with full shunt field, determine the external characteristic. Neglect any effect of field current in the armature at no load.

37. Using the machine in Table I as a long-shunt differential-compound generator, determine the external characteristic. Assume 100 per cent speed, hot-field resistance, and a noninterpole machine having 737 demagnetizing ampere-turns per pole at full load.

38. Assume the machine in Table I to be operated at 100 per cent speed as a long-shunt differential-compound generator with interpoles in the hot state. Determine the external characteristic.

CHAPTER VIII

Operation of Generators

Self-Excited Shunt Generator Building Up under Load. The building up of a shunt generator under load depends upon the same factors that determine this process at no load, plus the effects of the demagnetizing armature reaction and the armature-circuit resistance-drop due to the load itself. The building up under load may be studied by applying a graphical treatment to a special case.

A generator is assumed to be running at normal speed with the field switch open and with a 2-ohm resistance connected across the armature. An enlarged

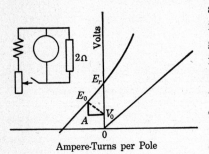

Fig. 1. Enlarged Lower Part of Fig. 2.

section of the lower part of the magnetization curve and excitation line for this generator is given in Fig. 1. The magnetization curve has been extended along $E_r E_0$ to include that portion which is obtained by reversed excitation. The generated voltage due to residual alone (without 2-ohm load) was E_r. The load current produces demagnetizing ampereturns equal to $A V_0$, giving a generated voltage of E_0. The armature resistance-drop represented by $E_0 A$ reduced the terminal voltage to $O V_0$. The triangle $V_0 A E_0$ is a load triangle and is identical in application to those used in the previous chapter. The sides of this triangle are proportional to a load current of $V_0/2$, since the terminal voltage V_0 is impressed across a 2-ohm resistance.

When the field switch is closed, a voltage of V_0 is impressed across the shunt field and the generator will start to build up if the conditions under which a generator will build up, as discussed in Chap. III, are fulfilled. As the generator builds up, the load current will increase in magnitude and the load triangle will grow in size. Both the current value and the sides of the triangle are directly proportional to the length of $O V_0$. The growing load triangle will slide up on the magnetization curve keeping its vertex E_0 or E on that curve as shown in Fig. 2. The lower vertex V_0 or E_1 gives the terminal voltage which is impressed across the field circuit. As the load increases, the voltage impressed

136

across the field increases with the ordinates of the dotted curve V_0E_1X. The initial accelerating voltage is V_0 and for the position of the load triangle EC_1E_1 it is $E_1 - V_2$. The generator will build up ultimately to a point corresponding to the point X on the excitation line. The accelerating voltage at no load is proportional to the distance between the full-line magnetization curve and the excitation line. This difference is always greater than for the condition under load so that a machine will always build up faster and more readily at no load.

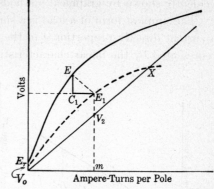

Fig. 2. Generator Building up under Load.

The size of the voltage triangle is governed by the value of the load resistance. Thus, a higher value of load resistance would produce a smaller load triangle and raise the position of the dotted line E_1X. Such a change would increase the accelerating voltage and cause the generator to build up more quickly. On the other hand, a lower value of load resistance would increase the size of the load triangle and reduce the rate of building up. It is evident that a very low value of load resistance might cause the dotted curve to intersect the excitation line at a low value and thus prevent the generator from building up. That load resistance at which the generator just fails to build up is called the **critical load.**

The preceding discussion has neglected the effect of the self-inductance of the armature and the load upon the building up of a generator. When the load is inductive, it will take a *longer time* for the *armature current* to come to the same value. For any given terminal voltage, the armature current will be

$$I_a = \frac{V - L \, di/dt}{R_a}$$

where L represents the self-inductance of the load and the armature. The effect of L is to reduce the instantaneous value of I_a, reduce the size of the load triangle, and thus *increase* the rate of building up of the generator.

A cumulative-compound generator under load will build up in a manner similar to the shunt machine, though its series field will serve as a definite aid in the process.

The Characteristics of Loads. Most loads which are placed upon sources of electrical supply have a definite *voltage-current characteristic*. The current taken by some loads is limited only by their resistance, while others produce a counter voltage or back voltage which opposes the voltage of the source and thus limits the amount of the voltage which is effective in producing current through the resistance of the load. The characteristics of loads can be conveniently shown by graphical methods.

The simplest form of a load is a single constant resistance. This load takes a current directly proportional to the voltage impressed across it and can be represented by the linear characteristic shown in Fig. 3.

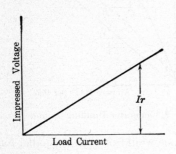

Fig. 3. Characteristic of a Resistance Load.

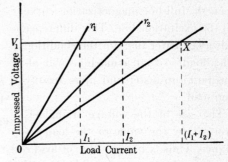

Fig. 4. Construction of Combined Load Characteristics of Two Resistances in Parallel.

In the constant-potential system, two or more loads are usually operated in parallel. A load consisting of two resistances, r_1 and r_2, can be represented by two individual load characteristics as shown by lines Or_1 and Or_2 in Fig. 4. The combined load characteristic for these two resistances must be a straight line because these two resistances may be replaced by an equivalent resistance whose value is $r_1r_2/(r_1 + r_2)$. The current through this equivalent resistance varies directly with the voltage impressed. At the voltage V_1 in Fig. 4, the combined current for the resistances r_1 and r_2 must be $(I_1 + I_2)$. This must be the current on the combined load characteristic at the voltage V_1. Thus, one point X on the combined load characteristic is defined by the ordinate V_1 and the abscissa $(I_1 + I_2)$. When the voltage is zero, the current must be zero. Hence the combined load characteristic is a straight line passing through point X and the origin.

A storage battery which is being charged is a different type of load than a simple resistance because it has an emf due to chemical action in addition to a resistance. Thus one component of the applied voltage must overcome the battery emf. The other component of the applied voltage causes current to flow through the battery against its internal resistance. The terminal voltage of the load must be equal to the sum of the two components $(E + IR)$, E being the emf of the battery and R its internal resistance. The load characteristic of a battery on charge is shown in Fig. 5. Since the emf of a battery varies with the state of charge, and the internal resistance varies both with the state of

charge and the temperature, the load characteristic curve holds only for a
given set of conditions.

Terminal Voltage of a Generator under Load. The operating characteristics of
generators depend to some extent on the type of load placed on them. It is
sometimes desirable to know the terminal voltage and the current that will be

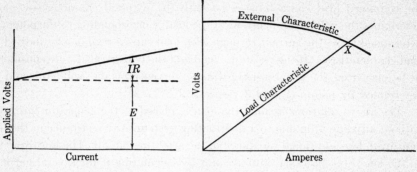

Fig. 5. Load Characteristic of a
Battery on Charge.

Fig. 6. Construction to Determine the Load
a Generator Will Carry When Connected to
a Given Resistance.

delivered by a generator when a certain type of load is placed on it. This information can be readily determined by plotting the load characteristic and
the external characteristic of the generator on the same sheet and to the same
scale as shown in Fig. 6. The intersection of these two characteristics at X
determines the voltage and current for the simple resistance load.

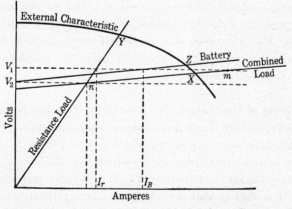

Fig. 7. Construction to Determine the Load on a Generator
Connected to a Battery and Resistance in Parallel.

A more complicated problem is to find the current and voltage delivered
to a resistance and a battery connected in parallel. The external characteristic
of a generator and the load characteristics of the resistance and the battery
are plotted in Fig. 7. The combined load characteristic is determined by adding

currents I_r and I_B for the two characteristics at the same potential V_1 and laying off the sum along V_1 at m. The same thing is done at some other potential V_2. The solution may be simplified by selecting a potential where the battery current is zero. This makes the total current V_2n equal to that taken by the resistance. The points m and n are the two points necessary to determine the combined load characteristic, since it is linear. The intersection of the combined load characteristic nm with the external characteristic at X determines the voltage and current at the load. Corresponding to the potential determined at X, the current through each load can be read on the individual load characteristics. If the resistance load and the battery load were considered to be placed on the generator separately, the current and voltage would be determined by points Y and Z respectively.

The above solutions assume the load is placed at the generator terminals without any line drop due to a distributing system. Any resistance in the line acts much like additional resistance in the armature circuit. The line drop due to the load may be taken into account by calculating it for several currents and by subtracting this drop from the voltage ordinates of the external characteristic at the corresponding currents. This yields a new curve somewhat lower than the external characteristic, which may be used instead of the latter to give actual line current and voltage.

The above method outlines the procedure for a solution of problems involving generators and different kinds of loads. It is possible to perform the solutions outlined above analytically if the equations of the external characteristic and the load characteristics are known. These equations are easy to find for the loads, being of the form $y = mx + b$, but the one for the external characteristic may be difficult to obtain and generally will have to be an approximation. The equations must be solved simultaneously for V and I. The analytical solution is rather involved, while the graphical solution is simpler and equally satisfactory.

Parallel Operation of Generators. The load on an electrical power-generating system fluctuates, usually reaching a minimum sometime during the night and having its peak value sometime during the day. When the load upon the system is small, it is undesirable from the standpoint of efficiency to have a large generator lightly loaded. It is better to have a smaller generator operating near full load. If a shift in load is made from a large generator to a small one or vice versa, the operation must be carried through without an interruption to service. *Continuity of service is not only desirable but also an economic necessity.* Generally, it is not desirable or perhaps possible to have one generator large enough to carry the peak load on a large system. With several machines required to supply the load, it becomes necessary to operate them in parallel so that their combined outputs may be transmitted from the same bus bars over outgoing lines. The problems that arise in the parallel operation of generators are important and interesting.

Parallel Operation of Shunt Generators. A circuit illustrating the connections for operating shunt generators in parallel is given in Fig. 8. Generator G_1 is assumed to be in operation and carrying the load L. As the load continues to increase, it ultimately will become necessary to place generator G_2 in parallel with G_1. This step is initiated by closing the circuit breaker CB and the switch S_2 on generator G_2. The closing of the field switch causes generator G_2 to build up, and its voltage will be indicated by the voltmeter V_2. The voltage of generator G_2 is adjusted until it is equal to V_1. It is very important that the voltages of the two generators are opposed in the series circuit of the two ma-

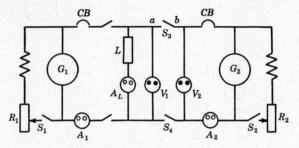

Fig. 8. Parallel Operation of Shunt Generators.

chines, which requires that the polarities of points a and b are the same, either both positive or both negative.* If this is not the case, a serious short circuit will result when the machines are placed in parallel. Assuming that the polarities are correct, the switches S_3 and S_4 may be closed. Generator G_2 will supply no current if the voltage V_2 has been adjusted exactly equal to V_1, since its generator voltage would be exactly opposed by the voltage V_1. Generator G_2 may be caused to take on some load by lowering the resistance in its field rheostat R_2. The lower resistance permits more current through the field, and the rise in generated voltage of G_2 above the terminal voltage V_1 causes G_2 to carry part of the load. The current supplied by G_2 automatically adjusts itself so that the generated voltage minus its armature-circuit resistance drop equals the terminal voltage of generator G_1.

In the actual operation of two generators in parallel, the field rheostat of generator G_1 is manipulated (resistance increased) at the same time as that of G_2 is decreased so that the terminal potential of the two machines is held constant. If this procedure is carefully carried out, the load can be shifted to generator G_2, and the transfer of the entire load to this generator would be

* A simple test can be made by closing S_4 and placing a voltmeter across points a and b. A zero or low reading indicates a correct polarity, while a reading of two times line potential shows a dangerous situation.

indicated by a zero reading of ammeter A_1. The circuit breaker CB of machine 1 can be opened and no arcing will occur. By this procedure, a generator may be taken off or placed on the bus bars without any voltage disturbance of the system. The proper order of procedure in switching operations is to open or close circuit breakers before the corresponding switches. A diagram of suitable switchboard wiring for the parallel operation of two shunt generators is given in Fig. 9.

When placing one shunt generator in parallel with another under load, it is better to have the voltage of the incoming machine a little higher than the terminal voltage of the machine under load. This higher voltage will cause the

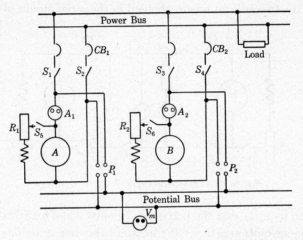

Fig. 9. Switchboard Wiring Diagram for Parallel Operation of Shunt Generators.

incoming machine to assume a part of the load at once, whereas a voltage less than the line would cause the incoming machine to act as a motor and would place a still greater load on the already heavily loaded generator.

Division of Load between Shunt Generators in Parallel. The division of load between shunt machines in parallel may be determined by a study of their external characteristics. These external characteristics should be obtained by loading the generators and measuring the corresponding voltages at speeds determined by their own prime mover and with the usual field rheostat setting. The external characteristic thus obtained is a combination of the external characteristic of the generator and the speed-load characteristic of the prime mover. It is the over-all volts versus load characteristic of the generator and its prime mover. Consider the case of two generators A and B which have external characteristics as shown in Fig. 10. In this figure, the field excitation of generator B is adjusted so that it produces a higher voltage at no load, when acting alone, than that of A. The terminal voltage of the two machines when operating in parallel must always be identical. At any terminal voltage V_2, the output of the generators will be the currents $I_A{}'$ and $I_B{}'$ corresponding to this voltage on the individual external characteristic curves. For this division of load, the total current on the system is $(I_A{}' + I_B{}')$. When the load on the system is zero, the output of one generator must equal the input to the other. Thus, at terminal voltage V_1 the current output of generator B is I_B (positive), while the equal current I_A of generator A is negative, and the sign indicates that current is flowing counter to the direction of its generated voltage. Therefore dynamo A is being driven as a motor by generator B. (See page 177.)

As load is placed on the system of Fig. 10, the resultant terminal voltage will drop. When the terminal voltage has dropped to V_3, the generator A is carrying no load and generator B supplies all of the load current $I_B{}''$. For a

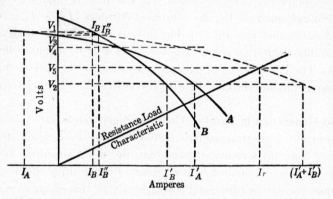

Fig. 10. Construction for Determining the Division of Load between Two Shunt Generators in Parallel when Connected to a Resistance Load.

further increase in system load, generator A begins picking up load until both generators are equally loaded, and the voltage of the system drops to V_4. As still more load is placed on the system, the voltage drops still further and generator A carries more than half of the load.

If the no-load voltages of both generators when acting alone were adjusted to equality, the external characteristic of generator B would be lowered until its intersection with the axis of ordinates coincided with that of generator A. With such an initial adjustment, it can be seen that generator A with the least drooping characteristic will always carry the greater load. These two generators would divide the load equally only when their external characteristics are identical. In general, it is desirable to have the generators divide the load in proportion to their capacities. Thus, if one generator is twice the capacity of another, it would be desirable for the loads to be divided so that the larger generator always carries just twice the load of the smaller. Therefore both generators would come to full load at the same time. When generators are to divide the load in exact proportion to their rating, their external characteristics must coincide when plotted in terms of per cent load.

Since the effect of varying field excitation on the external characteristic of a generator is to raise or lower it without producing any marked change in shape, the loads on direct-current generators can be divided in any desired ratio by manual control or with the aid of some automatic type of control.

Sometimes two generators with different external characteristics are adjusted to carry equal loads at a certain voltage. When the load is removed, it can be shown that the generator with the least drooping characteristic will carry the smaller part of the load.

The load on each of two generators operating in parallel on a certain resistance load may be determined from the load characteristic and the combined external characteristic. The combined characteristic is obtained by plotting for each voltage, such as V_2, the combined currents $(I_A' + I_B')$. This gives the dotted curve shown in Fig. 10. The intersection of the load characteristic and the combined external characteristics shows a total current I_r flowing at a voltage V_5. The current output of each generator can be read at the point of intersection of the line through V_5 with the individual external characteristic.

Compound Generators in Parallel. Compound generators are commonly used in direct-current generating station service because they automatically give more nearly constant terminal voltage than the shunt generator and because they may be overcompounded to compensate for line drop. Shunt generators with voltage regulators (discussed subsequently in this chapter) can be used to hold the terminal voltage more nearly constant than compound generators and can also be made to compensate for line drop. However, shunt generators with regulators need more attention and are somewhat less trouble free than the simple compound generator. Also the cost of the compound generator should be somewhat less than that of a shunt generator with its regulator. In applications where the increased precision of voltage regulation as given by a shunt generator with regulator is not required, the compound generator finds extensive application. While shunt generators without regulators operate in parallel quite satisfactorily, the adoption of over compound generators gave rise to unexpected difficulties. The compound generators were found to be unstable when operated in parallel, due to their rising voltage characteristic.

While parallel operation of compound generators is unstable only when one or both generators have rising *external* characteristics with increase in load, it is simpler to understand the cause of instability by visualizing the variation of the generated voltage with load. This results from the fact that the terminal voltages of generators in parallel at the point of paralleling must always be identical and also because the external characteristics do not show the terminal voltages during the transient conditions of instability as will be explained presently. A curve showing the variation of generated voltage with load is called the **internal characteristic,** and is obtained by adding to the ordinates of the external characteristic the total armature-circuit resistance drop between terminals. Figure 11 shows three curves representing (1) an external characteristic of a compound machine, (2) the armature plus series-field resistance drop, and (3) the sum of curves (1) and (2) which gives (3), the internal characteristic.

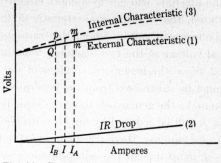

Fig. 11. External Characteristic Plus the Armature-Circuit Resistance Drop Yields the Internal Characteristic.

A simplified circuit for the parallel operation of two compound generators is given in Fig. 12. Both generators A and B are assumed to be overcompounded, to have characteristics similar to Fig. 11, and to be carrying equal load currents represented by I. Let it be supposed that the equilibrium of parallel operation be disturbed by something such as a slight momentary increase in speed of generator A. Under this momentary increase of speed, generator A will develop a little higher emf which will cause a little more current to be supplied by generator A. Generator B, in turn, should supply a little less current since the resultant load voltage and load current will not be affected appreciably. The slightly increased current output I_A of A increases the series-field excitation and raises its generated voltage (see Fig. 11). Conversely, the slight decrease in the current output of B (through its series field) decreases the voltage it generates (see Fig. 11). The increasing current of generator A produces another increment in the generated voltage of this machine, while the decreasing current in machine B causes another decrement in its generated voltage.

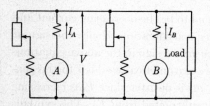

Fig. 12. Parallel Connection of Compound Generators without Equalizers (Generally Unstable).

Therefore the current of machine A continues to increase, while that of B decreases until it finally goes to zero, and machine A supplies all of the load. Beyond this point the current in A continues to increase and the current in machine B reverses in direction, causing this dynamo to act as a differential-compound motor driving its prime mover.

The rapid rise of current due to this instability continues until a circuit breaker opens or damage to the machines stops the process. A serious stage in this transient action will exist when the increasing current in the machine acting as a differential-compound motor finally becomes large enough to completely neutralize its shunt field. Then there will be no field flux through the armature, no counter-emf developed, and the machine will act as a short circuit on the other generator. As previously stated, the external characteristic of the individual machines does not show the terminal voltage under the transient conditions just discussed. The terminal voltage of the two machines must always be equal, as is evident from Fig. 12. Since the generated voltages of the two machines are different, a voltage must be subtracted from the generated voltage of machine A and added to B to make the generators have the same terminal voltage. The generated voltage of A will be reduced by an IR drop mn due to I_A, Fig. 11. Furthermore, since I_A is changing, there will be induced in the series field and armature a voltage $-L\ di/dt$ due to the self-inductance of the windings. Lenz's law states that this voltage opposes the increase of current and is opposite to the generated voltage. Thus the terminal voltage of generator A is its generated voltage minus a voltage due to armature and series-field resistance drop and a drop due to inductance and the changing current, or

$$V_A = E_A - I_A(R_{aA} + R_{SA}) - L_A \frac{dI_A}{dt}.$$

The current in generator B is decreasing and the voltage due to inductance, according to Lenz's law, will tend to prevent the decrease by being in the same direction as the generated voltage. Therefore the terminal voltage of generator B is the generated voltage minus the resistance drop due to the armature and series-field resistance minus the inductance drop, or

$$V_B = E_B - I_B(R_{aB} + R_{SB}) - L_B \frac{dI_B}{dt}.$$

Since $V_A = V_B$,

$$E_A - I_A(R_{aA} + R_{SA}) - L_A \frac{dI_A}{dt} = E_B - I_B(R_{aB} + R_{SB}) - L_B \frac{dI_B}{dt}. \quad (1)$$

It should be remembered that I_B was assumed to be the decreasing current and I_A the increasing current for the case under consideration. Hence the sign of dI_B/dt is negative and this will change the negative sign in the above equations to plus. The voltage $L_B(dI_B/dt)$ is therefore arithmetically added to the generated voltage E_B. For machine A, $L_A(dI_A/dt)$ is positive since I_A is increasing and this voltage is therefore arithmetically subtracted from E_A. The symbols R_{aA} and R_{SA} are the resistances of armature and series field respectively of machine A. Similarly, R_{aB} and R_{SB} are those for machine B. The symbol L_A is the effective inductance in machine A which is responsible for the voltage of self-induction due to the changing current. The symbol L_B is the similar quantity for machine B.

As stated above, the current must continue changing to equalize the terminal voltages as the generated voltages deviate more and more. Equation 1 shows that, when E_A and E_B are unequal, the terms $E_A - I_A(R_{aB} + R_{SA})$ and $E_B - I_B(R_{aB} + R_{SB})$ which are represented by n and Q respectively on Fig. 11, are unequal and the terms containing the changing currents are essential to produce equal terminal voltages. The current change therefore continues until a circuit breaker or some other means separates the two machines. The time taken to complete the whole sequence of events outlined is generally quite short. It may vary from only a fraction of a second to a few seconds from the time the currents start to deviate from equal values.

The instability of compound generators in parallel is due to the rising external voltage characteristic which causes the generator taking on more load to establish the conditions for taking on still more load, while the decreasing load on the other lowers its voltage, which causes it to drop more of its load. The development of instability is independent of the initial load upon the two machines. For simplicity, equal loads were assumed above.

Equalizer Connection. The inherent instability of overcompound generators operating in parallel can be overcome by means of an equalizer connection. The equalizer is simply a copper bar or other connection of low resistance which places the series fields of the two machines in parallel, as shown in Fig. 13. This parallel connection of the series fields causes the total load current from the armatures of A and B to be divided between the series fields S_A and S_B in a ratio inversely proportional to the resistances of these fields. As long as the

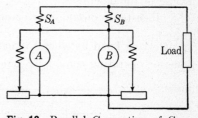

Fig. 13. Parallel Connection of Compound Generators Showing the Equalizer Connection.

combined output of machines A and B is the same, there will be no change in the current through series fields S_A and S_B regardless of the distribution of current between the two armatures. Because of this, an increase of emf of one machine while the total line current remains constant causes this machine to deliver more current and the other machine less, but the mmf produced by the series fields does not change. Hence the increment of emf produced by additional current in the series field of one machine when no equalizer was used is absent when the equalizer connection is added. Therefore the primary cause of instability has been removed by the use of the equalizer. An increase of current in one series field is accompanied simultaneously by an increase through the other, so that the voltages of both machines are increased. The tendency toward inequality of voltages due to a change in current in the series field is eliminated by the use of the equalizer and the machines operate satisfactorily.

Requirements for Operating Two Compound Generators in Parallel. In order that compound machines may be operated in parallel so as to share the loads in proportion to their ratings, the following conditions should exist.

1. Both machines should have the same regulation (that is, the same external characteristics if plotted v.s. per cent load).

2. The series fields of both machines should be connected so as to make the generators cumulatively compound.

3. The machines must have an equalizer connection, if overcompounded.

4. Both generators should be brought to approximately the same voltage. (This is the condition for paralleling.)

5. The voltages generated should be opposed in the series circuit of the two machines (that is, positive terminal connected to positive terminal).

6. The series field of both machines must be on either the positive or the negative side of the line. If they are not, and all other conditions for parallel operation are fulfilled, the armature of each machine will be short-circuited by the series field of the other. This precaution is necessary when machines are connected for parallel operation for the first time.

7. The series fields should have resistances inversely proportional to the ratings of the machines.

8. Resistance of equalizer connection must be below a critical value.

Transferring Load between Compound Generators. The switchboard connections for operating compound generators in parallel are shown in Fig. 14. It

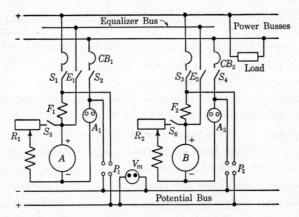

Fig. 14. Switchboard Connections for Operating Compound Generators in Parallel.

will be assumed that switches for generator A are closed, and that the generator is supplying the load connected to the bus bars. The load may be transferred to generator B as follows. Generator B is brought up to rated speed, and then its field switch S_6 is closed. The rheostat R_2 is adjusted so that the voltage of machine B shows a few volts under the voltage of A. The voltage of machines A and B may be determined by the insertion of a switchboard plug P_1 and P_2, respectively. Circuit breakers CB_2 are then closed, followed by the closing simultaneously of switches S_3, E_2, and S_4 if they consist of a triple-pole switch. If the switches must be closed singly, S_3 and E_2 should be closed first, though the order of closing these two is immaterial. Last of all, S_4 is closed. If E_2 were closed last, the machines would be operating for a short interval without the equalizer, and instability might develop. The voltage of machine B was adjusted to a few volts below the voltage of A because the voltage of B will rise a little as soon as the series field becomes energized. This occurs when S_3 and E_2 are closed and it is then possible, but not generally necessary, to readjust the voltage of B to exact equality with A by manipulating R_2.

After the generators are placed in parallel, the rheostats R_1 and R_2 are adjusted to give the desired voltage and load distribution. If generator A is to be taken off of the system, rheostat R_1 is "cut in" until ammeter A_1 reads zero or thereabout. The circuit breakers CB_1 may then be opened. If there are no circuit breakers, and switches S_1, E_1, and S_2 are single-pole switches, switch S_2 should be opened first. Opening E_1 first causes the machines to operate without an equalizer, while opening S_1 first causes machine A running as a shunt machine to be paralleled through the equalizer with machine B as a compound generator. Either of these latter conditions leads to instability. It may be necessary to manipulate rheostat R_2 to maintain the desired line voltage while "cutting in" resistance R_1.

Voltage Control. The voltage of either a shunt or compound generator can be kept constant by adjusting the field rheostat. The compound machine tends to maintain constant voltage as the load increases and can be designed to compensate for drops in voltage due to resistance, armature reaction, and speed. However, if the speed varies due to some other reason than the load, such as low steam pressure on the prime mover, the series field will not automatically maintain constant voltage. Where it is desired to hold a constant or rising voltage regardless of the cause of speed fluctuations, and regardless of resistance drop, armature reaction, or any other agency, a voltage regulator should be employed.

One form of voltage regulator functions by short-circuiting a field rheostat intermittently, thus maintaining a certain average value of field resistance and field current for each different load. The field rheostat consists of a resistance sufficient to reduce the voltage to about 35 or 40 per cent below normal when it is in the field circuit continuously. A short circuit placed on this resistance for a part of the time will produce an average resistance of such a value as to maintain rated voltage. The short circuit is placed around this resistance by a vibrating relay. The relative periods of open and short circuit determine the average resistance in the field, and hence the field current. The common regulator of this type was known as a **Tirrell regulator.*** While a large number of these regulators have been applied to direct-current generators and many are still in service, they have been superseded for this use by another type which will be explained presently. Occasionally, the vibrating type is used to regulate the voltage of alternating-current generators when it is desired to operate the exciters (direct-current generators) for these machines in parallel. Such applications as these probably comprise somewhat less than 10 per cent of the number of regulator applications.

Nearly all the regulators which are now applied to regulate the voltage of direct-current generators are of the rheostatic type. This type operates by varying directly the magnitude of the resistance in series with the field circuit. In principle it is similar to the usual manual method of adjusting the voltage of a generator except that the operation is performed automatically. The regulator operates when a change in excitation is required. At all other times no part of the device is in motion.

The principle of operation of one form of voltage regulator may be explained from the arrangement shown in Fig. 15. The resistance R_0 which is connected in the shunt field circuit has a number of taps each connecting to a leaf spring as shown in the figure. These springs are separated near one end by insulating strips shown cross-hatched. At the other end each spring has a silver contact button. A coil spring H pulls on an armature A which pivots at point P. Instead of actually pivoting, the equivalent effect is obtained through mounting the armature on a flexible support, thus eliminating the use of pivots and bearings. This coil-spring action closes successively the contacts on the leaf springs, thus short-circuiting the resistance R_0. One end of the armature is attracted by a magnet C which is energized by a winding M connected across the generator terminals. During normal conditions of operation this attraction balances the pull of the coil spring and causes the armature A to assume a position where only a portion of the leaf-spring contacts are closed. Hence only a portion of the resistance R_0 is in the field circuit. To illustrate the operation assume the generator voltage increases. More voltage is then impressed upon coil M which increases the magnetic pull on the armature A. This in turn relieves some of the pressure on the leaf springs, thus opening some of the silver contacts and causes more of R_0 to be inserted in the shunt field. The excitation is thereby decreased and the generator voltage returns to a voltage only slightly above normal. If the generator voltage should fall below normal, the electromagnet is weakened, the pull of the coil spring causes some of the silver contacts to close, thus short-circuiting part of R_0 and allowing more field current to flow in the field F. In this way the generator voltage is increased to a value only slightly under normal where a balance between the electromagnetic

* For a more complete discussion of the Tirrell regulator refer to the first edition of this text.

and coil-spring forces is restored. The action explained above is made more precise by the addition of a damping transformer T and stabilizing winding S on
the electromagnet. This combination provides an electrical method of doing
the same thing that might be done by the more familiar mechanical dash pots,
namely, damping. To illustrate the operation of this device, assume the generator voltage is low. The field current and corresponding voltage drop across
the field will then be increased as explained previously. The increasing field
voltage impressed across the primary of the transformer T causes an induced

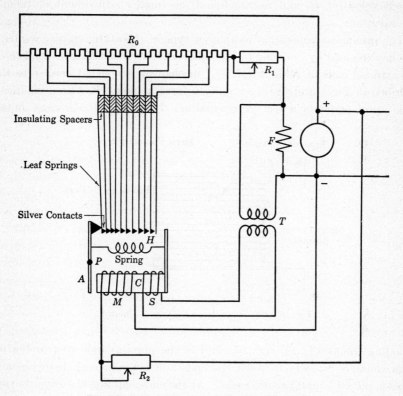

Fig. 15. Rheostatic Type of Voltage Regulator.

voltage in the secondary. This secondary voltage causes a current to flow in
coil S and the connections are made so as to add to the magnetic effect produced in winding M by the generator terminal voltage. Thus in effect, this
causes the magnet C to come to the final value of magnetic attraction that
will be caused by the increased generator terminal voltage when normal voltage is attained. Over-running the final position is thereby eliminated or greatly
reduced. In the steady state no voltage is produced in the stabilizing transformer secondary since only a *change* in primary voltage can cause an induced
secondary emf. Thus, under steady conditions, coil S carries no current and is

inoperative. In some arrangements the damping transformer secondary is connected in series with the terminal voltage of the armature and this resultant voltage impressed upon coil S. In this case coil S always carries current, the current being steady when there is no change of excitation but modified so as to produce damping action when the excitation changes. Rheostat R_1 is adjusted until the total field circuit resistance has a value which permits R_0 to be most effective. Rheostat R_2 permits some adjustment in the value of the voltage which will be held constant at the generator terminals. After the desired values of R_1 and R_2 are found, no further adjustment of them is necessary.

The principle of operation of another type of rheostatic voltage regulator may be explained by referring to Fig. 16. Terminals a and b correspond to the two extreme ends of R_0 in Fig. 15. A mechanism somewhat similar to that described in Fig. 15 operates to apply a force at point P. The resistance is made up of plates of a special composition. Each plate has a silver button

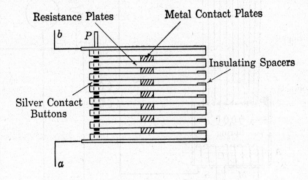

Fig. 16. Rheostatic Type Voltage Regulator.

extending completely through one end of the plate as indicated in Fig. 16. Approximately midway between the ends and between each two resistance plates is placed a metal contact plate. At the ends opposite the silver buttons are placed thin strips of insulation. A spring arrangement tends to tilt the resistance plates so that the silver buttons are separated. For the relations shown in Fig. 16 the current path is from a through the lower resistance plate, thence through alternate metal contact and resistance plates to the top plate, and out at b. As a force is applied at P the ends of the plates containing the silver buttons tilt downward. This tilting action gradually decreases the contact resistance between the metal contact plates and the resistance plates, this action becoming progressive along the stack, and starting at the top. After the contact resistance between the top resistance plate and the metal contact plate gradually decreases to a low value; the silver buttons in the two top resistance plates make contact and assure a very low resistance. As the tilting continues the action described progresses in sequence from one plate to the next until finally all silver buttons are in contact. The current path is then in at a through all the silver buttons and out at b. Thus the resistance has been reduced to a negligible value. For the normal voltage which is being held at the generator terminals several of the plates toward the top of the stack shown in Fig. 16 will be short-circuited through the silver buttons, while the rest of the plates will be effective in inserting resistance in the field circuit. Thus the actuating mechanism can either increase or decrease the field resistance as required to hold a predetermined generator voltage.

Another method of varying the field resistance of a shunt generator to maintain constant voltage automatically is illustrated in Fig. 17. The resistance R_0 has taps connected to copper segments insulated from each other and resembling a portion of an ordinary commutator. A rocking sector S may make contact with any of these segments as it rocks or rolls from segment B to C. As seen from the electrical connections in the figure, when the rocking sector is in contact with segment B all resistance R_0 is inserted in the shunt field circuit, while when making contact with C all resistance R_0 is short-circuited, and therefore cut out

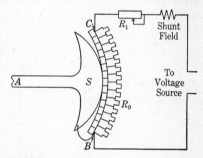

Fig. 17. Rheostatic   Type   Voltage Regulator.

of the field circuit. At other positions the amount of R_0 between segment C and the segment contacted by sector S is inserted in the field. The sector is rocked or rolled in position by a solenoid through a linkage mechanism connected to arm A. The solenoid is actuated by the terminal voltage of the generator in a way which maintains the voltage at a practically constant value similar to the mechanisms described previously. Through an elastically coupled damping mechanism the regulator is prevented from hunting or overshooting the resistance required to maintain constant voltage.

Regulators of the rheostatic type as described above are trouble free, need little maintenance, and perform satisfactorily over long periods of time with very little attention. Depending upon the class of regulator, they may be obtained to hold voltage constant within as small a range as $\pm\frac{1}{2}$ of 1 per cent to as great a variation as ± 3 per cent.

In addition to the types of voltage regulators described above, there are electronic regulators and rotary multifield exciters for accomplishing voltage regulation. In general, the electronic regulators are more sensitive, and therefore maintain the regulated voltage within closer limits than the rheostatic types previously described. For many applications in practice the very low limits of voltage regulation maintained by electronic regulators are not essential. A description of these electronic devices is beyond the scope of this text. Rotary multifield exciters which may be used for voltage regulation are explained in Chapter XIV.

Parallel Operation of Generators with Regulators. Generators equipped with individual rheostatic-type regulators may be made to operate in parallel and divide the load as desired regardless of the characteristics of the generators. A schematic diagram of two shunt generators with their regulators connected for parallel operation is shown in Fig. 18. In addition to the regulator potential winding, each regulator has a compensating winding placed on the same core with the potential winding as shown in the figure. The compensating windings are connected in series between points A and B which are located between the

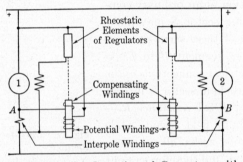

Fig. 18. Parallel Operation of Generators with Regulators.

armature and interpole field winding connections. Instead of an interpole winding a low resistance could be substituted. To illustrate the operation, assume generator 1 takes more than its share of the load. This will cause the potential at A to be lower than that at B. A current will therefore flow through the compensating windings on the regulators in a direction from B to A. This current decreases the magnetic field in the regulator torque element for machine 2 and increases the field in that for machine 1. Therefore the field excitation of machine 1 will be decreased while that of 2 will be increased. This action causes the load on 1 to decrease and that on 2 to increase until the loads are equalized. If machine 2 is assumed to take more than its share of the load, a similar analysis will show that the reverse effect from that explained above will occur.

The above principle of maintaining a desired load division between machines in parallel may be extended to any number of generators in parallel. An application using four generators on airplanes is shown on page 290. Not only is this system applicable to more than two machines, but it may also be employed to operate successfully in parallel, compound generators without equalizers, compound generators with shunt generators, or to divide the load equally between compound generators in parallel regardless of the amount of compounding.

PROBLEMS

1. The dynamo (page 129, Table I) is to operate in cold state, self-excited, with inter-poles, and at rated speed, but without series field. Find the critical load resistance that will just permit the generator to reach a terminal potential equal to residual voltage of 10 volts.

2. Operate the dynamo (pages 129–131) as self-excited, shunt generator with inter-poles, cold state, and at 1150 rpm.
   a. To what terminal potential will the generator build if connected to a load resistance of 2 ohms?
   b. How much accelerating voltage exists in the field as the potential passes 140 volts?

3. Operate the dynamo (pages 129–131) as a self-excited shunt generator in cold state at 1150 rpm but with the brushes shifted $3\frac{1}{2}$ commutator bars from the mechanical neutral in the direction for good commutation.
   a. How far will the generator build up self-excited while connected to a 2-ohm resistance load?
   b. What current will be delivered to the load?
   c. How much accelerating voltage exists in the field circuit as the potential passes 100 volts?

4. Three generators, A, B, and C, have the following external characteristics:

CURRENT	VOLTAGE A	VOLTAGE B	VOLTAGE C
−10	258	224	212
0	240	220	208
+20	206.5	214.5	200
40	162	206	189 and 7
50	134	201	179 and 23
60	90	194.5	165 and 43
70	28	187	140 and 75
74		184	112
90		166	
100		150	

   a. What load resistance would draw 50 amp from generator A?
   b. What current would a 4-ohm resistance draw from generator A?
   c. How many amperes would be drawn from each of generators A and B in parallel, with a 4-ohm resistance for a common load? What will be the voltage on the load?
   d. Find the current taken by a 2-ohm load on generator C and also 1/5-ohm load. Does lower resistance always draw more current from a generator?
   e. Place a parallel combination of 4 ohms and 5 ohms across the combination of generators A and B in parallel. Find the resulting potential, the current from each generator, and the current in each load.

5. Generators B and C (Prob. 4) are connected in parallel and supply a load consisting of a storage battery and two resistances, all loads being in parallel. The battery has an emf of 180 volts and an internal resistance of $r_1 = 0.3$ ohm. The resistances are:

$r_2 = 6$ ohms, and $r_3 = 3$ ohms. Find the generator potentials, and all currents of both generators and loads under the following conditions:

    a. Generators B and C paralleled, but all loads off.

    b. Generator B, load—the battery alone.

    c. Generators B and C, load—the battery alone.

    d. Generator B, load—battery and r_2.

    e. Generator C, load—battery and r_3.

    f. Generator B, load—r_2 and r_3.

    g. Generators B and C, load—battery, r_2, and r_3.

6. Two generators having the following external characteristics are operated in parallel. Find the total current output and the output of each generator when a 1-ohm resistance load is connected to the system.

EXTERNAL CHARACTERISTIC OF MACHINE A

Volts	120	116.4	112.6	108.8	104.5	100	95	88.8	80.4
Amp	0	10	20	30	40	50	60	70	80

EXTERNAL CHARACTERISTIC OF MACHINE B

Volts	130	123.2	116.2	118.9	101.3	93.1	84	72.5
Amp	0	10	20	30	40	50	60	70

7. Assuming the shape of the external characteristics in Prob. 6 to be unaffected by varying the field excitation (this only raises or lowers the curves), find the load voltage at which the external characteristic of each machine intersects the ordinate corresponding to zero current when the machines are adjusted to supply equal currents and the same total current and voltage for the resistance load of Prob. 6.

8. If an additional 5-ohm load resistance is connected to the generators in Prob. 6, find the current output of each generator and the current through the 5-ohm resistance. Has the current through the 1-ohm resistance changed? How much?

9. A battery of 50 cells each having an emf of 2.1 volts and 0.004-ohm resistance is connected across generator A of Prob. 6, operating by itself. Find the current and terminal potential.

10. Find the resistance of a load that will draw 50 amp from generator B of Prob. 6 when operated by itself.

11. Find the resistance of a load which will draw 100 amp when placed across the generators of Prob. 6 when they are operating in parallel. How many amperes does each generator supply and what will be the terminal potential?

CHAPTER IX

Motor Speed and Torque Characteristics

Torque and Speed Characteristics. The voltage characteristics considered in Chap. VII are of particular interest when the dynamo is operated as a generator. However, these characteristics have two relationships to the dynamo when used as a motor. First, the generated or counter emf of a shunt dynamo serving as a motor may have a trend similar to the emf of the generator when operated under like conditions of load. Second, the curve of the voltage impressed across a motor under load may droop with load, because of line drop, in a manner similar to the decrease in terminal voltage of a shunt generator under load (external characteristic).

The speed and torque characteristics suggested on page 102 are of particular interest when the dynamo is operated as a motor. Yet it is well to note that the mechanical torque input to a generator under load follows the same trend as the torque developed when the dynamo is operated as a motor under similar conditions of load, speed, and voltage. The speed at which a dynamo acting as a generator operates is determined by the speed-load characteristic of its prime mover. Prime movers have a drooping speed-load characteristic which is similar to the speed characteristic of a shunt motor. If a synchronous motor is used to drive the generator the speed will be constant and independent of the load.

Dynamos having shunt, series, or compound fields will serve as motors as well as generators, but each will have different characteristics with respect to torque and speed under load. These differences will now be considered.

Motor Torque. A motor develops torque because of the electromagnetic force exerted on a conductor when it is carrying current in a magnetic field. Each inductor on the armature, when in a magnetic field, is acted upon by a force which follows the definition of current and may be expressed as

$$f = BI_m l. \qquad \text{[16, page 358]}$$

This force acts on the inductor at a radius of r centimeters and represents a torque of

$$T' = fr = BI_m lr \qquad \text{dyne centimeters.}$$

157

For Z effective inductors in the same magnetic field, the total torque on the armature would be

$$T = ZBI_mlr \qquad \text{dyne centimeters.}$$

The flux density B in any machine is proportional to the flux per pole ϕ which links the armature coils. The effective number of inductors Z, the length of each inductor l, and the radius r are all constants. Therefore the torque equation may be reduced to

$$T = \left(Z \frac{lr}{A} \right) \phi I_m = K_2 \phi I_a, \tag{1}$$

where I_a is the total armature current. The constant K_2 depends on the machine dimensions, and it may be evaluated by calculating torque from the expression (ZBI_mlr) and substituting the values in equation 1. The general equation for torque (equation 1) shows that the torque of any given dynamo is determined solely by the variables of (1) armature current, and (2) the flux which links the armature coils and the field.

The expression for torque may be obtained in terms of motor power and speed. The general equation (3, page 105) for the motor is $V = E + I_aR_a$. When this equation is multiplied by the current I_a and the terms transposed, the following equation for power is obtained:

$$EI_a = VI_a - I_a^2R_a. \tag{2}$$

The power EI_a is equal to the total power input to the armature minus the copper loss in the armature. All of this power EI_a must be used to produce rotation of the armature, and it represents the total *electromagnetic* or *developed* motor power. It is greater than the power delivered at the shaft of the motor by the amount of the rotational losses. The rotational losses are friction, windage, hysteresis, and eddy current losses due to rotation. Therefore the motor or electromagnetic power developed is the product of the generated voltage and the armature current. In order to arrive at the developed torque, the following relations between power and speed may be considered:

$$P_m = EI_a, \qquad P_m \text{ is expressed in watts.}$$

$$P_m' = \frac{2\pi nT}{33,000}, \qquad \text{or} \qquad T = \frac{33,000}{2\pi n} P_m'$$

where P_m' is expressed in horsepower; and

$$T = \frac{33,000}{2\pi n} \left(\frac{EI_a}{746} \right) = 7.045 \frac{EI_a}{n}. \tag{3}$$

Since

$$E = \frac{p}{a} \frac{\phi Zn}{60} 10^{-8}$$

we have

$$T = \left(\frac{33,000}{2\pi n} \right) \left(\frac{p}{a} \frac{\phi Zn}{60} 10^{-8} \right) \frac{I_a}{746}$$

$$= 0.1173 \frac{Zp\phi}{a} I_a 10^{-8} \qquad \text{pound-feet} \tag{4}$$

In the derivation of equation 4 the speed n canceled out of the equation for torque. Hence, as long as the effective flux and the armature current are the same, the torque developed in a motor will be the same, regardless of whether the armature is stationary or in motion. If the constant terms of equation 4, $0.1173(Zp/a)10^{-8}$, be represented by a constant K_2, equation 4 reduces to the simpler form of equation 1.

Torque Characteristics of Motors. The torque of a motor has been shown to be proportional to the product of field flux ϕ and the armature current I_a. In

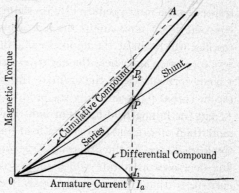

the shunt motor *without* armature reaction, the field will remain constant as long as the line voltage is constant (the usual assumption). The torque developed by the motor will then be directly proportional to the armature current. This will give a straight-line graph for the shunt motor, as shown in Fig. 1.

In the series motor, the mmf of the series field depends directly upon the load current. For small-load currents, when the magnetic

Fig. 1. Torque Characteristics of Motors.

circuit of the motor is being operated on the lower and straight portion of the magnetization curve, the field flux is nearly proportional to the load current I_a. Therefore

$$T = K_2\phi I_a = K_2(K'I_a)I_a = K_3 I_a^2 \tag{5}$$

and for this lower range of I_a the torque of the series motor follows a parabolic curve, as shown in Fig. 1. However, when the magnetic circuit approaches saturation, the flux will not continue to be proportional to the armature current and the field mmf, but will tend to reach a constant value. Here the torque approaches

$$T = K_2(K_1')I_a = K''I_a$$

which is the equation of a straight line. Thus, the torque curve for the series motor will begin as a parabola and then straighten out to a linear form at high values of armature and field current, as illustrated by the curve of Fig. 1. The point P, where the shunt and series torque curves cross, is the point where the field flux produced by each type of field winding placed on the same machine would produce an equal field flux. It should be noted that the series type of field gives a greater torque than the shunt type for high values of current, and hence the series motor would be better adapted for loads requiring a large starting torque and a strong pulling torque when the machine is operated at low speeds.

The cumulative-compound motor combines the properties of the shunt and series motor in producing its torque characteristic. This motor has a constant component of mmf, due to the shunt field, plus an increasing component directly proportional to the load. This resultant mmf causes a rising field flux (convex upward), and a rising torque curve (concave upward), as shown in the cumulative-compound curve for Fig. 1. This curve is higher than the one for the shunt motor, and its height indicates that this compound motor would be better than the shunt for applications requiring a heavy starting torque.

The differential-compound motor has its series field mmf reversed with respect to the mmf produced by its shunt field. The resultant field mmf is the constant shunt mmf minus the increasing mmf due to the series field. Thus, the flux will begin at the no-load value due to the shunt field and decrease to zero for that point where the negative series mmf equals the shunt mmf. Such a point corresponds to the ordinate through point P on Fig. 1. The resultant torque is that represented by the product of a steadily rising armature current I_a and the falling field flux. For light loads, the increase in armature current more than offsets the decrease in field flux, so that the torque increases with the load. Later, as the opposing series field becomes more effective, the field flux decreases at a rate which more than offsets the increase of armature current, so that the torque decreases, reaching zero at point I_1 on the curve of Fig. 1. If the armature and series-field current be increased beyond this point, the series field will reverse the field flux and reverse the direction of the torque. Obviously the torque characteristic of the differential-compound motor is a very undesirable one.

Speed Regulation and Control. Speed regulation is a term which describes the change in speed of a motor as load is placed upon it. The change in speed is due to inherent properties or characteristics of the motor in question. The rules of the American Institute of Electrical Engineers define the **speed regulation** of an electric motor, when operating at constant terminal potential, as the *ratio* of the *difference* between *no-load* and *full-load* speed to the speed at *full load*. Thus

Speed regulation expressed in per cent

$$= 100 \, \frac{\text{no-load speed} - \text{full-load speed}}{\text{full-load speed}}. \tag{6}$$

Speed control refers to the manipulation or control of the speed of a motor by *manual operation or by an automatic device*. Speed changes produced in this way are *independent* of the inherent changes in speed due to load upon the machine. For example, the varying of the speed of an electric railway car by a motorman operating the controller would be referred to as speed control.

Generated Electromotive Force. The voltage equation for motor action in a dynamo is $V = E + I_a R_a$ (equation 3, page 105). This equation may be explained by saying that the impressed voltage V has two components: the generated voltage E, and the component I_aR_a which causes current to flow through the armature resistance R_a. This equation may be transposed to a form for giving the motor current.

$$I_a = \frac{V - E}{R_a}. \tag{7}$$

This equation shows that the current is limited by the generated voltage E. The generated emf is opposed or counter to the direction of the current, and hence is called a **counter or back emf.** It is also opposite and nearly equal to the impressed voltage so that it may be considered as a back voltage or counter voltage with respect to the impressed voltage. Another transposition of equation 3, page 105, gives an expression for counter emf; thus,

$$E = V - I_aR_a.$$

The counter emf is an important factor in the speed characteristic of a motor.

The relative direction of counter emf, current flow, and rotation of a motor can be determined from a consideration of Fig. 2. If the current is assumed

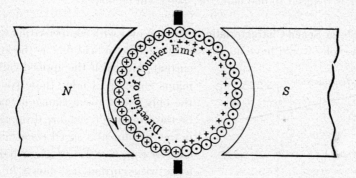

Fig. 2. Relative Directions of Current Flow, Rotation, and Counter or Generated Emf for a Motor.

flowing in the direction indicated by the signs in the circles, the direction of motion will be found by applying Ampere's right-hand rule. A further application of this rule and the conventional method of determining the direction of emf shows the emf generated to be as indicated. These considerations show the induced or generated emf to be of a polarity which opposes the current flow.

Factors Affecting Motor Speed. The factors affecting motor speed can be readily found by combining the equation for generated voltage

$$E = \frac{p}{a}\frac{\phi Zn10^{-8}}{60} = K_1\phi Z_an, \qquad [8, \text{ page } 65]$$

and the motor voltage equation $V = E + I_a R_a$

This gives

$$V = K_1 \phi Z_a n + I_a R_a$$

or

$$n = \frac{V - I_a R_a}{K_1 \phi Z_a}. \tag{8}$$

This latter equation is called the **fundamental speed equation** because it contains all of the variables which determine the speed of a motor and shows the precise manner in which each variable affects the speed. The major factors are the line potential V, armature circuit resistance R_a, flux per pole ϕ, and the number of inductors in series Z_a. Since Z_a is generally a constant for a given machine, and K_1 always is, it may be seen that the speed of motor varies *directly as the generated emf* $(V - I_a R_a)$ and *inversely as the field flux* ϕ. These facts form the basis for speed determination in various kinds of motors. Thus, if the field flux remains constant, the speed will be directly proportional to the counter emf. Conversely, if the counter emf remains constant, but the field flux is reduced to one half, the speed will be doubled.

Shunt Motor Speed Characteristic. A shunt motor with compensating windings and interpoles would have no appreciable change in field flux as the armature current changed if the applied voltage remains constant. Under these conditions, the only reason for a change in speed will be the armature resistance drop, as shown in the fundamental speed equation 8. The counter emf, $E = V - I_a R_a$, will drop linearly with current, as shown in Fig. 3. Since the speed varies directly with the counter emf, the sloping line shown in Fig. 3 will also represent the speed to some scale. If $(I_{a1} n_0)$ corresponds to a no-load speed of 1400 rpm, 1400 divided by the distance $(I_{a1} n_0)$ in inches would give the rpm per inch and establish the scale of ordinates for the diagram. A current such as I_{a1} would correspond to the no-load speed, since a small current is required to supply rotational losses. The speed-load characteristic of a shunt motor without armature demagnetization is a straight sloping line. It should be noted that this curve is similar to the external characteristic of this same dynamo operated as a separately excited generator at constant speed.

When a shunt motor has armature reaction which produces field demag-

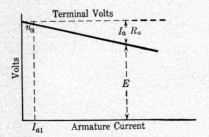

Fig. 3. Generated Emf of a Shunt Motor with Constant Field Flux.

netization, the speed changes under load are due to both armature resistance drop and the decrease in field flux caused by the demagnetizing ampere-turns. The latter factor tends to cause an increase in speed, while the former tends to decrease it, as shown in the preceding example. The resultant effect of these opposing factors may be inferred by considering a particular case.

The speed changes on a shunt motor may be studied and determined by a semigraphical method similar to the graphical method used for determining the external characteristics of generators. A shunt motor will be assumed to have a magnetization curve as shown in Fig. 4, part (2). The field resistance gives a field resistance or excitation line OL. The intersection of the magnetization curve and the excitation line at point A determines the line $FA = OV_0$. This line represents the voltage generated for no armature current (that is, with the applied and counter emf equal to OV_0). The speed for this condition will be assumed to be 1400 rpm. The full-load demagnetizing ampere-turns

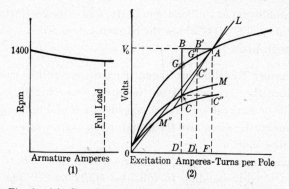

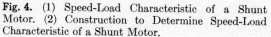

Fig. 4. (1) Speed-Load Characteristic of a Shunt Motor. (2) Construction to Determine Speed-Load Characteristic of a Shunt Motor.

will be assumed to have a magnitude represented by AB. These ampere-turns subtracted from the shunt-field ampere-turns OF leave $OD = V_0B$ as the net excitation, similar to the case of a generator. If the speed remained constant at 1400 rpm, a generated voltage of DG would be produced by the net excitation $OD = V_0B$. The generated voltage or counter emf must be equal to the applied voltage minus the full-load I_aR_a drop. To find this voltage at full load, the I_aR_a drop represented by the line BC must be subtracted from the applied voltage OV_0. This subtraction is accomplished graphically by laying off BC on a line drawn vertically downward from B, leaving the remainder DC as the generated voltage for full load. The flux corresponding to points C and G is the same since the net excitation is the same for both points. Therefore the speeds corresponding to generated voltages of DG and DC must be directly proportional to these generated voltages. Since DG would have been the generated voltage with a speed of 1400 rpm, the speed for the generated voltage DC must be $(DC/DG) \times 1400$. This product gives the speed at full-load armature current.

Since AB, BC, and AC are proportional to the armature current, the line AC may be used as a load line and be divided into proportional parts. Thus AC', which is one half of AC, represents half-load armature current and determines the half-load triangle $C'B'A$. The half-load speed is $(D'C'/D'G') \times 1400$. This process repeated for other load currents gives the points for the speed-load characteristic of the shunt motor, as shown in part 1 of Fig. 4.

It should be noted that new magnetization curves would pass through points C, C', etc. Since points C and G correspond to the same field flux and different speeds, the new magnetization curve will have each of its ordinates reduced in proportion to the speeds or to DC/DG times the corresponding ordinates of the original magnetization curve. This new curve would pass through point C for equilibrium at full load. Similarly, a new magnetization curve with ordinates equal to $D'C'/D'G'$ times the corresponding ordinates of the original will pass through point C'.

Effect of Armature Reaction on Speed. Armature reaction will demagnetize the field, reduce the flux, and cause the speed to be higher than otherwise. This effect can be understood from a consideration of Fig. 4, part (2). If the I_aR_a drop remains the same and the armature demagnetization is reduced, the line AB becomes shorter.

For the limiting case of zero demagnetization, line AB reduces to zero, and the point C corresponding to full load shifts to C''. The speed now is $(FC''/FA) \times 1400$, which is less than that in the previous case, since $FC'' = DC$ and FA is greater than DG. Considered in another way, a lower magnetization curve $M''C''$ passes through C'' than through C, and a lower magnetization curve corresponds to a lower speed. Reducing the armature demagnetization has reduced the speed for the same armature current. Therefore armature reaction tends to improve speed regulation. An inspection of Fig. 4, part (2) shows that speed would increase with load if the armature resistance drop were small enough to make the load line AC tangent to the magnetization curve at A. Under this condition, the load line would pass between B and G and DC/DG would be greater than one. Therefore a decrease in armature resistance causes less drop in speed and improved regulation. Conversely, an increase in armature resistance gives a lower speed at the same armature current and produces poorer regulation.

Effect of Field Resistance on Speed. An increase in the field resistance of a shunt motor reduces the field current and the field flux ϕ, provided that the applied voltage remains constant. This reduction in field flux causes the speed to rise in accordance with the fundamental speed equation

$$n = \frac{V - I_a R_a}{K_1 \phi Z_a}.$$ [8, p. 162]

The reduction in the denominator $K\phi Z_a$ causes the value of the fraction to rise. Looked at in another way the reduction in ϕ reduces the value of the counter emf ($E = K_1 \phi Z_a n$). The reduction in counter emf permits more current to flow in accordance with equation 7: $I_a = (V - E)/R_a$. This increase in current develops more torque and causes the motor to accelerate until the counter emf rises to its former value if we assume the same developed motor power.

A reduction in field resistance will cause the speed of a shunt motor to be reduced for similar reasons. Thus, there will result an increased field flux and an increased counter emf. The greater counter emf will reduce the armature current and the torque below the value needed to overcome the load and the rotational losses. Thus, the motor will slow down until the decrease in the counter emf and the rise in motor current will carry the load again.

Effect of Field Resistance on Torque. When the field flux is reduced by inserting resistance in the field, the speed was shown to increase. The increase in speed required additional torque to be developed by less field flux. Since torque is equal to $K_2 \phi I_a$, the only way the torque can increase with a decreasing ϕ is for I_a to increase more than enough to offset the reduction in flux. This is exactly what happens, as shown by the following example. Assume a motor having an armature-circuit resistance of 0.2 ohm, a current of 20 amperes, and an applied voltage of 110. The counter emf under these conditions is 110 − (20 × 0.2) = 106 volts. The torque is $K_2 \phi_1 20$. Now, assume the field resistance to be increased so as to reduce the flux to $0.95 \phi_1$. The speed cannot change instantaneously, and this new value of flux would give a counter emf of 0.95 × 106 = 100.7 volts. With this reduced counter emf, the current will be (110 − 100.7)/0.2 = 46.5 amperes. The torque now will be $K_2(0.95\phi_1)(46.5) = K_2\phi_1 44.18$, or 2.21 times its former value. This increase in torque will cause the motor to accelerate, thereby increasing the counter emf until the current is reduced to a value which will just produce the torque demanded by the load plus that for rotational losses of the motor itself. It is thus seen that a 5 per cent reduction in flux caused a 121 per cent increase in torque at the same speed.

Speed-Torque Characteristics. When motors are operated at constant terminal voltage, constant armature resistance, and constant field-circuit resistance, there is a definite relation between speed and torque. Data for the speed-torque curve may be obtained from curves of speed versus armature current and torque versus armature current. In a modern shunt motor with interpoles the pole flux is practically constant. Under these conditions torque is directly proportional to armature current (equation 1, page 158). The speed versus armature current curve will therefore be similar to the speed versus torque curve since the scale of torque will differ from that for armature current by only a constant. Such a speed torque curve is shown in Fig. 5.

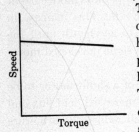

Fig. 5. Speed-Torque Characteristic of a Shunt Motor.

The Differential-Compound Motor. The differential-compound motor acts much like the shunt motor having strong demagnetizing armature reaction. The principal point of difference between these two types lies in the magnitude of the demagnetizing action. The series field of the differential-compound motor directly opposes the shunt field, and the resulting speed characteristic depends upon the relative magnitude of the series-field mmf with respect to the shunt field. A weak series field will produce a drooping speed characteristic like that of a shunt motor, whereas a powerful series field may produce a rise in speed under load. These extremes may be studied through the semi-graphical method outlined on page 163 and illustrated in Fig. 4.

Let line AB of Fig. 6 represent the demagnetizing ampere-turns due to both the armature reaction and the series field. The line BC represents the

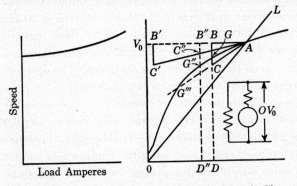

Fig. 6. Construction to Determine Speed-Load Characteristic of a Differential-Compound Motor.

total armature-circuit resistance drop due to the series field plus the armature, interpoles, etc. The resulting load triangle ABC applied in accordance with the preceding method will give a drooping speed characteristic curve like that of the shunt motor. Now, assume that many turns are added to the series field so that for the same armature current the total demagnetizing ampere-turns are represented by the line AB'. The new armature-circuit drop may equal $B'C'$, giving a new load triangle $AB'C'$. Using this load triangle for the half-load condition at B'', the speed will be $D''C''/D''G''$ times the speed corresponding to A. This ratio is greater than one and the speed at half load has risen above that at no load. A study of Fig. 6 will show that as the load increases the ratio corresponding to $D''C''/D''G''$ will increase and will give a rising speed characteristic, as shown on the left of Fig. 6. Since a differential-compound motor may be designed to give either a falling or a rising speed characteristic, a proper selection of the number of series turns will give a nearly constant speed or flat speed characteristic throughout the range of stable operation. This speed characteristic is very desirable for some applications of motors in experimental work.

Instability of Motors. A motor is said to be unstable when it fails to attain equilibrium in speed or armature current for a given set of conditions, or when, for loads equal to or less than rated value, the motor tends to run at either excessively high speed or armature current. Excessive speed and armature current are the more common results of instability.

Instability of a motor is likely to occur whenever it has a rising speed-load characteristic. Such a characteristic has been shown to result when strong demagnetization of the field is present. Such demagnetization may be caused by brush shift in noninterpole motors, faulty brush setting in interpole machines, or by a differential series field.

One form of instability may be understood from a consideration of the motor speed and torque equations in conjunction with the inertia of the rotating part. If the field flux in a motor is constant the motor will not usually become unstable. These conclusions are obtained as follows:

Since
$$n = \frac{V - I_a R_a}{K_1 \phi Z_a},$$

the speed decreases linearly with armature current (constant ϕ assumed), at the same time the torque $T = K_2 \phi I_a$ increases linearly with armature current. Hence the motor speed continues to fall until the torque developed increases to the value which overcomes rotational losses of the motor and carries the load. Should the speed drop somewhat after this point is reached (due to inertia of the rotating parts) the counter emf will be lower, the armature current higher, and the torque consequently greater than that necessary to overcome rotational losses and carry the load. The excess torque developed will then cause the motor to accelerate until the increasing counter emf reduces the current to that required to produce the necessary torque. Inertia may cause a further increase in speed but the torque developed will then be too small and the motor will again start to decrease its speed. It is apparent therefore that the motor will ultimately approach equilibrium unless the load itself demands a cyclic variation in torque.

Next, let us consider the case where the flux ϕ decreases when the armature current increases. Such a decrease may be due to armature reaction or a series field as in a differentially compounded motor. If the demagnetization due to armature current causes a sufficiently rapid rate of decrease of field flux ϕ as compared with the counter emf $(V - I_a R_a)$, the speed

$$n = \frac{V - I_a R_a}{K_1 \phi Z_a}$$

will increase. However, this increase will take place only in the event that sufficient torque to drive the motor is developed. Under the conditions imposed an increase in I_a is accompanied by a decrease in ϕ. Hence the torque $T = K_2 \phi I_a$ may either increase, remain constant, or decrease. At some armature current I_a, the flux decreases enough to offset the increase of I_a and the torque ceases to increase. (See the torque curve for the differential-compound motor, page 159). If the load torque is greater than this value, the difference between the total torque required and the developed torque decelerates the motor. Under these conditions the counter emf decreases and the armature current increases to excessive values. The phenomenon just described might be called **torque instability.** To encounter this kind of instability the torque versus armature-current curve must increase, come to a maximum, and then decrease as armature current increases.

A motor with sufficient demagnetization is subject to another form of instability. For this discussion assume the reduction of flux ϕ occurs at such a rate when armature current increases that permits the torque $T = K_2 \phi I_a$ to increase with armature current. If some disturbance requires the armature current to increase, the increased demagnetization reduces the field flux, thus lowering the counter emf. More torque will now be developed and the motor will accelerate according to the law in mechanics ($T = I\alpha$ where I is the moment of inertia, T the torque, and α the angular acceleration). If the moment of inertia of the motor and load is sufficiently large, the angular acceleration will be so small that the motor will not be able to raise its speed fast enough to keep pace with the decreasing field flux caused by the demagnetization. The counter emf will then continue to decrease which, in turn, causes the armature current to increase. The increase in armature current results in more demagnetization, a further reduction of field flux, and a repetition of the trend of events outlined. The armature current thus increases until protective apparatus or damage to the installation opens the circuit. This form of instability might be termed **current instability.**

Another form of instability where the current may be held to safe limits but never reaches a state of equilibrium occurs when a series generator supplies current to a separately excited shunt motor, as shown in Fig. 7.

When the motor armature M is connected to the series generator G, the series generator builds up its voltage quite rapidly as the current increases through the motor armature. The motor begins to rotate and accelerates. Its rapid acceleration builds up a counter emf, which reduces the current taken

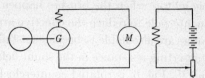
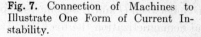

Fig. 7. Connection of Machines to Illustrate One Form of Current Instability.

from the series generator, and results in a gradual decrease of the generator voltage. Since the back emf of the motor is rising while the emf of the generator is falling, a condition is soon reached where the two are equal. The inertia of the armature M of a shunt motor overruns this point of balance and its back emf becomes higher than the emf of the generator. Thus the shunt motor acts momentarily as a generator due to the kinetic energy of its rotating armature and causes a current to flow through the series generator in the opposite direction. This reversal of current reverses the generator polarity, and it builds up in the opposite direction and causes the current to continue to flow in the direction in which it was started by the generator action of the shunt motor. Therefore the motor rapidly comes to rest, and then starts to accelerate in the opposite direction until a repetition of the events outlined above occurs. This process continues indefinitely and the system never reaches stability. This system offers an interesting laboratory experiment to demonstrate one form of instability. When preparing for this experiment in the laboratory, it is advisable to insert resistance in the armature circuit to limit the flow of current.

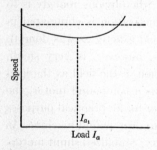

Fig. 8. Type of Speed-Load Curve in Which Instability May Eventually Occur.

It is possible for a motor to operate stably over a certain range of load and then become unstable for heavier loads. A motor with a load line as AG''', Fig. 6, will perform in this manner. As shown in a preceding article, the speed at which a motor runs in DC/DG times the speed for which the magnetization curve $G''GA$ is drawn. At point A, DC/DG is 1 and as the load increases DC/DG becomes less than 1; hence the speed decreases. At point G''', the ratio of DC/DG is again unity. Hence the speed is now equal to the no-load speed. The speed-load curve therefore takes the form

shown in Fig. 8. For loads up to I_{a1} the motor operation is stable, but for loads greater than I_{a1} instability may be expected. This point occurs somewhere between A and G''' in Fig. 6. The exact point is where DC/DG ceases to decrease and starts to increase.

The above analysis shows that shunt motors with demagnetizing armature reaction may become unstable at some loads. This is particularly true of interpole motors when the brushes happen to be shifted off neutral so as to allow the interpole to reduce the effective armature flux as the load increases. Shunt motors are also liable to become unstable when caused to operate at high speed by inserting resistance in the shunt field. Under these conditions the excitation line OL, Fig. 6, is rotated counterclockwise, the portion of the magnetization curve between O and L becomes steeper, and for the same armature resistance and demagnetization the load line AC will take the relative position with respect to the magnetization curve as represented by AC'. Looked at in another way, the reluctance of the magnetic circuit is reduced and a given demagnetizing mmf of the armature has a much greater effect in reducing the field flux, and hence increasing speed as the load increases.

A shunt motor operating on a line of high resistance may become unstable. As the load increases the voltage at the terminals of the motor is reduced because of the line drop. This reduces the field current, and hence the saturation of the magnetic circuit. The effectiveness of a given amount of armature demagnetizing mmf is thereby increased. This condition has been shown to be conducive to instability. For further discussion of this subject see page 174.

The preceding discussion shows the conditions under which instability may be expected. However, this treatment is only approximate because it has neglected the effects of such factors as the self and mutual inductance in armature and fields and the inertia of rotating parts. These factors may serve to retard or to help produce instability, depending upon their relative magnitudes and other conditions.

Since all cases of instability discussed depended upon the presence of demagnetization or weakening the field under load, the obvious remedy is to limit the amount of demagnetization. The demagnetization is eliminated in certain types of shunt motors by adding a series field exactly as was done to secure a compound motor. The number of turns, however, is very small, only sufficient to give a very slight net magnetization of the field as the load increases. While this motor might be thought of as a compound motor, the number of series field turns is so small that the motor for all practical purposes has the characteristics of a shunt motor rather than a compound machine. As a result, the motor is termed a **stabilized shunt motor.** Stabilized shunt motors are now very commonly used in industry.

Motors may operate satisfactorily with certain kinds of loads and be unstable for others. For example, consider a motor that has a rising speed torque curve ab, as shown in Fig. 9. For a load with a speed torque curve cd, the motor is unstable. At the speed s_1 the torque required by the load is T_1, while the motor develops a greater torque T_2. The excess torque $T_2 - T_1$ developed by the motor increases the motor speed. At a higher speed the difference in required and developed torques increases and the motor tends to "run away." If the motor were connected to a load having a torque curve *ef*, operation would be stable. At any higher speed than that corresponding to the intersection of the two curves, *ab* and *ef*, the load requires more torque than the motor can develop. Hence the motor speed decreases. At any lower speed the motor develops more torque than is required by the load. Hence the motor speed increases. The point of intersection of the curves *ab* and *ef* is therefore a speed corresponding to stable operation. Since the instability just described depends upon the relative torque characteristics of the load and the motor, it is sometimes called **load instability.**

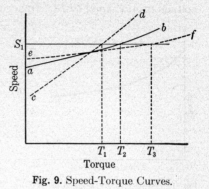

Fig. 9. Speed-Torque Curves.

The Cumulative-Compound Motor. The speed variation of the long-shunt cumulative-compound motor may be analyzed through the use of the fundamental speed equation of a motor: $n = (V - I_a R_{a_o})/(K_1 \phi Z_a)$. The shunt field produces a constant component of field flux for a constant impressed line voltage. The series field produces an additional component of field flux which increases with the load. The resultant field flux ϕ increases with the load, thus increasing the value of the denominator so that the speed decreases as the load comes on. Another small factor causing a decrease in speed is the greater value of the armature-circuit resistance R_{a_o} due to the added resistance of the series field. This additional resistance reduces the counter emf, and hence the numerator of the speed equation. The net result of both of these factors is to produce a falling speed-load characteristic.

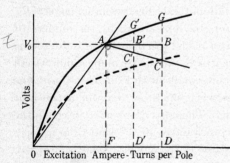

Fig. 10. Construction to Determine the Speed-Load Characteristic of a Cumulative-Compound Motor.

A quantitative analysis of the speed variation may be made by the semi-graphical method. The magnetization curve of a long-shunt compound motor is given in Fig. 10. The excitation line due to the shunt field is constructed as OA. The net excitation at zero armature current is represented by $OF = V_0 A$. At full load, the series field will add to this no-load excitation, and the armature demagnetizing action (if present) will subtract. Let the net addition be represented by the line AB, giving a total excitation equal to $OD = V_0 B$. The applied voltage at full load is $OV_0 = DB$, from which must be subtracted the armature-circuit resistance drop represented by BC, leaving the generated voltage proportional to DC. In accordance with the reasoning followed for the

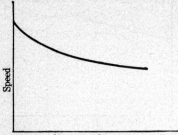

Speed

Armature Current

Fig. 11. Speed-Load Characteristic of a Cumulative-Compound Motor.

shunt motor, the full-load speed of the long-shunt compound motor is the ratio $(DC/DG) \times$ no-load speed. The no-load speed used is that corresponding to point A on the magnetization curve. The actual no-load speed would be that corresponding to the armature current required to overcome the no-load losses. The line AC determined above may be used as a load line to obtain the speed at other loads. Thus at half load, the speed is $D'C'/D'G'$ times the speed at A. A continuation of this procedure will give the speed-load characteristic shown in Fig. 11. The speed falls more rapidly than in the case of the shunt motor. With the rise in load, the *rate* of the decrease in speed becomes less and less as saturation of the magnetic circuit is approached. For the new loads corresponding to points C, C', etc., new magnetization curves may be considered to pass through these points.

Series Motor. All of the field flux of the series motor is produced by the armature current flowing through the series field. Thus the magnitude of ϕ in the denominator of the motor speed equation increases rapidly with the load until field saturation is approached. At the same time, the armature-circuit resistance drop $(I_a R_{a_0})$ increases directly with the load. The magnitude of $I_a R_{a_0}$ is a little greater for the series motor because of the added resistance of the series field (greater than for compound motors). The rise in value of $I_a R_{a_0}$ with load lowers the value of the counter emf represented by the numerator of the speed equation. Thus the numerator of the speed equation is *decreasing* in value more rapidly and the denominator is *increasing* more rapidly than for other motors, so that the speed falls off rapidly with load. At no load, the armature current and the field flux are very small, so that for a constant applied voltage the speed will be very high. Thus it is never safe (except in the case of fractional horsepower machines) to remove all the load from a series motor when rated voltage is applied, because of the danger of excessive speed.

The speed of the series motor may be analyzed by the semigraphical method. The analysis and construction will be simplified by considering the series motor as a special case of the compound motor with zero shunt excitation. The magnetization curve for a series motor running at 1400 rpm is given in Fig. 12. The line OV_0 may be considered as the excitation line since there is no shunt field (analogous to infinite shunt-field resistance). The symbol OV_0 also represents the applied voltage, which is constant. The ampere-turns of the series field for full load minus any demagnetizing mmf is represented by the line $AB = OD$. At full load the generated voltage is the applied voltage OV_0 $= DB$, minus the armature-circuit resistance drop (BC), which gives a value corresponding to the line DC. The generated voltage due to the field excitation AB at 1400 rpm is DG. Thus at full load the series motor speed is the ratio (DC/DG) $\times$ 1400 rpm. The hypotenuse AC of the load triangle may be used as a load line and may be divided proportionally to obtain speeds for various loads. Thus at one-half load the load triangle becomes $AB'C'$ and the motor speed is ($D'C'/D'G'$) $\times$ 1400 rpm. $D'C'$ is greater than $D'G'$, so that the speed has increased. A light load requiring a small armature current may produce an excitation corresponding to OD''. This condition would give a speed of ($D''C''/$ $D''G''$) $\times$ 1400, or about $9 \times 1400 = 12,600$ rpm. Obviously, this speed is excessive if the rated speed of the motor is 1400 rpm. The speed-load curve for this motor will vary as shown in Fig. 13.

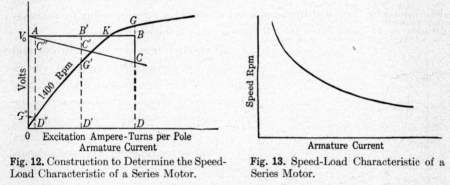

Fig. 12. Construction to Determine the Speed-Load Characteristic of a Series Motor.

Fig. 13. Speed-Load Characteristic of a Series Motor.

Series motors can usually be protected against the danger of excessive speeds by a positive connection to their load. A direct connection by a shaft coupling or through gearing is considered as a positive connection, but a belt connection is not so considered. In addition to the positive connection, the character of the load attached to a series motor should be such that it does not approach zero (for example, a shaper when not cutting material approaches zero load).

Torque and Speed Variation of the Series Motor. An inspection of Fig. 12 shows that the flux represented by the generated emf and the line DG increases almost directly with the armature current until the knee K of the magnetization curve is reached. Furthermore, at light loads, the armature circuit resistance drop is very small and might be neglected. Under these conditions the speed equation becomes

$$n = \frac{V - I_a R_{a_o}}{K_1 \phi Z} = \frac{V}{K_1 Z (K' I_a)} = \frac{K_4}{I_a}. \tag{9}$$

This is the equation of a rectangular hyperbola. When the magnetic circuit becomes saturated, the increase of flux with current becomes rather small, so that the flux might be considered approximately constant at high saturations. The current under these conditions will be large, so that the $I_a R_{a_0}$ drop is no longer negligible. Under these conditions, the speed equation approaches the form

$$n = \frac{V - I_a R_{a_0}}{K_1 \phi N} = \frac{V - I_a R_{a_0}}{K_1'} = K''(V - I_a R_{a_0}). \tag{10}$$

This is the equation of a straight line. Therefore the speed-load characteristic of the series motor starts from a high value, follows approximately a hyperbolic law, and then gradually changes to a nearly linear variation for heavy loads.

By way of contrast to the speed characteristic, the torque characteristic of a series motor was shown on page 159 to begin at low values, to rise following a parabolic law, and finally to straighten out to a nearly linear form. The exact shape of the torque characteristic may be determined graphically from the magnetization curve and the load-line of Fig. 12 by applying the torque formula $T = K_2 I_a \phi = K_2'(AC')(D'G')$. The value of the constant K_2' can be determined by the substitution of a value of torque corresponding to the magnitudes of AC' and $D'G'$, as determined from equation 3, page 158.

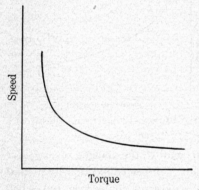

If speed versus armature current and torque versus armature current curves are plotted as previously explained, data for a speed versus torque curve may be obtained by reading both speed and torque corresponding to identical values of armature current. Such a speed versus torque curve for a series motor takes the general trend shown in Fig. 14.

Fig. 14. Speed-Torque Curve of a Series Motor.

Effect of Line Resistance on Shunt Motor Speed. Resistance inserted in series with the armature will cause a drop in the speed of the shunt motor because it reduces the counter emf or the numerator of the motor-speed equation. Applied to the graphical method of speed determination, it would increase the length of the leg BC of the load triangle and thus would produce a drop in motor speed under load.

The insertion of resistance in series with the line has a different effect upon the speed of a shunt motor. The drop through this resistance decreases both the voltage applied to the armature and that applied to the shunt field. The result is that the counter emf (numerator of speed equation) drops and the field flux (denominator) decreases. Thus these factors vary in the same direction and tend to neutralize each other. The resultant effect on speed for any given load can be determined by the use of the semigraphical methods previously outlined.

A magnetization curve for a shunt motor operating at 1400 rpm is given in Fig. 15. At zero load, the motor operated at point A with an applied voltage of OV_0. A resistance is placed in series with the line, which reduces the applied voltage by the amount AL and the excitation of the machine to that corresponding to the point A'. The load triangle $A'BC$ should be erected at point A'. The speed corresponding to the load triangle $A'BC$ is $(DC/DG) \times 1400$. As long as the load current remains the same, the load triangle will be the same size, but it must slide up or down along the excitation line as determined by the line drop AL. Speeds may be determined for other loads by constructing additional load triangles along the excitation line.

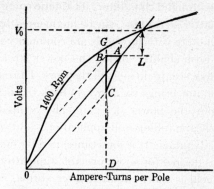

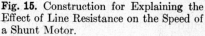

Fig. 15. Construction for Explaining the Effect of Line Resistance on the Speed of a Shunt Motor.

One unexpected effect of increasing line resistance may follow if the armature demagnetization and armature-resistance drop are of such proportions as to cause the line $A'C$ to fall to the left of the excitation line. Then an increase in line resistance may cause the point C to fall outside of the magnetization curve as the load triangle moves down. This condition would mean a rise in speed above no-load and the possibility of the development of current instability.

Classification and Application of Motors. Electric motors may be classified according to their speed characteristics as constant-speed, adjustable-speed, and variable-speed motors. A **constant-speed** motor will maintain its speed at practically the same value at all loads. An **adjustable-speed** motor is one whose speed can be varied (controlled) through wide limits, but whose speed for any particular adjustment is practically constant under varying loads. A **variable-speed** motor reduces its speed (inherently) as the torque required increases. Since power is proportional to the product of torque and speed, such a motor will not draw excessive power when the torque demand is large.

The shunt motor is essentially a constant-speed and an adjustable-speed motor. The amount of speed adjustment which can be obtained varies with the design of the motor. This type of motor has a good speed regulation, and it is widely used for applications requiring constant-speed service, such as line shafts, individual drives for lathes, milling machines, grinders, and shapers.

The cumulative-compound motor lies between the constant-speed and the variable-speed type. It has a definite zero-load speed, so that it is applicable to loads which may become very light. A compound motor having a weak series field approaches the constant-speed characteristic of a shunt motor, whereas one having a very strong series field has a widely variable speed. When a large demand for power comes on, it decreases its speed more than the shunt motor and thus allows its kinetic energy to help carry the peak of the load. This latter advantage can be augmented by the addition of a flywheel. Compound motors with flywheels are commonly used on punch presses. The motor slows down slightly during the power stroke and permits the energy stored in the flywheel to do most of the work. During the balance of the cycle, the compound motor brings the flywheel back to normal speed. This action serves to smooth out the power demand. The compound motor is used likewise for power shears, rolling-mill applications, and wherever the slightly variable speed is an advantage. It is sometimes used for hoists and elevators where a constant speed is desired for an appreciable time after starting. In such applications the series field is short-circuited after normal speed is attained.

For these last-named applications, a shunt motor would draw large peak currents when the heavy transient loads are applied. These peak currents would (1) produce undesirable voltage fluctuations on the line, and (2) would require a larger and more costly commutator on the motor to care for these current rushes and to give satisfactory commutation. Compound motors having a weak shunt field (strong series field) are used for driving power fans. The weak shunt field prevents an excessive motor speed if the mechanical load should become disconnected.

The differential-compound motor designed to give an exactly constant speed under small loads may find a very limited application for experimental and research work.

The series motor is of the variable-speed type and is applicable for loads requiring a high torque at low speeds and a moderate or small torque at high speeds. Series motors are used extensively for operating cranes, hoists, elevators, electric railway cars, trucks, and locomotives. The series motor characteristic of developing a high torque when the speed is low and a low torque when the speed is high is very desirable for these kinds of loads. Since power is proportional to speed times torque, the tendency is to approach a constant power demand from the supply lines automatically. Fractional-horsepower motors of the series types are used for electric fans, vacuum cleaners, sewing machines, hair driers, and other applications in which the load is rigidly connected to the motor or is under the control of the operator. Most of these motors are of the "universal" type and can be used on direct-current or alternating-current circuits.

Direction of Rotation of Motors and Generators. The direction of rotation of a dynamo acting as a motor is determined by (1) the polarity of the field, and

(2) the direction of the current in the inductors on the armature. When a shunt dynamo is operating as a generator, the current flowing in the inductors is in the same direction as the generated emf and the generator develops a back torque with respect to the driving torque of its prime mover. If the voltage across a generator from some external source be raised to a value greater than the generated emf, the current in the armature will reverse in direction while the field will continue to have the same polarity. The developed motor torque will reverse due to the reversal of the armature current and will be in the same direction as the driving torque of the prime mover. Thus the prime mover could be disconnected, and the dynamo would continue to rotate in the same direction as a motor. Hence a shunt dynamo on a railway train would automatically change to a generator when going down hill and would regenerate electrical energy.

A similar line of reasoning applied to a series dynamo will show that when it changes from generator action to motor action, or vice versa, the current changes direction through both the series field and the armature. Thus both field polarity and armature current reverse, and the direction of the torque does not change. It follows that the counter torque of the generator will *cause the machine to change its direction of rotation when it becomes a motor*. A series motor will not serve to regenerate electricity automatically when the train is coasting down hill. However, series motors are used almost exclusively for direct-current railway application, and regeneration is accomplished through a separate excitation of the series fields.

The compound dynamo has a field produced by both a shunt and a series winding. When this dynamo is caused to change from generator action (cumulative-compound) to motor action, the shunt field retains its same polarity while the series field reverses its mmf. The resultant field will be in the same direction but will be weakened in magnitude, so that the compound machine (like the shunt dynamo) will run in the same direction as a generator and as a motor. The *cumulative-compound generator changes to a differential-compound motor* with its tendency toward instability. For this reason it is never wise to charge a storage battery with a compound generator. Any failure of the prime mover will cause the compound generator to become a differential-compound motor with a possible rising speed characteristic, instability, and a heavy reversed current drain on the battery.

Condition for Maximum Motor Power and Torque. When the load upon a shunt motor is increased, the motor is required to develop more torque and power. When the line potential is constant, the increased load on the motor causes the speed and, in turn, the counter electromotive force to decrease, since the field flux remains constant. From equation (7), it is evident that the armature current will increase with the decrease in counter emf. This rise of current will continue until the product of the new generated voltage and arma-ture current gives sufficient motor power to supply all rotational losses in addition to the total load. There is a limit to the continuation of the phenomena outlined. This limit will occur when a decrease in speed no longer causes a greater motor power to be developed. The critical point for a constant impressed voltage is found as follows. From equation 2, page 158, we have

$$P_m = EI_a = VI_a - I_a^2 R_a.$$

The maximum motor power P_m will occur when $dP_m/dI_a = 0$. Therefore

$$\frac{dP_m}{dI_a} = V - 2I_a R_a = 0, \qquad V = 2I_a R_a$$

$$I_a R_a = \frac{V}{2}. \tag{11}$$

Equation 11 shows that the maximum motor power will occur when the armature-circuit resistance drop is one half of the impressed voltage. Under these conditions

$$E = V - I_a R_a = V - \frac{V}{2} = \frac{V}{2}. \tag{12}$$

Equation 12 shows that maximum motor power occurs for a constant impressed voltage when the generated emf (counter emf) is one half of the impressed voltage. This relation is known as **Jacobi's law.** With constant field flux, as assumed, the maximum motor power developed will occur at approximately one half of no-load speed. Below this speed, the decrease in power due to decrease in speed more than offsets the increase in power due to the increase in torque.

The above discussion illustrates clearly the difference between motor torque and motor power. With constant field flux and terminal potential, the motor power decreases as the speed falls below that at which $E = V/2$, but the torque continues to increase.

When the load is removed from a motor, the power developed will be greater than that necessary to supply the rotational losses, and the *excess* power becomes available for accelerating the motor. The speed of the motor rises until its counter emf and the resulting current develop sufficient motor power to overcome rotational losses. At this point, the motor is in equilibrium, and only a small no-load current flows through the armature.

The maximum possible developed motor power may be found by substituting for E and I_a in equation 2 their values for maximum electromagnetic power, as obtained from equations 12 and 11, respectively. Thus

$$P_m = EI_a = \frac{V}{2}\frac{V}{2R_a} = \frac{V^2}{4R_a}. \tag{13}$$

Equation 13 shows that the maximum possible motor power of a shunt motor is determined by the impressed voltage and the armature circuit resistance.

Division of Load between Motors Rigidly Coupled. Two motors may be rigidly coupled mechanically for driving a load. The division of the load between these machines may be determined by a suitable manipulation of the characteristic curves of the individual motors.

The current-speed curves should be plotted on the same sheet to a common scale of speed as abscissa. Similarly, the torque-speed curves should be plotted on a second sheet. The torque ordinates of the latter curves should be added to give the total developed torque at any speed. Now, assuming the torque required for a given load, a reference to the total torque curve will give the *speed* at which the motors will operate. This speed referred to the speed-current curves will give the *current* required by each motor. The *torque* produced by each individual motor can be obtained from its torque-speed curve.

PROBLEMS

1. A dynamo has 45 slots, 3 coils per slot, and 2 turns per coil. The coils on the armature are at an average distance from the center of the shaft of 4.65 in. The effective pole face covers 70 per cent of a pole span and has an average density over it of 50,000 maxwells per square inch, measured at a distance of 4.65 in. from the shaft center. The axial length of the conductors subject to this average density is 5.0 in. Find the torque in dyne-centimeters and also pound-feet that this dynamo produces when an armature current of 60 amp flows, if the armature is lap wound for four poles. Find the torque if this same machine is reconnected for a wave winding and the armature output current is 60 amp.

2. Evaluate the constant K_2 in equation (1) under the conditions of Prob. 1.

3. A 4-pole wave-wound dynamo having 270 turns on the armature has a flux of 500,000 maxwells per pole. If the armature current is 60 amp, what is the torque developed in pound-feet?

4. A 230-volt shunt motor takes 2 amp at no load and runs at 1200 rpm. The armature resistance is 0.25 ohm and the full-load current 40 amperes. Assuming no change in flux, find the full-load speed. What is the speed regulation?

5. A shunt motor takes 2 amp at no load and runs at 1200 rpm. The speed regulation at full-load current of 50 amp is 5.517 per cent and the armature resistance is 0.25 ohm. Assume no flux change with load and find the terminal voltage rating.

6. A shunt motor is operating at 230 volts, 1400 rpm, and requires 2 amp at no load. Assuming constant-field flux and an armature resistance of 0.3 ohm, what will be the armature current when a load causes the speed to drop to 1300 rpm?

7. If the machine of Prob. 1 is wave-wound and the armature resistance is 0.14 ohm, find the speed when the impressed voltage is 230 and when the armature current is 50 amp. What is the developed motor power?

8. The magnetization curve of a 4-pole shunt dynamo is shown in the chart on page 131. The dynamo is operated as a motor from a 240-volt source and has a field resistance of 165.5 ohms. The number of field turns per pole is 2000. The armature resistance is

0.16 ohm and the demagnetizing ampere-turns per pole at full-load rated current of 75 amp are 200. Use the descending branch of the 100 per cent magnetization and calculate and plot points for the speed load characteristic (rpm *vs.* I_a) for 0, ¼, ½, ¾, full, and ⁵⁄₄ rated load current. The 100 per cent magnetization curve was taken at 1200 rpm.

9. Solve Prob. 8 when there is no armature demagnetization and assume that the addition of interpoles and compensating windings is used with an armature winding that makes the total armature-circuit resistance 0.16 ohm. Compare these results with those in Prob. 8.

10. What will be the full-load speed of the motor of Prob. 8 if 100 ohms are added to the field resistance? Find the no-load speed if the no-load current at this speed is 3 amp.

11. What field resistance will be necessary to give a full-load speed of 1680 rpm for the motor in Prob. 8?

12. Find the full-load speed of the motor in Prob. 8 when 0.533-ohm resistance is added to the armature circuit.

TABLE I

A dynamo has the following constants:

Wave wound	4 poles
Shunt field turns per pole	1970
Series field turns per pole	3
Interpole turns	76
Armature resistance	0.31 ohm
Shunt field resistance	400 ohms
Series field resistance	0.0065 ohm
Interpole field resistance	0.057 ohm
Armature current at full load	37.2 amp
Speed	1150 rpm
Terminal volts	230

DATA FOR THE MAGNETIZATION CURVE AS FOLLOWS TAKEN AT 1150 RPM.

I_f	0	0.05	0.1	0.15	0.2	0.25	0.3	0.35	0.4	0.45	0.5	0.55	0.575
E	10	45	79	112	141	165	185.5	201	211.5	218.7	224	228	230

I_f	0.6	0.65	0.7
E	232	235.5	238

13. The dynamo in Table I is operated as a shunt motor with interpoles from 230 volts. What will be the speed at full load? How much field resistance should be inserted to make the full-load speed 1150 rpm?

14. The dynamo in Table I is operated as a long-shunt differential-compound motor with interpoles from 230 volts. What will be the speed at full load?

15. A series field having 10 turns per pole and 0.02-ohm resistance is added to the motor of Prob. 8 and the dynamo connected differential-compound, long-shunt. Interpoles and compensating windings having a combined resistance of 0.06 ohm are used so that no armature demagnetizing turns exist. Find the speed-load characteristic by determining speeds for no-load, ¼, ½, full, and 1¼ of rated armature current.

16. Repeat Prob. 15 when the number of series turns is doubled. The series-field resistance is also doubled.

17. Is instability a possibility in Prob. 14? Explain.

18. Is instability a possibility in Prob. 15? Explain.

19. Is instability a possibility in Prob. 16? Explain.

20. Find the speed-load characteristic of the motor under conditions referred to in Prob. 15 except with the series field reversed so as to make the motor cumulative-compound.

21. Repeat Prob. 20 when the number of series-field turns is tripled. This is assumed to triple the series-field resistance also.

22. The dynamo in Table I is operated as a long-shunt, cumulative-compound motor with interpoles from 230 volts. What will be the speed at full load? (*Note:* This is a stabilized shunt motor). What is the speed regulation?

23. Work Prob. 22 if the series field turns and resistance are increased to twice the values given in Table I.

24. Assume that the dynamo in Table I is operated as a long-shunt, cumulative-compound motor with interpoles and twice the series field turns and series field resistance from a potential of 120 volts. Also assume the field resistance is increased so that the dynamo runs at 1150 rpm at no load (zero armature current assumed). Determine the speeds at $\frac{1}{4}$, $\frac{1}{2}$, $\frac{3}{4}$, $\frac{4}{4}$, and $\frac{5}{4}$ of full-load armature current. Calculate speed regulation and compare with that in Prob. 23.

25. The magnetization curve at 1200 rpm of a series motor with 30 turns per pole is given by the 100 per cent speed descending magnetization curve in the chart on page 131. The full-load current is 100 amp and the total armature plus series field plus interpole field resistance is 0.16. If the motor is operated from a source of 240 volts, calculate the speeds at armature currents of 25, 50, 75, and 100 amp.

26. Calculate and plot the torque-current characteristic for the motor in Prob. 25.

27. A series motor rated at 50 amp has a total resistance between terminals of 0.16 ohm and operates from a 220-volt source. Data for the magnetization curve was taken in terms of field amperes and generated volts when the speed was 1000 rpm, as follows:

I_f	0	5	10	15	20	25	30	35	40	45	50	55	57.5
E	10	45	79	112	141	165	185.5	201	211.5	218.7	224	228	230

Calculate the speeds at 12.5, 25, 37.5, and 50 amp load.

28. Calculate torque for the motor in Prob. 27 for each of the load currents specified.

29. If interpoles are omitted in the motor of Prob. 25 and the brushes are shifted so there are 700 demagnetizing ampere-turns per pole at full-load, calculate the speed at rated current. The armature circuit resistance without interpoles is 0.12 ohm.

30. Plot the speed-load characteristic for the motor of Prob. 8 when a 2-ohm resistance is inserted in the line that connects to the common connection of the field and the armature.

31. Calculate the full-load speed of the motor in Prob. 8 when a 1-ohm resistance is inserted in the line that connects to the common connection of the field and the armature.

32. A load has a speed-torque characteristic given by the equation $T = 22 \times 10^{-9} n^3$, where T is in pound-feet and n in rpm. If the motor of Prob. 25 is used to drive this load, find the speed, assuming the rotational T required for the motor itself to be constant at 2 lb-ft.

33. A shunt dynamo without armature reaction and connected to a line of 250 volts has an armature circuit resistance of 0.2 ohm. When driven at 1200 rpm, the armature current is zero. Theoretically, what is the maximum possible motor power that this machine can develop? At what speed will this occur?

34. Determine and plot the torque-current characteristic of the motor referred to in Prob. 8 when a series field of 30 turns, interpoles, and a compensating winding are added (armature demagnetization eliminated). The series field is connected cumulative and has a resistance of 0.06 ohm. The combined resistance of the interpole and compensating windings is 0.06 ohm. The shunt field is connected long-shunt.

35. Determine and plot the torque current characteristic for the motor of Prob. 8 when interpoles and compensating windings are used so as to eliminate any demagnetization due to armature reaction. The interpole and compensating field resistance adds 0.06 ohm to the armature resistance of 0.16 ohm.

36. Determine the torque at $\frac{1}{4}$, $\frac{1}{2}$, $\frac{3}{4}$, $\frac{4}{4}$, and $\frac{5}{4}$ full-load current for the motor of Prob. 8 when operated under the conditions specified in Prob. 15.

37. Calculate the torque at half- and full-load currents for the motor in Table I when operated as a long-shunt, cumulative-compound motor with interpoles from a source of 230 volts.

38. Calculate the torque at full-load and half-load current for the dynamo in Table I when operated as a long-shunt, cumulative-compound motor with interpoles from a source of 230 volts but with the series field turns and resistance increased to twice the values given in the table.

CHAPTER X

Starting and Speed Control of Motors

Requirements in Starting Motors. The two requirements for the starting of direct-current motors are (1) maximum developed torque, and (2) a protection from excessive current through the armature. A large torque is desirable during starting because (a) a motor may be started under load, and (b) because it is usually important that the motor reach full speed in a minimum period of time. Protection from excessive current through the armature is necessary to prevent damage to the motor and associated equipment.

The fundamental motor speed equation $V = K_1 \phi Z_a n + I_a R_{a_o}$ shows that the voltage impressed across a motor is balanced by a counter electromotive force ($K_1 \phi Z_a n$) plus the effective fall of potential in the armature circuit. This effective fall of potential consists of the voltage drops across the armature, the series field, the commutating pole field, and the compensating winding. The counter electromotive force is directly proportional to the speed (n) if the field (ϕ) is constant. At the initial time of starting a motor, the speed is zero, and the counter electromotive force is zero. Hence it follows that the voltage impressed across a motor for starting must be balanced by the $I_a R_{a_o}$ drop in the armature and any other series resistances. The resistance of the armature and the series field is relatively low, so that the current I_a flowing will be relatively large if full-line voltage is impressed across the armature. For example, take the case of a 120-volt, 5-horsepower shunt motor having an armature circuit resistance of 0.25 ohm and a full-load current of 40 amperes. With full-line voltage impressed across the armature, the resulting current would be 120/0.25 or 480 amperes. This is twelve times full-load current, and such a current might damage the armature because of the mechanical forces set up, or would "burn out" the winding if this value of current were maintained for a few seconds. Such a large current would also cause vicious sparking, would cause a large voltage drop on the line, and might develop a torque which would damage the machinery to which it was connected. For these reasons, an external resistance must be placed in series with the armature during the starting period in order to limit the starting current of a motor. It is common practice to permit a maximum value of approximately two

183

times full-load current to be used during the starting period. Hence the maximum value of such external resistance R_x for the above example would be the total resistance minus the resistance of the armature circuit, that is $R_x = (120/80) - 0.25 = 1.25$ ohms.

As soon as the armature of the motor starts to rotate, a counter electromotive force will be generated, which will balance part of the impressed potential and will reduce the flow of current through the armature. The reduction in the current produces a lowering of the torque developed. When the current falls to or below the normal full-load value, part of the external resistance R_x may be cut out of the circuit. This reduction of R_x will cause a momentary increase of current with the accompanying increase of torque developed. As the motor continues to accelerate under the increased torque, the counter electromotive force also continues to rise, and again reduces the armature current. Thus, the resistance R_x can be cut out in successive steps until the full speed of the motor is reached. The decrease of the IR drop within the armature circuit and the rise of the counter electromotive force as a shunt motor comes up to speed are pictured in Fig. 1.

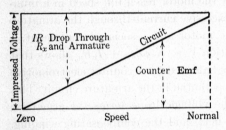

Fig. 1. Diagram Showing the Changes in Potential in a Shunt Motor during the Starting Period.

An exception to the general rule that an external resistance must be placed in series with the armature during starting is found in the case of fractional-horsepower motors of ⅓ horsepower and less. These motors may be connected directly across the line for starting. This procedure is permissible because (1) the armature of the small motor has a relatively high resistance which makes it semi-self-protecting, (2) a small motor with a low moment of inertia comes up to speed very quickly, and (3) the momentary starting current is not large enough to produce any disturbance to the voltage regulation of the supply lines.

The torque of any motor during the starting period or under load conditions is represented by the formula

$$T = K_2 \phi I_a \qquad \text{[1, page 158]}$$

where K_2 is a constant, ϕ represents the effective field flux, and I_a is the armature current. In order to meet the first requirement for starting motors (maximum torque), both the effective field flux and the armature current should have the maximum permissible value.

The field flux of a shunt motor is derived from its shunt field. In order to secure a maximum value of flux while starting, the field should be connected directly across the supply line with all resistance cut out of the field-control rheostat. The armature current should be limited by an external resistance, as previously explained.

The requirements for starting a cumulative-compound motor are similar to those for the shunt motor. Here, again, a full or strong shunt field is desirable. This field is strengthened during the starting period by the current in the series field, which adds to the starting torque. The resistance of the series field is added to the resistance of the armature, and thus tends to make a small theoretical reduction in the external resistance R_x required for starting.

The differential-compound motor, while seldom used, may show an unexpected behavior if the same starting procedure is followed as for shunt motors. Since the series field opposes the shunt field, the resultant field will be weak and the starting torque low. Now, if the impressed voltage is applied to the shunt field and the armature and series field simultaneously, the series field will build up quickly, but the shunt field will build up much more slowly due to its higher self-inductance. The result may be that the series field will initially be stronger than the shunt field, and the motor, if lightly loaded, may start to turn backward. Then, as the shunt field builds up and becomes stronger than the series field, the motor will stop, start forward, and continue in that direction. This phenomenon, together with the low starting torque, can be overcome by short-circuiting the series field during the starting period so that the motor will function like a shunt motor.

All starting requirements are readily met by the series motor. Its field in series with the armature provides a maximum flux when I_a is maximum, and the added resistance of the field in series with the armature tends to limit the initial flow of current in the armature. Hence a variable external resistance in series with the line is all that is required for starting a series motor.

Electric Controllers and Starters. The general requirements for starting motors covered in the preceding article are provided in practice through the use of devices known as **electric controllers.**

An electric controller is a device, or group of devices, which serves to govern, in some predetermined manner, the electric power delivered to the apparatus to which it is connected (ASA definition). A controller performs the basic functions of acceleration, retardation, line closing, and reversing, and, in addition, usually provides certain safety features, such as protection against overload, open fields, and a temporary failure of supply voltage. Protection against overload cannot always be provided by fuses because the starting current may vary from one and one-half to two times normal, and a fuse rated at this current value would not protect against a 25 per cent overload. If the line voltage fails for a short time, the motor will stop. Then if the line voltage is restored, its full value would be impressed across an unprotected armature.

Electric controllers are classified as manual, drum, and automatic, and are rated in horsepower and voltage. They are interchangeable on motors of like rating because efficiencies and full-load current will be approximately the same.

A *starter is a controller designed for accelerating a motor to normal speed in one direction of rotation* (ASA). A starter does not provide for speed control, though some separate device may be used in conjunction with it to do so. The simplest form of starting device is a switch which is adequate for small d-c motors of $\frac{1}{8}$ horsepower and smaller. A manual starting switch for fractional-horsepower motors is shown in Fig. 2. The switch resembles a tumbler switch such as is used on lighting circuits but incorporates a thermal overload device as illustrated in the detail view of Fig. 2. This thermal overload device will permit the initial rush of current for starting without opening but will open on continuous overload which would damage the motor.

Two forms of manual starters for shunt and compound motors have been used and are known by the terms **three-point** (three terminals) and **four-point** (four terminals). The three-point type has not been manufactured in recent

(Courtesy General Electric Company)

Fig. 2. Starting Switch for Fractional Horsepower Motors.

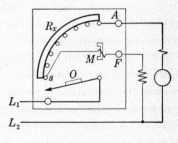

Fig. 3. Circuit for Three-Point Starter.

years, but since some of them are still in use and since the circuit of this starter is the one used in testing machines, it will be given here. The circuit of this box (starter) connected to a shunt motor is given in Fig. 3. The starting arm is normally held in its counterclockwise position by a strong spring. When the starting arm is moved to the first stud s, two circuits are closed. The first circuit leads from one side of the line L_1 to stud s, thence through the holding magnet M to one side of the shunt field, and then through the shunt field to the other side of the line. Current flowing over this path energizes the holding magnet and gives a full shunt-field flux (field rheostat cut out). The second circuit leads from one side of the line L_1 through the starting resistance R_x to A, and thence through the motor armature to the other side of the line. As the motor speeds up, the starting arm is advanced to cut out R_x in steps until full-line voltage is impressed across the armature. The starting arm is held in its final position by the attraction of the holding magnet M for a soft iron armature

(*O*) on the starting arm. If the field of the motor should be opened while the motor was running, the holding magnet M would be deenergized and the spring would bring back the starting arm and disconnect the motor. In like manner, if the supply circuit becomes opened, the starting arm will be restored to normal. This restoration will not take place instantly because the counter electromotive force developed by armature rotation which is sustained by inertia will serve to keep the holding magnet energized for a short time.

(*Courtesy General Electric Company*)

Fig. 4. Manual Starter for Direct-Current Motor.

In the operation of the three-point starter, the resistance R_x is inserted in series with the shunt field as the starting arm is advanced. This action would tend to increase the speed of the motor, but since the magnitude of R_x compared to the resistance of a shunt-field winding is very small, the change in speed is negligible.

The manufacture of three-point starters was discontinued because they did not permit the use of a resistance in the shunt field for a wide range of speed control. The holding magnet M in this type of box is in series with the shunt field and a large resistance inserted in series with the magnet will directly affect

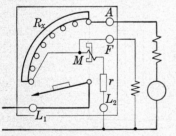

Fig. 5. Circuit for Four-Point Starter for a d-c Motor.

its holding power, whereas the circuit for the holding magnet of the four-point starter is separate from the field circuit.

The manual starter in general use today is of the four-point (four-terminal) type illustrated in Fig. 4. A simplified circuit of this starter connected to a compound motor is given in Fig. 5. This starter has an "undervoltage" release and operates similarly to the three-point starter just described. When the starting arm reaches the first stud, three circuits are closed. One leads from the line L_1 through the holding magnet M and a resistance r to the other side of the line L_2. The other circuits supply current to the shunt field and to the armature as in the three-point starter. When the supply-circuit voltage falls

to a low value or fails entirely, the holding magnet is deenergized and the starting arm is returned by the spring to the "off position" and stops the motor.

Many controllers of the type described above are designed to have the additional feature of speed control (hence they are not called "starters"). Figure 6 illustrates a controller having this feature, and Fig. 7 gives the circuit diagram for this device. Turning the starting arm in the clockwise direction serves to cut out the resistance R_x in series with the armature by steps. When this arm reaches the extreme clockwise position, a mechanical in-

(*Courtesy General Electric Company*)

Fig. 6. Controller for a d-c Motor.

terlock is formed and held closed by the retaining electromagnet M on the box. This interlock releases the spring tension on the starting arm, short-circuits the starting resistance in series with the armature R_x, and connects the field to a resistance R_f. The starting arm is now free to be rotated back (counterclockwise) and this action will serve to

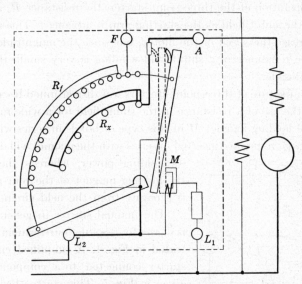

Fig. 7. Circuit for a Controller.

add resistance to the shunt-field circuit, step by step, and thus increase the motor speed. Upon failure of voltage, the retaining magnet M is deenergized, the interlock released, and the starting arm returned to the "off" position.

Some manual controllers are designed to reduce the motor speed below normal by inserting resistance in series with the armature. They are similar to the starter shown in Fig. 4, but contain a variable armature resistor having a heat dissipation capacity sufficient to carry full-load current continuously, whereas the ordinary manual controller is designed for intermittent starting duty only. A special form of manual controller which provides a speed both above and below normal uses the circuit of Fig. 8. The armature resistor has a capacity for continuous duty; hence the starting arm may be stopped at any

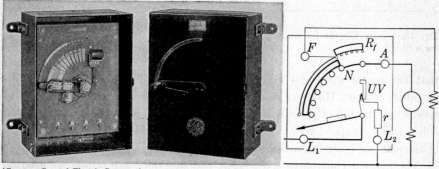

(*Courtesy General Electric Company*)

Fig. 8. Special Manual Controller for a d-c Motor.

stud to give a reduced (below normal) speed. If the starting arm is advanced to point N, the motor runs at normal speed under full field and full voltage across the armature. As the starting arm is advanced further clockwise, resistance is inserted in the series with the shunt field, thus raising the speed. This controller provides a speed range varying from 50 per cent to 125 per cent of normal. The holding or undervoltage (UV) magnet on this controller will hold the starting arm in any position under normal voltage but release it for undervoltage (75 per cent).

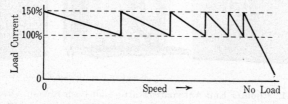

Fig. 9. Current-Speed Characteristic of a Manual Starter.

Manual starters and controllers are usually designed to give a maximum of 125 to 200 per cent of full-load current under starting conditions. A probable current-speed characteristic of a motor started with a manual controller designed for 150 per cent normal current is shown in Fig. 9. This curve indicates that six steps would be required for the starting resistance.

In connecting a starter to the supply line and the motor, wrong connections are sometimes made. A wrong connection using a three-point starter is given

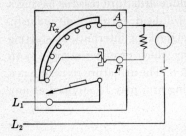

Fig. 10. Faulty Circuit for Starting a Shunt Motor.

in Fig. 10. This connection is very deceptive because the motor will seem, at first, to be starting satisfactorily, and then will race at a dangerous speed as the starting arm is advanced. A study of this circuit shows that when the arm reaches the first position, the current through the armature is properly limited by R_x, but that the voltage impressed across the shunt field is the fall of potential across R_x. With the motor at rest, this fall of potential approaches the full-line voltage so that the motor starts to revolve with nearly full-field strength and full-armature current. However, as the starting arm is advanced and the motor speeds up, the fall of potential across the shunt field decreases and the motor will increase its speed very rapidly to a dangerously high speed if the advance of the starting lever is continued.

The manual controllers of the type just described are ordinarily used on motors up to 50-horsepower rating. The satisfactory starting of the motor and life of the manual controller depends upon the intelligence, judgment, and care exercised by the operator. Since these qualities are often lacking, the use of automatic starters is becoming quite extensive.

An automatic starter is a starter designed to control automatically the acceleration of a motor (ASA). Automatic starters are usually of the "push-

(Courtesy Westinghouse Electric Corporation)

Fig. 11. Counter Emf Automatic Starter and Push-Button Assembly.

button" type in which the operator has one button marked "start" for starting the motor and another labeled "stop" for stopping the motor. Figure 11 (right) shows the push-button assembly.

The "start" and "stop" buttons may be located at a distance from the motor, thus affording remote control. These controllers may operate on three different principles: counter electromotive force acceleration, current-limit acceleration, and time-limit acceleration. All of the basic functions of starting and stopping are performed by electromagnets, and hence such starters and controllers are frequently called **magnetic controllers.**

A **counter electromotive force automatic starter** employs the counter emf developed across the armature for determining the operation of the electro-magnetic relays which, in turn, control the resistance in series with the arma-ture. A shunt or compound motor may generally be started with only three steps if the starting current is permitted to pass through the range of two times full load down to 80 per cent of full load and then up to two times full load, etc. Thus, assuming a 120-volt shunt motor having an armature resistance of 0.25-ohm and 40-ampere full load, the external starting resistance should be

$$Rx_1 = \frac{120}{2 \times 40} - 0.25 = 1.25 \text{ ohms (first step).}$$

If the motor speeds up until the current falls to 80 per cent of normal full-load value, the counter electromotive force generated will be

$$V = (R_x + R_a)I_a = E$$
$$120 - (1.25 + 0.25)(0.8) \times 40 = 72 \text{ volts}$$

and the potential drop across the resistances is 48 volts. Now, if the current be permitted to rise to twice normal, or 80 amperes, the external resistance could be reduced to

$$R_{x2} = \frac{48}{80} - 0.25 = 0.35 \text{ ohm (second step).}$$

Again, as the motor speeds up and the current drops to 32 amperes, the counter electromotive force becomes

$$120 - (0.35 + 0.25)32 = 100.8 \text{ volts}$$

and the potential across the resistances 19.2 volts. And, again, if the current be allowed to rise to 80 amperes, the external resistance would be

$$R_{x3} = \frac{19.2}{80} - 0.25 = -0.1 \text{ ohm}$$

and the motor armature could be connected directly across the line. Thus only three steps would be necessary for starting this motor.

Counter electromotive force starters frequently employ three steps in accordance with the preceding discussion. For starting small motors (up to 5 horsepower) a two-point starter having the circuit of Fig. 12 is satisfactory. The circuit employs one counter emf accelerating relay R and one main-line magnetic relay or contactor M. To start the motor the two-pole manual line switch $L+$ and $L-$ must be closed. Next the depressing of the "start" button closes a circuit from $L+$ through start button (normally open), stop button (normally closed), through coil M of main contactor relay to $L-$. Relay M on energizing closes its main contact M_1 and an auxiliary contact M_2. The closing of M_1 places full-line voltage across the shunt field (giving full field) and across the armature and starting resistor in series. The closing of M_2 places a shunt around the start contacts and locks relay M in so that the subsequent opening of the start button is ineffective. Accelerating relay coil R is connected across the armature and at the instant when M_1 closes the armature is at rest and the voltage across R is the R_aI_a drop over the armature which is likely to be 20 per cent of normal line potential. As the motor accelerates the counter emf of the armature rises, and when the voltage across R reaches a

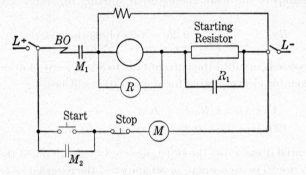

Fig. 12. Circuit for a Counter Emf Automatic Starter.

predetermined value (about 75 per cent of normal line potential), R is energized, closing the contact R_1. The closing of R_1 short-circuits the starting resistor causing an increase of current into the armature and a rise in torque which quickly accelerates the motor to full speed. The motor may be stopped by depressing the stop button or by opening the manual line switch. Operation of the stop button deenergizes relay M, thus opening its contacts M_1 and M_2. Since the main circuit might be opened under full-load current, a magnetic blowout (BO) is used for the contacts of M_1 in order to prevent arcing and burning of contacts. A counter emf starter is illustrated in Fig. 11. Three- and four-point starters use more accelerating relays adjusted for different operating voltages and designed to cut out the armature resistor in more steps.

A **current-limit automatic starter** functions through the use of current relays which operate when the accelerating current *falls below* full-load value. The circuit for a simple two-step current-limit starter is given in Fig. 13(a). In addition to the accelerating relay R and the main-line contactor M used on the counter emf system, this circuit requires a series current relay CR. The motor is started by closing the manual switch $L+$ and $L-$ and depressing the "start" button. The start button closes a circuit from $L+$, normally closed contact OL_1, stop button, start button, normally closed contact M_2, accelerating relay R to $L-$. Relay R is energized opening the shunt around starting resistor at R_1 and closing contact R_2. Closing of contact R_2 energizes relay M. Operation of relay M, in turn, closes its main-line contact at M_1, opens contact M_2, and closes contact M_3. The operation of M_1 energizes the motor for starting and the initial rush of current through the series current relay CR closes contact CR_1. The closing of contact M_3 establishes a locking circuit for coil M (ahead of start button). The closing of contact CR_1 serves to keep relay

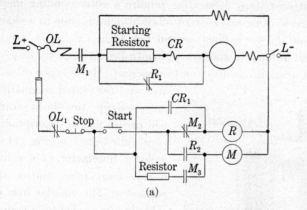

(a)

(Courtesy Allen Bradley Company)

(b)

Fig. 13. Current-Limit Automatic Starter and Circuit.

R energized after contact M_2 opens. The motor accelerates and as the counter emf rises the *current* through the armature and current relay falls. When this armature current reaches a predetermined value (approximately normal full load), relay CR becomes sufficiently deenergized so that contact CR_1 opens the circuit to relay R. Relay R deenergizes and its contact R_1 recloses and shunts out the starting resistor and the current relay. The motor now accelerates to normal speed. The motor is stopped by pressure on the stop button which deenergizes main-line relay M as in the preceding starter circuit. The circuit of Fig. 13(a) contains an overload thermal switch OL. On either transient heavy overloads or continuous moderate overload, the thermal switch operates and opens its contact OL_1 which in turn acts like the stop button in stopping the motor. Additional steps in starting require a corresponding increase in the number of accelerating and current relays which function in a chain sequence. A current-limit starter is illustrated in Fig. 13(b).

Time-limit automatic starters are controlled in steps by time-delay relays regardless of armature counter emf or current. Many types of time-delay relays and associated magnetic contactors are used for time-limit starters. Space will permit a brief description of only one type, illustrated in Fig. 14. This unit, called a **timetactor**, is a combination of a time-limit relay and a spring-closed contactor. The circular iron core for the relay is surrounded by a copper tube and two coils. One coil carries the main relay current for pulling up the armature. The second coil carries a much smaller reverse or neutralizing current which is subject to adjustment for timing the relay. When the main coil is energized, the armature is pulled up against the pull of a spring and the main contacts are opened. When the main coil circuit is opened, the flux in the magnetic circuit decreases but the decrease induces current in the copper tube (one turn coil) which delays the rate of the dying flux. When the magnitude of the flux decreases to a certain value, the armature releases and the spring restores the main contacts to normal (closed). The time required for the relay magnet to deenergize may be varied from $\frac{1}{2}$ to 6 seconds.

(Courtesy Westinghouse Electric Corporation)

Fig. 14. Time-Limit Relay and Contactor.

The circuit for a two-step time-limit starter using a timetactor is given in Fig. 15. The overload and mainline relays and start-stop buttons function as in the two preceding automatic starters. The start button closes a circuit from $L+$ through normally closed OL_1, stop contacts, start contacts, normally closed M_3, main timetactor coil TD to $L-$. The timetactor energizes, thus (1) opening the main contacts TD_1, (2) placing the starting resistor in armature circuit, and (3) closing auxiliary contacts TD_2. The closure of TD_2 energizes main-line relay M, thus operating main contacts M_1, auxiliary contacts M_2, and opening contacts M_3. M_2 closes the usual locking circuit around start button while the opening of M_3 opens the main coil winding on the timetactor TD. The flux in the magnetic circuit of the timetactor dies down and after a predetermined time drops its armature and recloses TD_1, shunting out the starting resistor. The motor quickly accelerates to full speed. The circuit, Fig. 15, includes a field rheostat relay FR which may be used on any automatic starter for the purpose of shunting out the field rheostat during the accelerating period until approximately full-line voltage is applied to the armature. It will be noted that relay FR is connected across the starting resistor so that when the main-line contactor M_1 closes, nearly full-line voltage is applied to FR, causing it to close contacts FR_1 and shunt the field rheostat. When the starting resistor is shunted by a relay, FR is shunted also and FR_1 opens. The opening of FR_1 reinserts the field rheostat in the field and causes the motor

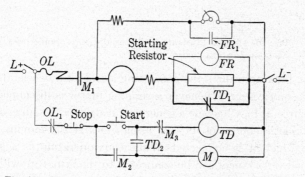

Fig. 15. Circuit for a Time-Limit Automatic Starter.

to accelerate to the final speed determined by the setting of the field rheostat. Additional steps in motor acceleration may be obtained through the use of more timetactors and taps on the starting resistor.

In comparing the three principles of automatic starting it may be said that the counter emf system is simple in construction, has a minimum of parts, and operates well under favorable conditions. It is not suitable for starting heavy loads or where great fluctuations of line voltages may occur. Thus if the load at starting is too heavy or the line voltage too low, the counter emf may not reach the magnitude necessary for operating the relay and the starting resistor will be burned out. The counter emf starters are limited to small motors up to 20 horsepower where low cost is important and favorable operating conditions prevail. Current-limit starters are more costly and complicated but are desirable for starting **heavy inertia loads.** The time-limit automatic starter works well under unfavorable conditions where rugged service is necessary. This type of starter is used for large motors where quick acceleration, stopping, and reversing are necessary in steel mills and similar applications.

Certain additional features are frequently incorporated with the manual and automatic starters covered in the preceding discussion. These features, the field discharge resistor and dynamic braking, are illustrated in Fig. 16. The field discharge resistor consists of high resistance in parallel with the field to absorb the inductive kick arising from sudden opening of the field circuit.

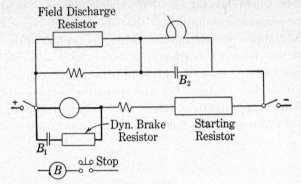

Fig. 16. Circuit Illustrating Special Features Sometimes Embodied in Automatic Starters.

Dynamic braking utilizes the generating action of a decelerating motor to bring it to a quick stop. Whenever a running motor is disconnected from its electrical source, it may become a generator utilizing as a source of mechanical power the kinetic energy of its own armature and the moving parts of the machine to which it is connected. While thus operating as a generator, an electrical load (resistance) can be connected to the armature which will bring the motor to rest quickly. This resistance may be applied in one or more steps with a final value of zero. Dynamic braking is important in industrial applications where it is desirable to stop a motor quickly in order to speed up production. Oftentimes it is desirable also to reverse a motor, and controllers, both manual and automatic, may be provided with circuits which arrange to reverse the connections to the armature to provide reversal after being stopped by dynamic braking.

The drum controller, (Fig. 17), is another device for starting shunt, compound, and series motors. It consists of an inclosed drum switch together with an auxiliary starting resistance. The drum switch consists of a central shaft supporting several copper cams which make contact with copper fingers. Contact between cams and fingers is made between fireproof baffles which prevent any dangerous short circuits due to arcing between "live" parts. Where high voltages (500 volts and higher) and heavy currents must be broken, magnetic blowouts are

(*Courtesy General Electric Company*)

Fig. 17. Drum-Type Controller.

incorporated in the drum switch. The magnetic blowout provides a strong magnetic field at right angles to the arc formed when a circuit is opened. In accordance with the fundamental action upon a conductor bearing current in a magnetic field, the arc is pushed (blown) out of the field until it breaks.

A drum controller for a series motor provides for a starting resistance in series with the motor, and it may provide for a reversal of direction by reversing the current through either the armature or the series field. Part of the starting resistance may remain in the circuit all of the time that the motor is running, because the speed control of a series motor is secured by the insertion of resistance in series with the line. Hence the resistor must be capable of withstanding full-load currents continuously. Fig. 18 gives the simple circuit for starting a series motor.

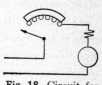

Fig. 18. Circuit for Starting a Series Motor.

Electric controls for hoists and cranes have an extensive application and an interesting theory of operation. Direct-current series motors are widely used because of their superior torque and speed characteristics where heavy loads and torques are encountered. In applying motor power to a hoist it is necessary to use a mechanical brake to lock the hoisted load in position when the power

(Courtesy Electric Controller & Mfg. Co.)

Fig. 19. Electromagnetic Brake for Crane Motor.

is shut off from the motor. Many forms of brakes are in use and either compressed air or electromagnets or both may be employed for actuation of the brakes. One form of electric brake which is applied directly to the motor shaft is illustrated in Fig. 19. Normally the brake shoes are locked to the brake's wheel by a strong spring which is capable of holding any load (weight) placed on the hoist which is within the rating of the device. The brake shoes are released by the armature of the electromagnet which overcomes the spring tension whenever the electromagnet is energized. Obviously, the brake must be released whenever the motor operates to hoist or lower the load.

The operation of crane hoists is controlled by a small manual master switch or controller like the one illustrated in Fig. 20. This master switch controls the operation of many relays and contactors for producing the needed steps in hoisting and lowering crane loads. The various relays, contactors, switches, and protective equipment for a five-point crane control using dynamic lowering are shown mounted on a switchboard panel in Fig. 21. The schematic line diagram for this five-point controller showing all main contacts but omitting relay coils and circuits is given in Fig. 22(a). Simplified step-by-step circuits for the five points of hoisting and lowering operation are given in Fig. 22(b). With the aid of these diagrams the following sequence of operation may be followed.

(Courtesy Electric Controller & Mfg. Co.)

Fig. 20. Controller or Master Switch for Crane Motors.

(Courtesy Electric Controller & Mfg. Co.)

Fig. 21. Panel Containing Switches, Relays, Contactors, and Protective Equipment for Five-Point Crane Motor Control.

Hoisting. Moving the master switch to the first hoist point simultaneously energizes coils of contactors M and H without sequential interlock delay, thus giving immediate power to the motor and brake. The spring closed contactor E remains closed connecting resistor A-E in shunt with the motor. The line current is limited to about 50 per cent of full-load value. All of the line current passes through the brake coil. The torque obtained is about 20 per cent full-load value, which is sufficient to take up slack cable except possibly on large cranes and those where the rope and gear reduction are large, resulting in a large amount of friction.

On the second point hoist contactor coil E is energized, causing E to open its spring-closed contacts removing the motor shunt connections. This in-

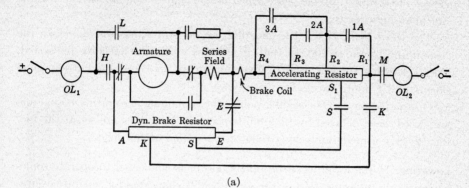

(a)

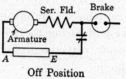

Hoisting   Off Position   Lowering

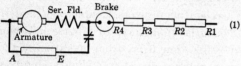

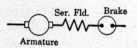

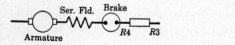

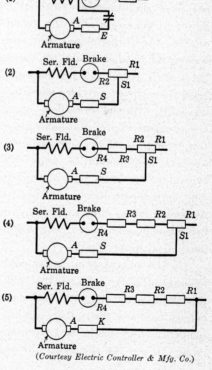

(Courtesy Electric Controller & Mfg. Co.)

(b)

Fig. 22. Simplified Circuits for Five-Point Crane Motor Control.

creases the torque to 40 per cent, which is sufficient to take up any slack cable and hoist light loads.

The third point closes $1A$, shorting out resistor R_1R_2, and increases the current and torque to 100 per cent, in case the motor has not already started. No accelerating relay is used to give time delay on $1A$ as the current upon closure of $1A$ is not excessive.

On the fourth and succeeding points the remaining acclerating contactors are closed, each delayed by time-limit relays. These relays are set at the factory to give a moderately long time of 0.6 second at full load.

Lowering. In the lowering direction the motor is connected to operate somewhat as a shunt motor, that is, the series field is connected for separate excitation from the line, but is also connected to the armature circuit, so that, on overhauling loads,* depending upon the speed, the armature supplies part or all of the field exciting current reducing the power taken from the line. In fact, on heavy overhauling loads, with the master on the last point, considerable power is returned to the line.

On the first point lower, contactors $2A$ and $3A$ close immediately to short out all but the first step of the series accelerating resistors. Contactors L and M also close simultaneously without sequential time delay to provide lowering power to the motor with the least possible time delay from operation of the master. The spring-closed contactor E remains closed providing a shunt of resistor AE around the motor. The line current is limited to 100 per cent by resistor R_1R_2. All of this line current passes through the brake for prompt release. This circuit provides lowering power to the motor to start nonoverhauling loads, with the series field separately excited to about full-load value and the armature excited through resistors AE and R_1R_2. This provides a lowering torque of 10 to 15 per cent, depending on contact resistance of trolley collectors, etc. This amount of torque will start the empty hook in the down direction unless friction is high, in which case moving the master to the second point will increase the torque. On overhauling loads, the resistor AE provides a dynamic braking circuit which prevents excessive speed. Full load will descend at approximately 35 per cent of full-load motor speed, and lighter loads will descend at lower speeds.

On the second point lower contactor S closes, immediately followed by opening of E. This leaves the field separately excited through resistor R_1R_2 but changes the dynamic braking circuit from AE to AS plus S_1R_2, which change increases the voltage applied to the armature to increase the speed of nonoverhauling loads, and increases the resistance in the dynamic braking circuit to increase the speed of overhauling loads.

---

* Overhauling load is a heavy load which will fall rapidly. The action described is analogous to dynamic braking.

On the third point contactor 3A opens, which inserts additional resistance in the field circuit giving weaker field strength and adds resistance to the dynamic braking circuit, and thus increases the speed of any load.

On the fourth point 2A opens to further weaken the field and increase the speed of all loads.

On the fifth point K closes immediately followed by opening of S. The closure of K is controlled by the counter emf relay, the coil of which is connected across the armature on the last point lowering. The operating point of the relay is adjusted to occur at approximately 105 volts, thus preventing closure of K until the motor is accelerated to about half speed. The operating point of the relay can be varied by adjustment of the opening spring pressure. On closure of K and opening of S, the field is left excited through all the resistor R_1R_4 with about 50 per cent full-load current. The transfer from S to K also decreases the resistance in the armature circuit from AS to AK, materially increasing the voltage applied to the armature, to give the highest lowering speed to drive the light loads. It also increases the resistance in the dynamic braking circuit to R_1R_4 plus AK and gives higher lowering speeds with heavy loads.

Motor Speed Control. The speed control of motors is a very important subject in the consideration of the applications of motors. The various methods of speed control follow directly from the fundamental equation of the motor which, for the purposes of this chapter, will be referred to as the **speed equation of direct-current motors.** This "speed equation" (equation 8, page 162) shows that the speed is directly proportional to the counter electromotive force $(V - I_a r_s)$ and is inversely proportional to the total effective flux where r_s represents all of the armature circuit resistance including any external resistor.

$$n = \frac{V - I_a r_s}{K_1 \phi Z_a} \tag{1}$$

There are four general methods of speed control for direct-current motors. Each of the four methods results from the control of one of the four possible variables in the "speed equation." The armature current I_a depends directly upon the load, and hence does not offer a usable method of speed control. The term K_1 is a constant which, in general, cannot be changed for a given machine. This leaves the variables r_s, ϕ, V, and Z_a available for manipulation for speed control.

Resistance Method of Motor Speed Control. The standard way of controlling the speed of a series motor on constant-potential systems is to insert a resistance in series with the line as covered on page 173. Since a series motor should always be operated under load, the torque for the motor will be determined by that load. The torque developed by any motor is expressed by the equation $T = K_2\phi I_a$. For the series motor, ϕ is proportional to some power of I_a, and for any given value of torque the necessary value of I_a to develop this torque is fixed. With this in mind, a study of the speed equation (1) will show that for a given load condition (fixed torque) and for constant potential, the only possible variable is the resistance r_s. Hence a resistance in series with the line may be used to control the value of the counter electromotive force $(V - I_a r_s)$, and, in turn, the speed of the series motor.

The torque required of a series motor may vary with the speed. In the case of a series motor direct-connected to a fan, the torque increases as some power of the speed. Here the analysis of the speed control is not so simple, although the same general results are obtained. In this case, a decrease of the external control resistance (R_x) will tend to increase the value of the numerator and to increase the speed. However, any increase of speed requires an increased torque, which, in turn, will require a larger value of I_a. This larger value of I_a will tend to decrease the value of the numerator $(V - I_a r_s)$ and at the same time to increase the value of the denominator by increasing ϕ. The net result of all these factors will be an increase in speed, but not such a large increase as would occur if the torque had remained constant.

In the application of the series motor to a load, the operating points can be determined readily if the torque-speed characteristics of both the motor and load are known. Thus in Fig. 23, the operating points lie at the intersections of the motor and load curves, or a, b, and c. For a constant-torque load, the speed would rise from c to b, whereas for the increasing torque load characteristic the speed would rise by the amount O to b only.

It might be assumed that the speed of a shunt motor could be controlled likewise by inserting a resistance in series with the line. In general, this assumption is not correct since the field of the shunt motor is connected across the line and since any reduced voltage across the motor terminals affects the field flux ϕ. For the purpose of analysis, first let it be assumed that the magnetization curve of a shunt motor is a straight line. Then a resistance inserted in series with the line will reduce the numerator of equation 1 by a certain percentage, and the field flux ϕ (proportional to I_f) will be reduced in the same ratio, resulting in no change in speed. In the actual case, the magnetization

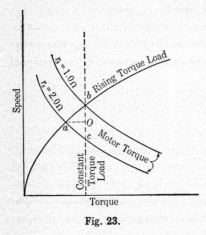

Fig. 23.

curve is not a straight line and the machine is normally operated at a point above the knee of the curve; hence for this case the field flux ϕ will not be reduced to as great an extent as $V - I_a r_s$. Thus there will be a small decrease in speed.* It can readily be seen that this method of speed control is wasteful of power ($I^2 r_s$ loss) and relatively unproductive in results. For these reasons, it is never used.

Speed control for shunt (and compound) motors can be obtained by inserting resistance in series with the armature only (not in line). Here all members of the speed equation except the $I_a r_s$ term remain constant. For a given value of load (fixed torque) I_a will be constant and the counter electromotive force (hence speed) will be controlled directly by varying a resistance in series with the armature. However, in practice, the torque required varies and the current I_a to develop this torque must vary likewise. With a fluctuation in the value of I_a, the value of the term $I_a r_s$ will fluctuate through wide limits since r_s is relatively large in value. For example, assume a 120-volt motor having an armature resistance of 0.3 ohm drawing 20 amperes of current. In order to reduce the speed to one-half, the $I_a r_s$ must equal 60 volts. Thus, $r_s = 60/20 = 3$ ohms. If an increased load required 40 amperes to produce the required torque, the $I_a r_s$ is $40 \times 3 = 120$ volts and the motor would stop. If all the load were removed from the motor ($I_a = 3$ amperes), the $I_a r_s$ is 9 volts and the motor would run at near normal speed. Hence, the motor has a widely varying speed, and its speed regulation using this method of speed control is very poor. Another disadvantage is that all the power consumed in the control resistance is wasted, and the over-all efficiency for the motor is low. For example, at one-half speed, one half of the applied voltage is impressed across the armature and the other one half across the control resistance. This condition results in an efficiency of less than 50 per cent. Similarly, at one-fourth speed, the efficiency is less than 25 per cent.

This method of speed control of shunt motors has the slight advantage that it is simple and does serve to reduce the speed below the normal value (most other methods serve to increase speed). Its applications are limited to experimental work, in emergencies where no other method is available, for temporary work where the waste of power is not an important consideration, and for fractional-horsepower motors.

Flux Methods of Speed Control. The field flux of shunt motors can be varied in two different ways for controlling the motor speed. One means of flux control is by varying the shunt-field current and the other is by varying the reluctance of the magnetic circuit.

A variable resistance inserted in series with the shunt field (Fig. 24)

---

* A quantitative treatment of this subject has been given on page 175.

furnishes a simple means for varying the shunt-field current and, in turn, the field flux ϕ. Reference to the speed equation shows that a decrease in ϕ gives an increase in speed, and vice versa. For any given setting of the field rheostat, the speed of the motor will follow the characteristic speed regulation curve of a shunt motor, which curve indicates practically constant speed at all loads.

Fig. 24.

With this method of speed control, the maximum speed may be as much as five or six times the minimum speed if interpoles are used. On noninterpole motors, a speed increase of approximately 30 per cent may be obtained through the variation of the field resistance. Any attempt to obtain higher speed range meets with commutation difficulties and a tendency toward instability because of the greater distortion (when the field is weakened) of the field flux due to armature reaction. This distortion of the field flux shifts the magnetic neutral and produces an electromotive force in the coil undergoing commutation. The emf is in the same direction as the reactance voltage, and hence results in poor commutation.

This field-resistance method of speed control is simple, efficient, and inexpensive, and it furnishes a wide range of adjustable speeds with good regulation throughout the range for both shunt and compound motors. Consequently this method has wide application today for adjustable speed motors up to approximately 50 horsepower.

A new system of speed control using the field resistance method and giving a speed range of eight to one was announced in 1947*. The system is adapted to a four-pole motor having a wave winding and two shunt field circuits. One field circuit called the main field is wound for line voltage to excite the poles A and B of Fig. 25a. The second circuit, called the variable field is placed on

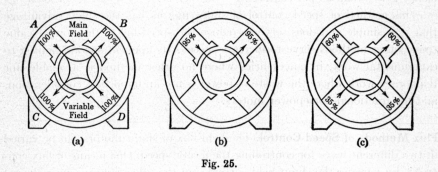

Fig. 25.

poles C and D and designed to produce 100 per cent pole flux at one-half of

* R. W. Moore, "Application Engineer," *Westinghouse Engineer*, Nov. 1947.

line voltage. The two fields are connected to the line through a field rheostat R and a potential divider resistor PD (with a mechanical interlock), as shown in Fig. 26. With the field control F to the extreme left the main field is subject to full-line voltage and supplies 100 per cent field flux and the variable field is subject to one-half line voltage and also supplies 100 per cent field flux, as suggested in Fig. 25a. With this adjustment and full-field flux the motor operates at minimum speed. Now as the control F is moved to the right, both fields are weakened; the main field because of the insertion of resistance and the variable field because of the reduced voltage drop across a part of the potential divider. When the control is moved right to the point Y, the voltage across the variable field is zero and the main field is reduced so that its field flux is approximately 95 per cent. This condition is illustrated in Fig. 25b and the speed has risen to about 210 per cent of minimum. Now as the control F is moved into the region shown by X, the voltage across the variable field

and its current reverses in direction, thus reducing the effective or algebraic net flux being cut by the armature inductors. In the extreme position of F at the right the respective fluxes reach the condition shown in Fig. 25c, giving a net flux just one-eighth that shown in Fig. 25a. For this setting the speed will be eight times the minimum speed for equal condition of load.

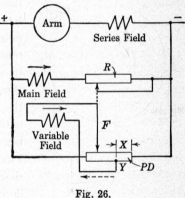
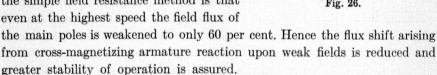

Fig. 26.

The advantage of this system over the simple field resistance method is that even at the highest speed the field flux of the main poles is weakened to only 60 per cent. Hence the flux shift arising from cross-magnetizing armature reaction upon weak fields is reduced and greater stability of operation is assured.

The speed of a shunt motor can be varied by controlling the reluctance of the magnetic circuit. From the fundamental formula $\phi = (\text{mmf})/\mathcal{R}$, it is obvious that any change in the reluctance $\mathcal{R}$ will change the resultant flux, and hence the motor speed. The expression for reluctance is

$$\mathcal{R} = \frac{l}{\mu A}.$$ [60, Appendix]

The major part of the reluctance of the magnetic circuit of a motor lies in the air gap. Hence a change in either the length (l) or the cross-sectional area (A) of the air gap will change the speed of the motor. Both of these changes have been embodied in the motors which have been designed and manufactured to use the reluctance method of speed control.

The Stow motor, constructed as shown in Fig. 27a, was the first to use the reluctance system of speed control. The field poles are hollow and fitted with cylindrical cores of soft iron, which may be set flush with the fixed pole face or may be drawn away from the inner pole face. A hand wheel controls the position of the pole cores through a system of bevel gears and screw-threaded shafts. The withdrawal of the cores increases the length of the air gap under the movable core and, in another sense, decreases the area of the air gap. Both changes increase the reluctance of the magnetic circuit and increase the speed of the motor. The Stow motor has not been manufactured since 1900.

The Reliance motor (formerly the Lincoln motor) produces a similar result through the construction shown in Fig. 27b. This motor has an armature which is slightly conical, and the entire rotating part is arranged so that it can be moved laterally along the center line of the shaft. The magnetic pull of the field upon the armature tends to hold the armature "in" and is balanced by a strong spring which pushes the armature in the opposite direction. With the armature "in," the air gap is short, the reluctance of the magnetic circuit is low, the flux is large, and the speed is a minimum. As the armature is withdrawn, the length of the air gap increases due to the conical shape of the armature and the area of the air gap decreases due to the lateral shift; both of these actions cause the reluctance to increase, the flux to decrease, and the speed to rise. This motor may be built to give a speed range of 5 to 1 or 10 to 1, as desired. Interpoles are placed on these motors to assure excellent commutation. The Reliance motor has been out of production since 1930.

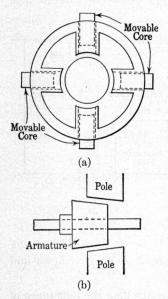

Fig. 27. Variable Reluctance Methods of Speed Control.

Both the Stow and the Reliance motors give a finely graduated system of speed control with good speed regulation and commutation at all speeds. It will be noted that the magnetomotive force of the field circuit (ampere-turns) is the same at all speeds. Thus, while the increase of reluctance does decrease the flux, the armature reaction (mmf) must act through the same increase in reluctance; hence there is little change in the relative distortion of the field. This means that better commutation can be obtained at all speeds on noninterpole motors using field-reluctance control than with the field-resistance control. Both of these motors were developed before the interpole came into general use, and, at that time, they were the only motors which could give a wide range of adjustable speed with fair commutation throughout the range.

The mechanical control features on the motors just described add to the cost of manufacturē. Today it is standard practice to place interpoles on all machines above 1 kilowatt in size, so that this system of control no longer has any marked advantage over that using the variable resistance in the field.

The flux method of speed control may be applied to series motors in two ways. One method is to place a resistance in parallel (shunt) with the series field. This will weaken the effective field flux and thus increase the motor speed if other factors remain constant. In the second method, taps are placed on the winding of the series field so that the number of turns, and hence the field flux, may be reduced by changing the connection to the taps.

Potential-Difference Method of Speed Control. The speed equation of the motor shows that the speed can be controlled by varying the potential difference V if all other factors remain constant. This was one of the early forms of speed control. In the multivoltage system, multiple lines and a circuit diagram like that of Fig. 28 were necessary. The field is always supplied with a voltage for which it is designed, such as 220 volts in the illustration. The armature was connected to any two lines giving the voltage combinations 40, 70, 110,

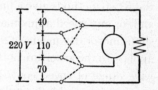

Fig. 28. Multivoltage Circuit for Speed Control.

150, 180, and 220, with resulting speeds almost directly proportional to the voltage impressed across the armature. This system was very costly because it required several generators in series and a special controller. It is no longer in use except where the three-wire system of 220 to 110 volts may be used to give a 2 to 1 range of speed.

The **Ward Leonard** system of speed control varies the voltage across the armature of the motor through the use of a special motor-generator set.* This system is also known by the terms **variable voltage** and **adjustable voltage.** The fundamental circuit for the Ward Leonard system of speed control is given in Fig. 29. The principal parts of the system consist of two shunt dynamos, one serving as the motor M and the other a generator G, having their armatures connected in series. The shunt fields of the two machines are separately excited from a constant voltage supply line or an exciter E driven by the same prime mover or driving motor which powers the generator G. The driving motor may be either alternating or direct current depending on the available source of electrical supply. Normally the motor M has a constant full-field flux

* The Ward Leonard system of motor speed control was invented by H. Ward Leonard and covered by a series of eight patents issued over the period of 1890–1899. Licenses to use this system for electric elevators, rolling mills, cranes, etc., were granted to several electrical manufacturers during the lifetime of the patents.

and its speed can be varied through a wide range from zero to normal by changing the voltage impressed across its armature by the generator G. This voltage variation can be readily obtained by control of the generator field rheostat (g). After the speed corresponding to full motor field and normal armature

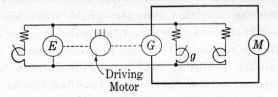

Driving Motor

Fig. 29. Circuit for Ward Leonard System of Speed Control.

voltage is reached, an additional increase and range of speed may be attained by inserting resistance in the shunt field of the motor M. The combination of these two methods give a finely graduated and wide range of speed of motor M, and for any speed adjustment the speed regulation under load will be that of a shunt motor. By means of a reversing switch for the generator field the voltage applied to the armature of the motor may be reversed, thus providing the same wide range of speed control of operation in either direction of rotation. The system of control indicated also permits a smooth and quick starting and acceleration of the motor M. In like manner, a quick and smooth deceleration of the motor M may be secured by the principle of dynamic regeneration. A rapid weakening of the generator G field will cause (1) the motor M to act as a generator, (2) the generator G to develop motor action, and (3) cause the driving motor to pump power back into the line.

It is obvious from the preceding statements that the Ward Leonard system provides an ideal system where a wide flexibility in speed, acceleration, deceleration, and reversals is desired. Accordingly, this system finds extensive use for high-speed passenger elevators, large hoists, power shovels, rolls in steel mills, drives in paper and textile mills, and propulsion of small ships. The Ward Leonard system also finds application as a "spot conversion" method

(Courtesy Reliance Electric & Engineering Company)

Fig. 30. Three-Unit Conversion Set Using Ward Leonard Principle.

of supplying direct-current power for operating d-c motors on alternating-current systems. There are many applications in factories where the wide range of speed control afforded by the Ward Leonard system is desirable for operating lathes and other machines. Small compact conversion units may be placed close to the machine or be built into the machine needing the special speed range. A unit of the power-package type is illustrated in Fig. 30. A two-unit, a-c motor, d-c generator is shown at the bottom belted to a small d-c exciter. Automatic starter, protective equipment, and other controls are located in the power cabinet.

The over-all efficiency of the Ward Leonard system is low where small amounts of power are needed but where great flexibility in speed is required this system may show a higher efficiency and a lower cost than some alternative plan. The initial cost of the Ward Leonard system is high because three and frequently four dynamos are required.

Many modern applications require that the speed of a motor be controlled automatically and that the necessary speed shall depend on varying factors in other machines or some phases of a manufacturing process. The Ward Leonard system may be used for such automatic and complicated control by introducing another link in the system in place of the rheostat (g) of Fig. 29. The added link may be an electronic device or, more often, a rotating machine like the

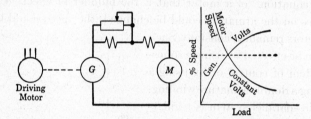

Fig. 31. Modified Ward Leonard Circuit Using Series Dynamos.

amplidyne or a multifield exciter like the Rototrol. These rotating machines will be discussed in a later chapter.

Some modifications of the Ward Leonard system have been employed to simplify the circuit and lower the cost*. The circuit for one modification is given in Fig. 31. Two series dynamos are employed instead of shunt. This change eliminates the need of a separate d-c supply or an exciter. The generated voltage is now controlled by a variable resistor in parallel with the series field of the generator G. A variation of armature voltage for starting M or controlling the speed of M may be attained also by varying the speed of the driving motor. The characteristic curves for a series generator and motor for load variation are shown at the right of Fig. 31. A study of these curves will reveal that they are complimentary so that for any given setting of the generator field rheostat the speed of the motor will be nearly constant with load as indicated by the

* Caldwell, G. A., "Adjustable-Speed D-C Drives," *Westinghouse Engineer*, Aug. 1942.

dotted line. For other setting of the field rheostat other speeds will be established. The normal range of speed by this system is 10 to 1.

A second modification of the Ward Leonard system of speed control is illustrated by the circuit of Fig. 32. This circuit uses shunt instead of series dynamos for the generator and motor. A combination or interlocked pair of field rheostats is used for controlling the fields of the generator and motor. When the generator field resistance is "all in" the motor field resistance is "all out," and vice versa. Thus for a low speed the generator field is weak and the generated voltage is low, while the motor shunt field is strong (field rheostat zero resistance). Conversely, for high motor speeds the generator field is strong and generated voltage high with the motor field weak. This system uses standard dynamos and gives a speed range of about 12 to 1.

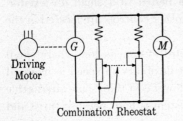

Driving
Motor

Combination Rheostat

Fig. 32. Modified Ward Leonard Circuit Using Shunt Dynamos.

Speed Control by Changing Conductors. It is obvious from an inspection of the "speed equation" of a motor that if the number of effective conductors (Z_a) in series on the armature could be changed, the speed could be varied if all other factors remained constant. Such a change can be effected by using a series-parallel system of control or by using a motor having a double armature winding.

The series-parallel system is regularly used on electric railway cars where either two or four series motors are required. The operation of this system is illustrated in Fig. 33. In part 1, the two motors are in series with a starting resistance R_x. At 2 the two motors in series are across the line and this constitutes a regular running condition. This connection gives one-half normal speed and is equivalent to changing the conductors in series from (Z_a) to $2Z_a$. This connection gives a high efficiency and should be contrasted with the method of inserting resistance in series with the motor where one half of the power would be wasted at this speed. Part 3 of Fig. 33 illustrates the full-speed connection for the series-parallel control where a current-limiting resistance R_x is in the external circuit. Part 4, Fig. 33, shows the final full-speed running connection. This gives a speed corresponding to Z_a conductors in series in the armature.

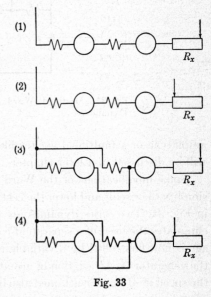

Fig. 33

Similar results can be obtained for a shunt or compound motor by having two like windings on the armature which are connected to a commutator on each end of that armature. Thus, the double-wound armature will offer a means of changing Z_a in the ratio 2 to 1 through series-parallel connections if the windings are identical. Other speed ratios could be obtained with windings having different ratios of Z_a if used for single or series armature connections (not parallel).

Summary of Methods of Speed Control. The chart on the following page contains a summary of the characteristics and applications of the principal methods of speed control.

PROBLEMS

1. A 115-volt, $\frac{1}{4}$-hp motor has an armature resistance of 8.5 ohms and a field resistance of 660 ohms. What will be the initial instantaneous line current if this motor is thrown across a 110-volt circuit? At no load, the counter emf equals 106.5 volts. How much line current does this motor take at no load?

2. A series fan motor has an armature resistance of 1.8 ohms and series field resistance of 0.6 ohm. If operated on a line of 115 volts potential, what will be the starting current if no starting resistance is used? What starting resistance will limit the initial transient current to 25 amp?

3. A 1-hp, 115-volt, 8.7-amp, 1800-rpm shunt motor has an armature resistance of 1.25 ohms and shunt field (I_f) of 1 amp. If the starting current must be limited between a minimum of normal to a maximum of 25 amp, determine the resistances R_x and the number of steps required.

4. A 5-hp, 230-volt, 21-amp, 1150-rpm shunt motor has an armature resistance of 1 ohm and a shunt field (I_f) of 1.5 amp. What should be the resistance (R_x) of a starter to limit the initial current to 200 per cent of normal load? What will be the counter emf when the starting current drops to normal with full starter resistance in series?

5. A 10-hp, 230-volt, 38.5-amp, compound motor (long shunt) has an armature resistance (R_a) of 0.23 ohm, series field (R_s) of 0.03 ohm, and a shunt field resistance (R_f) of 115 ohms. What will be the instantaneous current taken by the motor if it is thrown across the line without a starting resistance? What is the ratio of this instantaneous current to the normal load current? What would be the ratio of the heat developed in armature only by this transient current, if continuous, to the heat developed by the normal load current?

6. What should be the total resistance of a starter for the motor of Prob. 5 (assume series field shorted) in order to limit the initial armature current to 50 per cent greater than normal? Assuming a no-load speed of 1000 rpm and a current range of 150 per cent down to 100 per cent, then up to 150 per cent, and down to 100 per cent, etc., calculate the value of the resistance steps and the number of steps for a starter for this machine operated as a shunt motor. Plot resistance *versus* points.

7. A 50-hp, 230-volt, 180-amp, 600-rpm, compound motor has the following resistances:

$$R_a = 0.05 \text{ ohm}$$
$$R_s = 0.003 \text{ ohm}$$
$$R_c = 0.007 \text{ ohm}$$
$$R_f = 46.0 \text{ ohms}$$

SUMMARY OF METHODS OF SPEED CONTROL

METHOD	SPEED RANGE	REGULATION	EFFICIENCY	COST	CLASSIFICATION	APPLICATIONS
Resistance in armature circuit	0-normal	Poor	Low for low speeds	Low	Variable speed	Emergency use and small motors
Resistance in field circuit	5-1 Small motors 2-1 Large motors	Excellent	High at all speeds	Low for motors 1-25 hp	Constant adjustable speed; constant hp	General for motors 1-25 hp where constant speed of range 5-1 desired
Mechanical flux change	6-1	Excellent	High	High	Constant adjustable speed; constant hp	No longer manufactured
Resistance in line	None for shunt motors; wide for series motors	Poor	Variable; low for low speeds	Low	Variable speed; constant torque	Starting and speed control of series motors
Multivoltage line	2-1 for 3-wire system	Excellent	High	Low	Constant speed	Rarely used
Fundamental Ward Leonard system	As high as 120-1	Excellent	Variable	High	Constant adjustable speed	Passenger elevators; rolls in steel mills; paper & textile mill drives
Ward Leonard series machines	10-1	Good	Variable	High	Constant torque	Conveyors, machine-tool feeds, and other constant torque loads
W L self-excited shunt machines	12-1	Good	Variable	High	Constant hp	Machine-tool spindle drives

Calculate R_x for the starter on the basis of a maximum initial current of 150 per cent of normal load.

8. A 500-volt series railway motor has a normal current rating of 90 amp, an armature resistance of 0.05 ohm, and a series-field resistance of 0.03 ohm. What should be the resistance of an external resistor if the maximum current is to be limited to three times normal?

9. A 7½-hp, 230-volt, 1140-rpm, shunt motor has a full-load armature current of 27 amp and an armature resistance of 0.12 ohm. If a counter emf starter is to be designed for this motor to give a current range of 200 per cent to 80 per cent, calculate the resistance steps for the starter.

10. Make calculations for a counter emf starter for the motor of Prob. 5 for an armature current range of 200 to 80 per cent of rated current for the motor.

11. A 20-hp, 230-volt, 73-amp shunt motor has the following constants: I_a (full load) = 70, R_a = 0.11 ohm. If a current-limit starter for this motor permits a range of 300 per cent normal down to 100 per cent normal, calculate the number of steps and R_x values.

12. Assume that a time-limit starter is applied to the motor of Prob. 11 and that on the first R_x step after the current has dropped to 200 per cent normal the time relay operates and the second step cuts in. What instantaneous current will flow?

13. If a dynamic brake circuit is applied to the starter in Probs. 9 and 11 and at an instant when the counter emf of the motor is 225, the supply power is cut off, and the full value of R_x applied as the dynamic brake resistor, what instantaneous currents will flow?

14. A crane hoist having the controls covered by Fig. 22 is lifting a 3-ton load above a workman's head at an instant when a complete electric-power failure occurs. What happens?

15. For what type of motor loads are the starters of Probs. 9, 11, and 12 designed?

16. A 230-volt shunt motor has an armature resistance of 0.15 ohm and a full-load armature current of 50 amp. The no-load speed of the motor is 900 rpm and the no-load armature current is 2 amp. Two ohms resistance have been placed in the armature for speed reduction for some given load. Neglecting the effect of armature reaction, calculate the speed regulation of this motor with the 2 ohms resistance left in the armature circuit.

17. A series motor has an armature resistance of 0.3 ohm and a series field resistance of 0.1 ohm. For a given load (torque) an impressed potential of 120 volts causes 78 amp to flow and the motor to operate at 650 rpm. What will be the resultant speed when steady conditions are reached for the following cases?

  a. If the torque remains constant and the series resistance be increased by 0.4 ohm?
  b. 0.6 ohm?
  c. 0.90 ohm?
  d. If the load is changed so that the resulting current is 50 amp (assuming ϕ proportional to I)?

18. If the reluctance of the magnetic-field circuit of a Stow motor be increased 50 per cent, what will be the speed change of the motor, assuming other factors affecting speed remain constant?

19. The motor of Prob. 4 is operating under a constant torque load which requires 20 amp through the armature. With no external resistance in the armature circuit the speed is 1150 rpm. Calculate the speed as external resistances (R_x) of 1, 3, 5, 7, and 9 ohms are inserted with line voltage and shunt field remaining constant.

20. What would be the no-load speeds for the motor of Prob. 19 assuming speed equals 1190 and I_a equals 2 amp for zero value of R_x? Assume I_a equals 2 amp for all values of R_x.

21. An adjustable-speed shunt motor has a full-load and full-field speed of 600 rpm. What will be its full-load speed if the resistance R_f in its field circuit be increased so as to change the field flux to values of 75, 50, 37½, and 25 per cent?

22. How many running speeds could be obtained with a 220/110-volt, three-wire system of supply and a 220-volt motor having two 220-volt armature windings and two commutators, without resorting to field-resistance control? Give connection diagrams.

23. A certain shunt motor has the following constants: volts, 230; full-load armature current, 37 amp; armature resistance, 0.22 ohm; shunt-field resistance, 90 ohms; armature demagnetizing factor,* 0.006 (assumed constant); no-load armature current, 2.5 amp; magnetization curve at 500 rpm is the 100 per cent speed curve (descending branch) of the chart on page 131. With a line voltage of 230 volts and a field current of 2.5 amp, the motor has a no-load speed of 500 rpm. There are 1000 turns per pole.

a. What resistance should be inserted in series with the shunt field to raise the no-load speed to 1500 rpm?

b. If the armature current is 50 amp, line volts, 230, and the shunt-field current 2 amp, what will be the motor speed?

c. What will be the speed of this motor with a line voltage of 190, a field current of 2.1, and a load current of 40 amp? (Use the fundamental motor speed equation for the solution of this problem.)

---

* The armature demagnetizing factor is that factor which multiplied by the armature current gives the number of amp by which the effective field current is reduced due to armature demagnetization (that is, for a no-load field current of 2.0 amp, an armature current of 100 amp, and an armature demagnetizing factor of 0.006, the effective field current would be 2.0 − 0.006 × 100 = 1.4 amp).

CHAPTER XI

The Three-Wire Distribution System

Edison Three-Wire Distribution System. The Edison three-wire distribution system is a constant potential system in which the voltage between the two outside conductors is twice the voltage between the neutral and either outside wire. This system was first suggested and applied by Thomas A. Edison at the time of his invention of the incandescent lamp in 1879.

As applied today for both direct-current and alternating-current distribution, this system uses voltages of 220/110, 230/115, 240/120, and 250/125. The important advantages which have contributed to the widespread adoption of this system will be treated in the following paragraphs.

The Edison three-wire system represents a saving in the weight of copper required for the distribution of electrical energy for light and power. If the same amount of power is to be transmitted by two wires at a voltage of E_1 or E_2 with corresponding currents of I_1 and I_2, it will follow that $E_1I_1 = E_2I_2$. If the power lost in the line is to be the same fraction (p) of the total in either case, then

$$pE_1I_1 = pE_2I_2$$

whence
$$\frac{pE_1}{pE_2} = \frac{I_2}{I_1} = \frac{E_1}{E_2}.$$

Now, if the resistances of the transmission line are to be r_1 and r_2, then for equal power loss in the line $I_1{}^2r_1 = I_2{}^2r_2$, and

$$\frac{r_1}{r_2} = \frac{I_2{}^2}{I_1{}^2}$$

and since the weight of a conductor is directly proportional to its cross-sectional area, which, in turn, is inversely proportional to the resistance,

$$\frac{W_2}{W_1} = \frac{A_2}{A_1} = \frac{r_1}{r_2} = \frac{I_2{}^2}{I_1{}^2}$$

and
$$\frac{W_2}{W_1} = \frac{E_1{}^2}{E_2{}^2}. \tag{1}$$

This proves that where *the same amount of power is to be transmitted a fixed distance with the same power loss, the weight of copper required is inversely pro-*

215

portional to the square of the voltage used. Applying this directly to a comparison between a 230-volt and a 115-volt distribution line, it follows that

$$\frac{W_{220}}{W_{110}} = \frac{\overline{115}^2}{\overline{230}^2} = \frac{1}{4}$$

or, that for the same loss *it requires only one-fourth as much copper to transmit power at 230 volts as at 115 volts.*

A large part of the electrical energy consumed in the home today is used for lighting. Incandescent lamps built for 115-volt service (1) cost less money, (2) are more durable, (3) have a longer life, and (4) are more efficient than those for 230-volt service. These advantages result from the fact that the 115-volt lamp has a shorter and heavier filament. This filament of larger cross section costs less for the drawing and mounting the tungsten wire, it gives a stronger and more durable lamp with a longer life, and it also has a higher efficiency because it can be operated at a higher temperature, thus giving out more lumens of light per unit of energy consumed. Similar points of advantage for 115-volt units apply to the heating elements of socket appliances, such as electric irons, toasters, and percolators, and to small motor-driven appliances. As a final advantage, 115-volt service is much safer than 230 volts where accidental contacts by human beings are possible.

It has been shown that the 230-volt line requires only one-fourth as much copper as a 115-volt line for the same power loss. This means that each conductor of the 230-volt system has only one-eighth of the total weight of copper required on the 115-volt system. It is frequently desirable for mechanical reasons that the conductors on the three-wire system be of the same size. Hence it follows that for this condition the three-wire system will require 3/8 or 37½ per cent as much copper. Where a large amount of power is to be transmitted in the downtown districts of the larger cities, it has been found that the neutral wire need be only one half the size of the outer ones. For such cases the three-wire system would require 31¼ per cent as much copper as a 115-volt, two-wire system. Thus it is evident that *the Edison three-wire system gives the advantage of a saving in the weight of copper required and at the same time permits the use of lamps and appliances of the most desirable and efficient types.*

The Edison three-wire system has an *inherent voltage regulation* which may be puzzling when considered for the first time. This regulation varies with the degree of unbalance of the system and can be explained most satisfactorily by examples. Part 1 of Fig. 1 shows the currents in a certain balanced three-wire system. For a resistance of 0.1 ohm per conductor, the voltage relations for this system will be as given in part 2 of Fig. 1. It will be noted that for this balanced condition (no current in the neutral wire) the voltages at the end of the line are each equal to 110 volts. Assuming, now, the partially unbalanced load condition of Fig. 1, part 3, for the same system, it is observed that there is no apparent drop in voltage between the conductors N and B (part 4), although they are each carrying a load of 25 amperes. An analysis of the condition will show that there has been a drop of 2.5 volts along conductor B which has been offset by a rise (with respect to line B) of 2.5 volts along N. The net result is in contradiction to the usual conception of a load on a line producing a lower potential at the loaded end. A condition for the maximum unbalance (all load on one side) is shown in Fig. 1, part 5. Here the voltage at the load

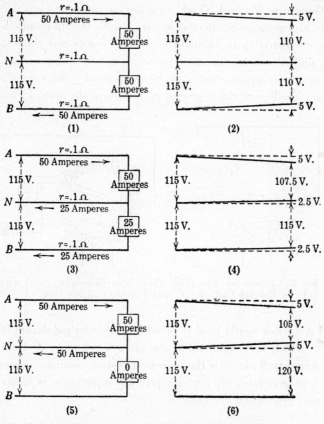

Fig. 1. Three-Wire System Voltage Diagrams.

end of line NB (shown by part 6) is actually 5 volts higher than at the supply end. In residences and factories using the three-wire system, it is not uncommon for an increase in load on one side of the three-wire system to cause the lights on the other side to burn brighter.

The three-wire system of power distribution may be energized by (1) connecting two generators in series, (2) by using a three-wire generator, or (3) by using a two-wire generator and a balancer set to subdivide the main generated voltage. A fourth method which is practically universal with the larger power companies is to use a rotary converter operating directly from a bank of power transformers with the neutral point brought out from the transformer bank. In principle this system is essentially the same as the three-wire generator.

The three-wire system of distribution is widely used in both direct-current and alternating-current systems. The theory developed for the weight of copper and the inherent regulation applies equally well to alternating current for all unity power factor loads.

The Two-Generator Method. The Edison three-wire system was first produced by using two generators connected in series with the midpoint between the generators connected to the neutral wire. Two compound generators direct-connected, and driven by the same prime mover, were generally used. Since they were acting as separate units, each gave a good voltage regulation at the powerhouse regardless of the degree of unbalance of the lines. In fact, an over-

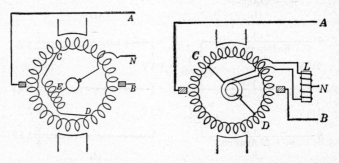

Fig. 2. Circuits for Two-Pole, Three-Wire Generator, (left) with Interior Balance Coil, (right) with Exterior Balance Coil.

compound generator would tend to offset the inherent regulation of the three-wire system which was explained in the preceding article. A disadvantage of this system for small plants is the increased cost of two machines over that of the three-wire generator so that its present application is limited to large direct-current generating stations.

The Three-Wire Generator. This generator employs a principle first suggested by Dobrowolsky and is illustrated in Fig. 2. This generator is a modified two-wire machine having taps on the armature 180 electrical degrees apart. These taps (C and D) are connected to the ends of a coil placed on an iron core. The mechanical and electrical midpoint (E) of this inductance coil is connected to the neutral wire of the three-wire system. Some manufacturers place the inductance coil on the rotating element of the machine (Fig. 2 left) and bring out the third wire from a single slip ring. Other manufacturers bring out the taps C and D through two slip rings and place a stationary inductance coil outside of the machine (Fig. 2 right).

The potential across the brushes will be constant (say 230 volts) as in any two-wire direct-current generator. But as the armature rotates, the potential between C and D will vary from $+230$ volts (CD horizontal) to zero (CD vertical), then to -230 volts (CD horizontal and reversed), and to zero (CD vertical again), and then back to $+230$ volts (first position). Thus there will be an alternating potential across points CD having a maximum voltage equal to the potential across the brushes. This alternating voltage would cause a large current to flow through an ordinary resistance (ohmic), but the inductance between C and D will "choke" the current down to a very small value. This inductance coil has a large number of turns of heavy copper wire wound on an iron core. When any difference of potential exists between C and D, it tends to send a current through the inductance coil. But as soon as any current starts to flow through the inductance coil, a flux is produced in the iron core and this rising flux links with the turns of the coil and produces a change in flux linkages; this produces an opposing emf ($e = - N \, d\phi/dt$), which restricts the flow of current. Since the potential across CD alternates very rapidly (40 to 80 times per second), only a small alternating current flows across CD.

A study of Fig. 2 will show that for any position of C and D the potential of E at the electrical and mechanical neutral will be midway between that of A and B, thus making the potential across $A N$ equal to the potential NB. If a load is placed on the line $A N$, current will flow out on the line A and return along the neutral wire to the point E. Here the current will divide with one half flowing through EC and the other half through ED. This division will take place naturally because the resistances of EC and ED are equal. The equal direct currents through CD are in opposite directions, and hence the magneto-motive forces (NI) which they produce are equal and opposite. Thus, since they are on the same iron core, the magnetic circuit is not saturated by the direct current. If the core were saturated, the coil would lose most of its self-induction and the alternating component of the current would demagnetize alternately one coil and the other, producing a large alternating potential on the neutral wire. Hence, on the one hand, the alternating emf between C and D will not cause any appreciable current through the inductance coil CD, while on the other hand the direct emf between A or B and N causes direct current to flow readily in the neutral through the two halves of the inductance coil.

It is general practice to assume that the neutral current shall not exceed 10 per cent of the full-load current in the outside mains though specifications may be made for any value up to 25 per cent. The neutral current flowing through the combined parallel resistance of EC and ED produces a fall of potential which results in an unbalance of the voltages across $A N$ and NB because such resistance has the same action as the resistance of the neutral wire. The voltage regulation of a three-wire generator shall be such that when operating at rated current (on the heavier loaded side) and voltage, and carrying in the neutral 10 per cent of its rated amperes, the resulting difference in voltage between the two sides of a circuit will not exceed 2 per cent of the

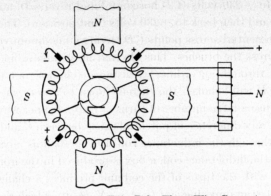

Fig. 3. Circuit for a Four-Pole, Three-Wire Generator
Having External Balance Coil.

normal rated voltage across the outside mains. A compound winding on a three-wire generator tends to raise the voltage across both sides of the lines regardless of the condition of unbalance, and hence will not help to balance the voltage drops due to unbalanced loads.

A schematic diagram for a multipolar three-wire generator is shown in Fig. 3. Points under like poles which should be at the same potential are connected to a common slip ring and thence to one side of the inductance coil. It is also possible to place several inductance coils on the armature and use only one slip ring, as in Fig. 4. Here it is necessary to have the two leads from each inductance coil connected to points just 1 pole pitch apart. The theory of operation of the multipolar machine follows that of the bipolar machine previously explained.

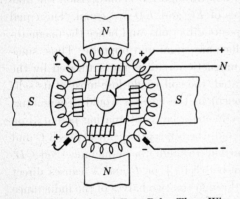

Fig. 4. Circuit for a Four-Pole, Three-Wire Generator Having Interior Balance Coils.

The three-wire generator is simple, is lower in first cost, and gives a higher over-all efficiency than any of the other systems in use. Three-wire generators are used on many ships and in a few industrial applications where three-wire direct current is needed.

The Three-Wire Balancer System. This system employs two shunt or two compound dynamos directly coupled mechanically and connected in series electrically across the main supply line. This set of two dynamos may be located in the powerhouse if the three-wire voltage is to be used near by, or it may be placed some distance away at the point where the three-wire system is needed. The latter location saves the cost of the neutral wire and the losses in it from the power plant to the point of distribution. The two dynamos used may have their shunt and series fields connected in a number of different ways, each giving a somewhat different inherent voltage regulation.

A balancer set may be formed by connecting two shunt machines in series, as shown in Fig. 5. If there is no load upon the three-wire system, the two shunt machines will operate as two motors in series running idle on the line. If the machines are identical and the field strength the same, the potentials V_1 and V_2 are equal, and, if we neglect the $R_a I_a$ drop in the armature, the generated or counter electromotive force E will be equal to V_1. Hence $E = V_1 = V_2 = V/2$.

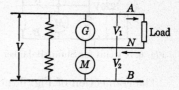

Fig. 5. Circuit for Shunt Balancer Set.

The ideal condition for the three-wire system is to have the same (balanced) loads across $A N$ and $N B$ at all times. With this condition, there is no current flowing in the neutral wire and no unbalance of voltages at the balancer set. In actual practice, the ideal condition rarely exists and there is a load on one side only, or a greater load on one side such as $A N$. In either case, the unbalanced load will be taken care of (as in Fig. 5) by one dynamo G acting as a generator and the other machine M acting as a motor to drive the generator. If the armature-copper loss and core losses be neglected, it may be assumed that the neutral current will divide, with one-half going up through the generator (and being furnished by it), and the other half passing through the lower machine M and driving it as a motor. Then the potentials across the line, assuming an armature resistance of R_a for each machine, will be:

$$V_1 = \frac{V}{2} - \frac{I_n}{2} R_a = \frac{V - I_n R_a}{2}$$

$$V_2 = \frac{V}{2} + \frac{I_n}{2} R_a = \frac{V + I_n R_a}{2}.$$

(2)

These general equations serve very well for studying the action of balancer systems, even though they are based upon assumptions which differ from the actual operating conditions. Due to the losses in the balancing machines, that part of the neutral current passing through the dynamo acting as a generator may vary from 37 to 47 per cent of the total, depending on the size of the balancer set (the average value is about 42 per cent).

The inherent voltage regulation of a balancer set depends primarily upon the connection of its fields to the system. For the connection in Fig. 5, the machine acting as a generator under unbalanced load will have the external characteristic of a separately excited shunt-type generator. Under load, the terminal voltage will fall, due to the $R_a I_a$ drop in the armature and due to the effect of armature reaction. The fields of both motor and generator will remain constant, so that the speed will tend to remain constant, and the generated voltage will not be affected by any change of the generator field.

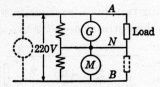

Fig. 6. Circuit for Shunt Balancer Set.

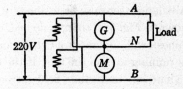

Fig. 7. Circuit for Shunt Balancer Set.

The connection of Fig. 6 (not practical in itself) is given to illustrate more clearly the regulation with other connections. The inherent regulation with this connection is very poor because of two factors. First, the external characteristic of the machine on the heavily loaded side of the line will follow that of a self-excited shunt generator wherein the reduced terminal voltage impressed across the shunt field acts to lower this terminal voltage. In the second place, the higher potential across the machine acting as a motor strengthens its field and tends to reduce its speed, which further lowers the terminal voltage of the generator over what it would be if the motor field remained constant.

The connection of Fig. 7 causes an action just the reverse of that explained in the preceding paragraph. With the interchange of the field connections, a slightly lowered voltage across the generator weakens the field across the motor, which in turn tends to increase the speed, and hence increases the generated voltage. In like manner, the lowered voltage across the generator means a higher voltage across the armature of the motor, which higher voltage is impressed across the generator field. Thus, as the load becomes unbalanced, the generator field becomes stronger and the speed of the set tends to rise. These factors cause this connection to be somewhat self-regulating and give much better results than the connections of Fig. 5 or Fig. 6.

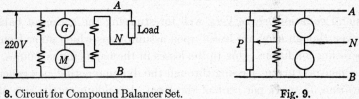

Fig. 8. Circuit for Compound Balancer Set.   **Fig. 9.**

The case just described requires some unbalance in voltages before the self-regulating action can take place. Another form of connection gives an automatic voltage regulation through the use of the unbalance of load currents. This connection, shown in Fig. 8, does not require a voltage unbalance for its action. Two compound dynamos are used having their series fields connected in series with the neutral wire. Each series field is connected so that it is cumulative in action when its machine is acting as a generator and differential in action when the machine is a motor. It should be noticed that any unbalanced current in the neutral must pass through both series fields and thus produces a double corrective effect. On the heavily loaded side of the line, the cumulative effect of the series field tends to boost the terminal voltage and thus counteract armature $R_a I_a$ drop and armature reaction, while on the motor side its differential action will tend to increase the motor speed and further help to raise the generator voltage. The magnitude of these corrective effects depends upon the number of turns on the series fields of the machines comprising the balancer set. It is obvious that if the number of series field turns is sufficiently large, the voltage on the heavily loaded side of the line may rise above the no-load voltage. This condition of voltage regulation would tend to offset the inherent voltage characteristic of the three-wire transmission line.

For experimental purposes, it may be desirable to control manually the voltages on the two sides of a three-wire system. This result may be accomplished with the balancer connection given in Fig. 9. Here a potential divider form of voltage control has been provided by means of which the voltage across the balancer fields can be controlled at will. This makes it possible to vary the potential from zero to 220 volts across either field, and this, in turn, will vary the armature generated voltage from zero to 220 volts. For any given rheostat setting, the field excitation is separate from the balancer armature so that the voltage regulation will be like that of a separately excited machine, and the machines will be stable in their operation for all rheostat settings.

Balancer sets are started by using a starting box as for a single motor. The two shunt fields and the two armatures in series are treated like the field and the armature of a single motor. However, for the connections as given in Figs. 6 and 7, it is absolutely necessary that the mid-point between the fields be disconnected from the neutral during the starting period. The same is true for the extreme settings of the rheostat in Fig. 9.

PROBLEMS

1. If No. 2 B. & S. gauge copper wire is required for satisfactory line regulation when supplying service to a distant customer at 115 volts, what size wire should be used for the same load at 230 volts? If 800 lb of copper were required in the first case, what would be the saving in the second case, assuming copper to cost 20 cents per pound?

2. What percentage of the weight of copper required to deliver power at a given loss at 220 volts will be required to deliver the same power with the same line loss at 2200 volts? 22,000 volts? 220,000 volts?

3. A household electric range is connected to a 220–110-volt, three-wire system with the surface cooking units (total 30 amp) on one side of the system and the oven (total 40 amp) on the other side. The range is connected by three No. 7 B. & S. gauge copper wires, 500 ft long, to the source. The housewife enters a service complaint stating that the surface units are "hotter" when both the oven and the surface units are on than when the surface units alone are on. Is she right? Calculate the probable voltages at the units in each case. Use 0.508 ohm per 1000 ft for resistance of No. 7 wire.

4. The powerhouse voltage on a three-wire system is held constant at 250–125 volts. The outside line conductors leading to a factory have a resistance of 0.025 ohm and the neutral 0.05 ohm. Determine the voltages at the factory for the following simultaneous loads:

SIDE A	SIDE B
500 amp	500 amp
500 "	400 "
500 "	250 "
0 "	300 "

5. Two identical flat-compound generators having a rating of 125 volts, 100 amp, 600 rpm, are direct-connected to furnish current to a three-wire system, each wire of which has a resistance (to load) of 0.05 ohm. Assuming a straight-line external characteristic, what will be the voltage at the generators and at the load at the time when *A* is carrying full load and *B* ¼ load? *A* ¾ load and *B* ¾ load? *B* full load, *A* zero load?

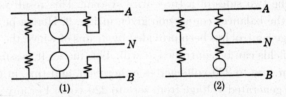

Fig. 10. Circuits for Compound Balancer Set.

6. A three-wire generator has an external inductance coil having a combined resistance of 0.2 ohm from end to end. For a given load, the terminal voltage across the outside lines is 230 volts. Neglecting armature resistance and reaction, what will be the voltage between each outside wire and the neutral when the neutral wire carries a current of 50 amp? What is the per cent change from no-load voltage?

7. Two identical shunt dynamos having a rating of 115 volts and 150 amp, are direct-connected to form a balancer set (Fig. 5). Each armature has a resistance of 0.2 ohm and each of the three wires of the distributing system has a resistance of 0.05 ohm. With a load of 150 amp on one side of the line and 50 amp on the other, calculate all voltages at the load and at the balancer set, assuming no rotational losses, 230 volts across the outside lines at the set, and balanced voltages at no load.

8. Give an analysis explaining what would happen if an attempt were made to start the balancer set of Fig. 6 by means of a starting box without disconnecting the mid-point between the shunt field from the neutral wire.

9. Compare the inherent regulation of the balancer-set connection of Fig. 10 (1) with that of Fig. 8.

10. Compare the performance of Fig. 10 (1) with Fig. 10 (2).

CHAPTER XII

Efficiency of Dynamos

Definitions of Efficiency. The efficiency of a direct-current commutating machine is the ratio of the useful power output to the total power input.* This leads to the simple algebraic relation

$$\text{Efficiency} = \frac{\text{output}}{\text{input}} \qquad (1)$$

in which both the output and the input must be expressed in the same units of power, as horsepower (746 watts) or kilowatts. In considering the efficiency of an electric motor, it is common to give its mechanical output in horsepower and its input in kilowatts. On the other hand, for a generator, the output is given in kilowatts and its input in mechanical horsepower. In each case, the difference between the output and the input is equal to the losses in the machine. And this leads to two other forms of the algebraic relation for efficiency:

$$\text{Efficiency} = \frac{\text{output}}{\text{output} + \text{losses}} = 1 - \frac{\text{losses}}{\text{output} + \text{losses}} \qquad (2)$$

$$\text{Efficiency} = \frac{\text{input} - \text{losses}}{\text{input}} = 1 - \frac{\text{losses}}{\text{input}} \qquad (3)$$

where the first equation is best adapted to the generator and the second to the motor. The last form of these equations is particularly convenient for accurate calculation using the slide rule.

The expressions given above for efficiency lead directly to two recognized methods of determining efficiency. These methods are as follows:

(a) *Efficiency by load test.*
(b) *Efficiency by determination of losses.*

The first method follows equation 1 and is applied to small machines and in special cases to large ones. Great care is required to obtain accurate results by this method. In this method the efficiency may be determined by simultaneous measurements of the input and output. Preferably the mechanical input or output is measured by a dynamometer, and the electrical output

* ASA C-50.

or input by carefully calibrated electrical instruments. As an alternate to this procedure, the total losses may be measured directly by suitably enclosing the machine and measuring the total quantities and temperature rises of the cooling media for the machine and bearings.

The American Institute of Electrical Engineers recommends the second method (b) of determining efficiency, except in the case of small machines, for the three following reasons. First, it is impractical to measure the efficiency of large machines directly because of the difficulty of driving a large generator or loading a large motor. Second, a large amount of energy would be wasted in making the test. Third, most of the losses are accurately measurable and those to which conventional values are assigned can be so closely approximated that the percentage of error in the determined efficiency is small. The high efficiency generally attained in electrical machines renders an error in the measurement or estimation of one or more of the losses of much less effect on the efficiency as obtained by the conventional method than an error of like magnitude in the measurement of the total input and output. For example, suppose that the true efficiency of a machine is 90 per cent and that an error of 1 per cent is made in determining either the output or the input by the directly measured efficiency method. This 1 per cent error would produce an error in the computed efficiency of approximately 1 per cent. On the other hand, if an error of 1 per cent were made in determining the total of the losses of this machine, the error in the computed efficiency would be 1 per cent of 10 per cent (losses) or only 0.1 per cent.

In the case of a small machine, the losses themselves constitute from 20 to 50 per cent of the total input of the machine. Hence, with the same error in determining these losses, computing the efficiency by the conventional method will result in a larger percentage of error than in the case of a large machine. This fact coupled with the ease and speed of a direct determination of efficiency of a small machine accounts for the general use of the direct method for small machines.

Losses in Direct-Current Commutating Machines. The calculation of the efficiency of a d-c machine by the method of losses requires a determination of such losses under load. The individual losses may be classified and listed as follows:

I. Electrical losses
    1. Ohmic losses
        a. I^2R_f loss in shunt field winding
        b. I^2R_a loss in armature windings
        c. I^2R_s loss in series field windings (and shunts if any)
        d. I^2R_{rheo} loss in rheostat (not chargeable to machine efficiency)
    2. Brush contact loss in brushes and contacts (brush voltage drop times armature current)

II. Rotational losses
  1. Mechanical
     a. Friction and windage
     b. Brush friction
  2. Core loss (iron loss)
     a. Hysteresis and eddy current
  3. Ventilating loss
     (Power input to any ventilating system for cooling machine)
  4. Stray-load loss
     (Miscellaneous load losses not covered above)

The I^2R or Ohmic Losses. These are based upon the current and the measured resistance corrected to 75 C. Resistances are corrected to 75 C because that is the average operating temperature for machines in service. The actual temperature of any winding varies with the cooling medium temperature and the load (See page 259). The armature loss is the current squared times the resistance of the armature at 75 C. For the series field, interpole field, and compensating winding, the copper loss is the resistance of the winding combined with any shunt around that winding at 75 C times the square of the current through the combined circuit. In like manner, the I^2R_f loss for the shunt field is its current squared times its resistance corrected to 75 C. The I^2R_{rheo} loss in the field rheostat is no longer included as a part of the machine losses but is chargeable to the loss of the plant or system in which the d-c machine is used.* A convenient way of correcting the resistances of copper circuits to a temperature of 75 C consists in the use of the following relation from equation 38, page 364:

$$\frac{R_{75°C}}{R_{initial}} = \frac{234.5 + 75}{234.5 + t_{initial}} = \frac{309.5}{234.5 + t_{initial}}$$

and
$$R_{75°C} = R_{initial} \frac{309.5}{234.5 + t_{initial}}. \tag{4}$$

Bearing-Friction and Windage Losses. These are two mechanical losses which are generally grouped together because of the difficulty in separating them. Theoretically, it would be possible to separate these losses by testing a machine in air and then in a vacuum at the same speed. Bearing friction depends upon the viscosity of the lubricant, the area of the rubbing surfaces, and the rubbing velocity. It is independent of bearing pressure as affected by the load on the machine so long as a film of oil is maintained between the journal and bearing. The latter statement follows from the fact that for fluid and gaseous friction, the resisting force is independent of the pressure between the surfaces in contact (in contrast to frictional resistance in solids). Windage loss depends upon the form of the moving surfaces and will increase with some power of the speed. For smooth-cored nonventilated types of armatures having peripheral

---

* ASA Standard C-50.

velocities of less than 6000 feet per minute, it has a very small value. Thus the combined bearing friction and windage is independent of the load (unless the speed changes with load) and is constant for a given speed. It is determined by driving the machine under test from an independent motor, the output of which shall be suitably determined. The machine under test shall have its brushes removed and shall not be excited. The differences between the *output* of the motor in this test and that when running idle represents the bearing friction and windage of the machine under test.

Brush-Friction Loss. This is a mechanical loss which can be separated from other losses. This loss is directly proportional to the coefficient of friction between the brush and the copper commutator, to the brush pressure, to the area of contact, and to the rubbing velocity. The coefficient of friction will vary with the polish of the bearing surface of the brushes, with the brush temperature, and with the velocity. The brush pressure may change with time. Hence the brush-friction loss may change slightly with the use of the machine and is properly classed as only approximately measurable or determinable.

The standardization rules of the AIEE give two methods of determining the brush-friction loss.

a. Drive the machine from an independent motor, the output of which shall be suitably determined. The brushes shall be in contact with the commutator, but the machine shall not be excited. The difference between the output of the motor in this test and that in the test previously given for bearing friction and windage is to be taken as the brush-friction loss. The surfaces of the commutator and brushes should be smooth and polished from running when this test is made.

b. Experience has shown that wide variations are obtained between tests of brush friction made at the factory and values obtained later in service after the commutator and brushes have received the smooth surfaces that come after continued operation. Conventional values of brush friction, representing average values of many tests, shall be used as follows:

	WATTS PER SQUARE INCH OF BRUSH CONTACT SURFACE PER 1000 FEET PER MINUTE PERIPHERAL SPEED
Carbon and graphite brushes	8.0 watts
Metal graphite brushes	5.0 watts

In the event that these conventional values are questioned in any case, the brush friction shall be measured as in *a* above.

The table under *b* would be applied as follows. Assume a machine having six sets of carbon brushes of four brushes per set, a commutator diameter of 12 inches, and a speed of 640 rpm. If the brushes are $\frac{1}{2}$ inch $\times$ 1 inch, the total area of brushes will be $6 \times 4 \times \frac{1}{2} = 12$ square inches, and the brush-friction loss would be $12 \times 8 = 96$ watts for a peripheral velocity of 1000 feet per minute. However, the actual peripheral velocity is $(12/12)\pi \times 640 = 2010$ feet per minute. Hence the brush-friction loss will be approximately twice that calculated above, or $2 \times 96 = 192$ watts.

Core Losses or Iron Losses. These are the hysteresis losses and the eddy-current losses in all parts of the magnetic circuit.

The flux in any portion of a direct-current dynamo armature passes through one complete magnetic cycle each time the armature moves through the angle covered by two magnetic poles. This hysteresis cycle is *not* represented by the hysteresis loop (curve) resulting from the experimental determination of the hysteresis loop of a machine, but the correct picture is obtained by thinking of the hysteresis loop in individual sections in the armature core. Thus, in Fig. 1 consider a small section of iron in the teeth in position a. The state of the flux in its hysteresis loop may be represented by the cross. When this same section of iron has traveled to position a', the direction of the flux through it has reversed and this iron has gone through one half of the hysteresis loop to a new point x.

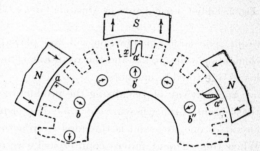

Fig. 1. Hysteresis Losses in Teeth and Armature Core.

Later at position a'', the flux has returned to its original direction and value. Thus, in passing a pair of poles, the iron in the teeth has been carried through a complete hysteresis loop and has undergone an energy loss which is proportional to the area of its hysteresis loop (page 381). In a similar manner, the change in the direction of the flux in the armature yoke is illustrated in the circles at b, b', and b'' in Fig. 1. Here the flux does not pass through a regular hysteresis loop as in the teeth by changing from a maximum value in one direction to zero and then to a maximum in the other direction, but rotates in the counterclockwise direction and changes in magnitude as the section under consideration moves from position b through b' to b''. This rotation of the flux and change in magnitude will cause the iron in the armature yoke to experience a hysteresis loss. The complete hysteresis loss in the armature is the summation of the losses in the individual sections.

The hysteresis loss in the teeth is represented by the following equation:

$$\text{Hysteresis loss} = K_h f V B^{1.6} \text{ watts.} \quad \text{[64, page 381, Appendix.]}$$

The production of eddy currents in the iron core of the armature can be visualized from Fig. 2. This figure assumes that the armature core is solid (not laminated) and that it is revolving counterclockwise within a bipolar field structure as shown. First, consider the elements of this armature core, such as the dotted lines *mn* and *qp*, as moving (cutting) through a stationary field of

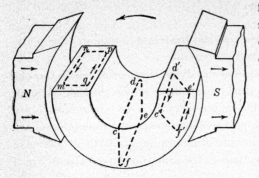

flux. There will be induced along *mn* an emf in the direction indicated. A smaller emf will be induced along the parallel line *qp* in the same direction, but since *mn* moves at a much higher velocity and cuts more flux, the emf induced will be much greater and a current will flow counterclockwise along the path *mqpn*. Since the resistance of this path is very low, a relatively large current will

Fig. 2. Eddy-Current Losses in Armature Core.

result. The same phenomenon will take place for an infinite number of other elements parallel to *mn* and the resultant sum of I^2R losses will be the energy losses due to eddy currents.

Another way of visualizing the production of eddy currents is to consider the element of the armature core *cdef*. This element constitutes a closed electric circuit of one turn and is threaded by practically one half the flux per pole. When this element moves counterclockwise one-half pole pitch (90° in this case), the flux threading it will have become zero. This change in flux linkages will induce an emf in the direction shown in the mid-position *d'c'f'e'*, and this emf will cause a circulating current to flow around the path *f'e'd'c'*. An infinite number of other paths could be taken approximately parallel to *cdef* and the same phenomenon noted in each. The summation of the I^2R loss in all of these circuits will represent the eddy-current loss in the armature.

The eddy-current loss may be reduced by constructing the armature of thin sections (laminations) cut by planes perpendicular to the shaft (page 382). This effect is shown in Fig. 3 where the armature of Fig. 2 has been divided into three sections. Here an emf will be generated in the element *mn* as before but since *mn* is only one third as long, the generated emf will be only one third as great. The axial length of the eddy-current path will be reduced to one third but

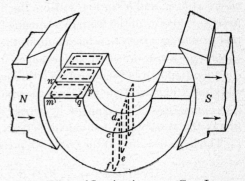

Fig. 3. Effect of Lamination upon Core Losses.

the radial length remains the same as before. Hence the ratio of e/r will be reduced and this reduction will increase rapidly in magnitude as the axial length or thickness of the sections is decreased. The eddy-current energy loss I^2R decreases more rapidly since the current (I) term enters the expression as the second power (square). In like manner, one can view the new element *cdef* (Fig. 3) and note that the area has been reduced to one third, and hence the change in flux linkages as it moves 90 degrees ahead is only one third its previous value.

Eddy-current losses are always reduced by subdividing or laminating the iron parallel to the direction of the magnetic field and along the plane of relative motion.

Eddy-current loss may be expressed by

$$\text{Eddy-current loss} = K_1 V f^2 t^2 B_m^2 \qquad \text{[65, Appendix]}$$

and it is important to note that the eddy-current loss varies as the square of the flux density, the frequency, and the thickness of the laminations.

In addition to the iron losses in the armature, there are others in the pole face. These are due to the difference between the reluctance in the air gap opposite the slots and opposite the teeth. Thus the flux will be highly concentrated or bunched opposite the teeth. This causes waves of flux to move across the face of the pole and produce both hysteresis and eddy-current losses therein. Figure 4 illustrates how this is done through the use of an armature having only one tooth. The wave of flux under the tooth will cause a change in flux density at the pole face. While the flux will never reverse in direction or fall to zero, it will change continually

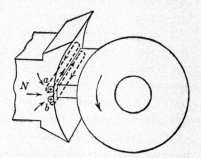

Fig. 4. Eddy-Current Losses in a Pole Face.

in value so that the iron in the pole face will pass through a small hysteresis loop and produce a small energy loss. However, on modern machines properly designed and having laminated pole faces, the losses due to eddy currents and hysteresis in the pole faces are very small and can generally be considered to be negligible.

The eddy-current loss in the pole face may be pictured by considering the cylindrical elements a and b in the pole face parallel to the shaft and opposite the tooth of Fig. 4. As the tooth moves downward, it is accompanied by a wave of flux which cuts these elements and induces an emf in each element and causes eddy currents to flow in the direction indicated. With all teeth present on the armature, a similar phenomenon will take place at all points on the pole face. The frequency of the flux waves across a pole face is very high because it is determined by the number of teeth on the armature and not by the number of poles. This high frequency makes the hysteresis and eddy-current losses in the pole face much higher than for similar flux changes in the teeth.

The magnitude of these losses depends upon the relative width of the air gap and the slot. With a poorly designed machine having a very wide slot combined with a very short air gap, it is possible for the losses in the pole face to exceed all other core losses in the machine. However, on modern machines with laminated pole cores, the eddy-current loss in the pole face is very small.

If the pole arc* divided by slot pitch is not an integer, there is likely to be a pulsation of the field flux throughout the magnetic circuit. Thus, if the pole arc divided by the slot pitch is $12\frac{1}{2}$, at one instant there will be 12 teeth opposite a pole and a fraction of a second later there will be 13 teeth opposite the same pole. This change in the number of teeth opposite the pole will change the reluctance across the air gap and produce small pulsations of the flux throughout the magnetic circuit. These pulsations of flux produce hysteresis and eddy-current losses in all parts of the magnetic circuit and become a part of the iron losses in the machine.

In comparing hysteresis and eddy-current losses, it should be noted that the hysteresis loss depends upon the peak value of B, whereas the eddy-current loss depends both upon the peak value of B and the distribution of the flux.

Core loss is produced by the flux in the magnetic circuit and the magnitude of the loss is determined by the magnitude of the flux. The magnitude of the flux is measured by the internal or generated emf of the armature which is determined by the rated or other voltage at which the machine is to be operated. The internal emf is the terminal volts $+$ load IR drop for a generator and terminal volts $-$ load IR drop for a motor.

The AIEE Standardization rules provide for the determination of core loss by using an independent motor to drive the machine with all brushes in contact with the commutator and with the machine excited, so as to produce at the terminals a voltage corresponding to the calculated internal voltage for the load under consideration. The difference between the independent motor output obtained in this case and that obtained under a, page 228, shall be taken as the core loss.

The copper conductors on the armature are subject to flux changes much the same as the iron elements in the armature yoke and teeth. If the cross sections of the conductors are relatively large, eddy currents will be induced in these conductors by the flux changes, and the energy consumed by these eddy currents constitutes a part of the losses of the machine.

Brush-Contact Loss. This is an I^2R loss due to the effective resistance between the brushes and the commutator. This resistance, in turn, depends upon the condition of the brush-contact surface, upon the brush pressure, upon the current density at the contacts, upon the temperature of the brushes, and upon the rubbing velocity.

---

* More closely, the pole arc plus twice the air gap.

Figure 5, page 325 shows the *steady-state condition* existing between the voltage drop (from a brush to copper) and the current density. For this condition, the voltage drop across the brush contact rises quickly and approaches a constant value of about 1 volt. Thus the combined contact loss of a direct-current machine for both positive and negative brushes is about 2 volts times the current flowing in the armature.

$$\text{Brush-contact loss} = 2 \times I_a. \tag{5}$$

The AIEE Standardization Rules state that a total drop (at positive and negative brushes) of 2 volts shall be assumed as the standard drop in determining brush-contact loss for carbon and graphite brushes with pigtails (brush shunts) attached. A total drop of 3 volts shall be assumed where pigtails are not attached and for metal-graphite brushes with shunts attached use 0.5 volts.

Ventilation Loss. Some machines are designed to be cooled by forced circulation either by self-contained or external fans. The power required to circulate the air through the machine itself should be charged against the efficiency of the machine. There are certain exceptions in the application of the ventilating loss and the reader should refer to ASA Standard C-50 for specific applications.

Stray-Load Losses. These losses are caused by the *load* on the machine. They cannot be calculated or measured directly and hence they are termed **stray losses.** With a uniform distribution of flux in the air gap of a dynamo, there is a definite maximum value of flux density in each part of the circuit and a definite time of change of flux (frequency). But when a machine is loaded, the armature reaction distorts the flux in the air gap and increases the flux density under one of the tips of each pole. Since hysteresis loss varies as the 1.6 power of the maximum flux density, this increase of flux density will increase the hysteresis loss in the teeth and to a lesser extent in the pole faces. The flux density being increased at one half of the pole tips causes the change of flux here to take place more quickly, so that the eddy-current losses in the teeth and pole face will also increase. The decreased losses under the other pole tips (proportional to 1.6 power) fail to compensate for the increase explained. Thus there is a considerably increased iron loss due to the flux distortion resulting from armature reaction.

Differences in flux density within the cross section of the armature conductors under load may be due to two causes, as follows:

a. The load current in each armature inductor sets up a magnetic field surrounding itself. This transverse flux cuts the inductor and other near-by inductors during commutation and will induce eddy currents in them.

b. Armature reactions produce high flux densities in some parts of the armature so that the iron in some teeth becomes saturated. This tooth saturation increases the flux passing through the slot where the inductors are located. Changes in flux density due to both of these causes increase the eddy-current losses in the copper and thus contribute to the stray-load losses.

Brushes usually cover three or more commutator segments, and the coils connected to these segments are short-circuited through the brush contact. Differences in potential induced in these coils due to flux distortions will cause a circulating short-circuit current and an I^2R loss which becomes a part of the stray-load losses. It is customary to assume a value for the *stray-load loss of 1 per cent of the output,* in accordance with ASA Standard C-50.

Efficiency of Conversion, Mechanical Efficiency, and Electrical Efficiency. The general definition of efficiency applied to an electrical machine was given by Equation 1. Efficiency as thus defined may be analyzed into two components based on the two classes of losses given in the preceding paragraph. One component of efficiency covers the conversion of electric power to mechanical power, or vice versa, and is called the **efficiency of conversion.** The other component of efficiency is the ratio of the power (electrical or mechanical) output to the power (electrical or mechanical) developed by conversion. To define these components by means of an example, suppose a direct-current motor has a full-load input of 100 kilowatts of electrical power. At full load, let it be assumed that there will be consumed in the machine 5 kilowatts in electrical losses. The motor converts the electrical power into mechanical power but the maximum electrical power converted is the input minus the electrical losses, $100 - 5$, or 95 kilowatts. Thus the *efficiency of conversion* in this case is the ratio of the total mechanical power developed to the total electrical power input, or 95 per cent, and it is identical with the electrical efficiency. Again, the actual mechanical power output of this motor will not be 95 kilowatts because an additional 5 kilowatts (assumed) of power will be consumed in overcoming the rotational losses. This leaves an output of 90 kilowatts. Thus the *mechanical efficiency* for this machine is the ratio of actual mechanical power output to the total mechanical power developed, or 94.8 per cent.

For a motor,

Efficiency of conversion

$$= \frac{\text{mechanical power developed}}{\text{electrical power input}}$$

$$= \frac{\text{electrical input} - \text{electrical losses}}{\text{electrical input}} \tag{6}$$

and

Mechanical efficiency

$$= \frac{\text{mechanical power output}}{\text{mechanical power developed}}$$

$$= \frac{\text{mechanical power output}}{\text{mechanical power output} + \text{rotational losses}}. \tag{7}$$

In a similar way, assume that a generator has a full-load output of 100 kilowatts. This 100 kilowatts does not represent all of the mechanical power which has been converted into electrical power because there has been perhaps 6 kilowatts of converted power which has been consumed in electrical losses. Hence the electrical efficiency of this generator is $100/(100 + 6)$, or 94.4 per cent. The prime mover driving the generator has supplied 106 kilowatts of power plus the various rotational losses of the generator. If we assume these rotational losses to be 6 kilowatts, then the *mechanical efficiency* or the efficiency of conversion of this generator is $106/112$, or 94.7 per cent.

For a generator,

Electrical efficiency
$$= \frac{\text{electrical power output}}{\text{electrical power developed}}$$
$$= \frac{\text{electrical power output}}{\text{electrical power output} + \text{electrical losses}} \tag{8}$$

and

Efficiency of conversion
$$= \frac{\text{electrical power developed}}{\text{mechanical power input}}$$
$$= \frac{\text{electrical power output} + \text{electrical losses}}{\text{mechanical power input}}. \tag{9}$$

The over-all efficiency of a motor or generator is the product of the efficiency of conversion and the mechanical or electrical efficiency, as may be seen by multiplying equations 6 by 7, or 8 by 9.

The two components of efficiency just outlined are rather academic in concept and are not of much commercial importance.

Condition of Maximum Efficiency. The condition for maximum efficiency is important in the study of all electrical machines. We know that all losses may be classified as *constant* and *variable*. Let $K =$ the constant losses, $AI =$ the losses which vary directly with the armature current, and $BI^2 =$ the losses which vary as the square of the armature current. Then

$$\text{Efficiency (generator)} = \frac{\text{output}}{\text{output} + \text{losses}}$$
$$\eta = \frac{VI}{VI + K + AI^* + BI^{2*}}.$$

To obtain the maximum efficiency, take the derivative of the expression for efficiency with respect to the current (variable) and set it equal to zero. In the first place, we have

$$\frac{d\eta}{dI} = \frac{(VI + K + AI + BI^2)V - VI(V + A + 2BI)}{(VI + K + AI + BI^2)^2}.$$

* This is armature current and differs slightly from the load current used in the numerator VI. The error involved can be neglected in this development.

Equating to zero gives

$$VI + K + AI + BI^2 - VI - AI - 2BI^2 = 0$$
$$K - BI^2 = 0$$
$$K = BI^2. \tag{10}$$

Thus, for maximum efficiency, the constant losses in the direct-current machine should be equal to those losses which vary as the square of the armature current. Since those losses which vary as the first power of the current are small, it is customary to state that the condition for maximum efficiency is that the constant and variable losses be equal. This is a general law which applies equally well to alternating-current motors, generators, and transformers. The student should note that the efficiency of a machine usually does not vary greatly from the maximum value over a range of loads near the maximum point. Hence it is not too important to load a machine at exactly its maximum efficiency.

All-Day Efficiency. The *all-day efficiency* of a machine is the ratio of the *total energy output during a day to the total input* during that same day. Thus

$$\text{All-day efficiency} = \frac{\text{output}}{\text{output} + \text{constant losses} + \text{variable losses}}. \tag{11}$$

The load upon a machine operated continuously usually varies throughout the day. The efficiency is high when operating under full load, but it is low at light loads, and the all-day efficiency is some intermediate value of these various instantaneous efficiencies.

A direct-current generator has a rating of 100 kilowatts with constant losses of 6 kilowatts and variable losses of 6 kilowatts at full load and 1.5 kilowatts at one-half load. If the generator runs for 4 hours at full load and 12 hours at half load and 8 hours at no load, the all-day efficiency would be

$$\frac{4 \times 100 + 12 \times 50}{4 \times 100 + 12 \times 50 + 24 \times 6 + 4 \times 6 + 12 \times 1.5} \times 100 = 100 \frac{1000}{1186} = 86 \text{ per cent.}$$

It was proved in the preceding article that for maximum efficiency the constant losses should be equal to the variable losses. Hence it lies within the control of the designer to determine the load at which maximum efficiency shall occur. The usual practice provides for maximum efficiency at full load but the customers specifications may warrant a departure from this practice. It is not unusual for a machine to operate at a fraction of its full load for the major portion of its time of use and at full load for only a short time. Obviously, in such a case, the constant losses of the machine which are effective throughout the time of use would lower the all-day efficiency. For such a special case, the machine might be designed to have lower constant losses and higher variable losses at full load. Such a design would increase the all-day efficiency of the machine.

The term **all-day efficiency** may be applied to a group of generators in a power plant. The plant efficiency may be kept high by operating just enough generators to carry the load with each one operating at near full load and at high individual efficiency.

Calculation of the Conventional Efficiency of a Compound Motor. The following rating and test data are taken from the records of a large electrical manufacturer:

Rating 10-horsepower, 230-volt, 4 main poles, 2 interpoles, 1150 rpm, shunt-wound, direct-current motor:

Armature resistance at 25 C	0.238
Shunt-field resistance at 25 C	262.0
Series-field resistance at 25 C	0.0166
Commutating pole field resistance at 25°	0.0352

No load (running light) test data as follows:

Line volts	230.0
Armature amperes	1.7
Field amperes	0.725 at 75 C
Rpm	1301.0

The running light test is performed, as the name signifies, by operating the motor at no load with normal shunt-field current, taking readings of speed, line volts, armature amperes, and field amperes. The rated speed of 1150 is for full load, whereas the running light speed is 1301, the difference being due to the regulation of a compound motor.

In order to calculate the conventional efficiency of this motor, it will first be necessary to correct all resistances for a temperature of 75 C. Thus:

Arm. res. at 75 C = $0.238[309.5/(234.5 + 25)]$	0.2850 ohm
Series-field resistance at 75 C	0.0197
Commutating pole field resistance at 75 C	0.0419
Total series resistance bearing armature current at 75 C	0.3466
Shunt-field resistance at 75 C	312.0

For a compound motor operating at a constant impressed voltage, the core loss, windage, and brush friction will be approximately constant. It will be equal to the no-load armature input minus the variable losses.

Core loss, windage, and friction (stray power) = armature input − armature $I_a^2R_a$ − series field $I_a^2R_s$ − commutating pole field $I_a^2R_c$ = armature input − $I_a^2R_{a_0}$ (sum of series resistances).

Core loss, windage, and friction (stray-power loss) = $230 \times 1.7 - I_a^2R_{a_0}$*

$$= 391 - 1$$
$$= 390 \text{ watts.}$$

The shunt-field loss excluding the field rheostat will be a constant loss on a constant-voltage line equal to $I_f^2R_f$.

Shunt-field loss = $0.725^2 \times 312 = 164$ watts.

---

* Since the $I_a^2 R_{a_0}$ loss is very small and usually less than the approximation used, it is often omitted in calculating the stray-power loss.

In order to plot the efficiency curve of the machine throughout its load range, it is usually sufficient to calculate the efficiency at approximately 25, 50, 75, 100, and 125 per cent of full load. Since the current taken by the motor at full load is not known, it is necessary to assume an efficiency which experience suggests for a motor of the size under consideration. Assuming a full-load efficiency of 80 per cent, the approximate full-load current of the motor in question would be calculated as follows:

$$\text{Full-load current} = \frac{10 \times 746}{0.80 \times 230} = 40.5 \text{ amperes.}$$

In order to simplify calculations, a value of 40 amperes armature current will be used, thus giving values of 10, 20, 30, and 50 amperes for the other loads.

A convenient aid in calculating the efficiency lies in the use of a tabulation like that of Table I, which is largely self-explanatory.

$$\text{The horsepower developed} = \frac{\text{watts output}}{746}$$
$$= \frac{2\pi \text{ rpm} \times \text{torque}}{33,000}$$

and

$$\text{Torque} = \frac{\text{horsepower} \times 33,000}{2\pi \times \text{rpm}}.$$

The results of the calculations and the speed regulation taken from test data are plotted in Fig. 5. The actual current taken by the motor when de-

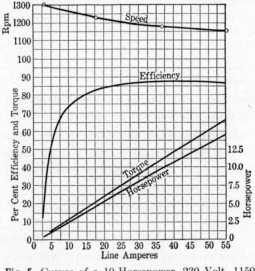

Fig. 5. Curves of a 10-Horsepower, 230 Volt, 1150 Rpm Motor.

veloping 10 horsepower can now be obtained from the curves or it can be calculated from the data given in the table. From Table I, the efficiency of the motor when developing 10.95 horsepower is 87.3 and when developing 8.22 horsepower is 86.9; hence the efficiency at 10 horsepower will be about the same as at 10.95 horsepower. Thus the full-load current should be

$$I_L = \frac{10 \times 746}{230 \times 0.872} = 37.2 \text{ amperes.}$$

The exact full-load efficiency could be obtained, if desired, by a calculation of the efficiency on the basis of a line current of 37.2 amperes. This method of calculating the full-load line current is essentially a method of successive approximation, which is the only practicable method to use before the motor is built.

TABLE I. EFFICIENCY OF A 10-HORSEPOWER, 230-VOLT, 1150-RPM COMPOUND MOTOR*

% FULL-LOAD CURRENT	25%	50%	75%	100%	125%
Armature current	10	20	30	40	50
Field current (shunt)	0.715	0.715	0.715	0.715	0.715
Line current	10.715	20.715	30.715	40.715	50.715
Armature I^2R_o loss	28	114	256.1	456	712
Series-field I^2R_s loss	2	8	18.0	31	49
Com. Fd. I^2R_c loss	4	17	38	67	105
Brush-contact loss ($2I_a$)	20	40	60	80	100
Shunt-field loss $I_f^2R_f$	164	164	164	164	164
Core loss and friction	390	390	390	390	390
Total losses	608	733	926	1188	1520
Input	2464	4760	7060	9360	11660
Output	1856	4027	6134	8172	10140
Efficiency	75.3	84.6	86.9	87.3	87.0
Horsepower	2.48	5.40	8.22	10.95	13.6
Torqu.[a]	10.4	23.2	36.3	49.0	61.5

* Stray load-loss is neglected.
[a] Use speed regulation curve of Fig. 5 for torque calculation.

Calculation of the Conventional Efficiency of a Compound Generator. The following rating and test data are taken from the files of a large electrical manufacturer:

Rating 100-kilowatts, 125-volts, 800-amperes, 6–6 poles, 870-rpm, compound generator.

Armature resistance at 25 C . . . . 0.002392 ohm
Shunt-field resistance at 25 C 20.2
Series-field resistance at 25 C 0.000823
Commutating-pole resistance at 25 C 0.000913

Results of tests show the brush friction to be 650 watts and the bearing friction and windage 1225 watts.

This machine was a part of a motor-generator set which was given a complete test for no-load saturation curve, core loss, voltage regulation, and speed regulation. The results of these tests are plotted in the curves of Fig. 6.

Correcting the armature and field resistance to 75 C gives:

Armature resistance at 75 C	0.002853 ohm
Series-field resistance at 75 C	0.000982
Commutating pole-field resistance at 75 C	0.001089
Combined armature-circuit resistance at 75 C	0.004924

The machine was connected long-shunt so the current through the armature, series field, and commutating pole field is equal to the line (load) current plus the shunt-field current. The curve shows that the shunt-field current was practically constant at 5.2 amperes from 25 to 125 per cent of full load.

The core loss is proportional to some power (1.6 to 2.0) of the flux entering the armature if the frequency (speed) is constant.

The flux entering the armature must increase with the load in order to give an increase of generated emf, to offset the $R_{a_0}I_a$ drop in the series circuit, to

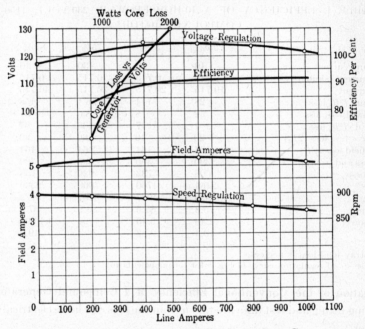

Fig. 6. Curves for a 100-Kilowatt, 125 Volt, 870 Rpm Generator.

offset the brush drop, and to produce a rise in terminal voltage if the generator is overcompounded. This rise in flux produces an increase in the core loss with load. The core loss for a given load may be obtained from a calculated core-loss curve or from core-loss test data. The core loss at full load was 2000 watts for the generator in this problem. The loss for other loads has been taken from the core-loss curve in Fig. 6. The generated emf is equal to the line volts plus the $R_{a_0}I_a$ drop in the armature-series circuit plus the brush drop (assumed 2 volts, constant). Hence we have

$$E = V + I_a(R_a + R_s + R_i) + 2.$$

The outline of the calculation for the efficiency of the generator is shown in Table II. The student should work out and check each step in these calculations. Note that stray load loss is neglected.

TABLE II. EFFICIENCY OF A 100-KW., 125-VOLT, 800-AMPERE, 6–6 POLE, 870-RPM COMPOUND GENERATOR

% FULL-LOAD CURRENT	25%	50%	75%	100%	125%
Line current	200	400	600	800	1000
Field current	5.2	5.2	5.2	5.2	5.2
Armature current	205.2	405.2	605.2	805.2	1005.2
Line volts	121	123	125	124	121
Generated emf	124	127	130	130	128
Armature I^2R_a	120				
Series field I^2R_s	41	810	1800	3190	4970
Com. Fd. I^2R_c	46				
Brush-contact loss $(2I_a)$	410	810	1210	1610	2010
Shunt-field loss $I_f^2R_f$	650	650	650	650	650
Core loss	1760	1880	2000	2000	1920
Brush friction	650	650	650	650	650
Bearing friction and windage	1225	1225	1225	1225	1225
Total losses	4902	6025	7535	9325	11425
Output	25000	50000	75000	100000	125000
Input	29902	56025	82535	109325	136425
Efficiency	83.6	89.2	90.9	91.5	91.6

Calculation of the Conventional Efficiency of a Series Motor. The following rating and test data are taken from the files of a large electrical manufacturer:

Rating 50-horsepower, 230-volts, 4–2 poles, 500-rpm, inclosed series motor.*

The designer knows from past experience that the efficiency of a motor of this type and size should be about 86 per cent. For this efficiency the full-load line current at rated voltage would be 188 amperes.

The test data are as follows:

Armature resistance at 75 C	0.0703 ohm
Series-field resistance at 75 C	0.0276
Com. pole-field resistance at 75 C	0.0137
Combined resistance	0.1116

SPEED–REGULATION TEST (SERIES MOTOR)

RPM	VOLTS	ARM. AMP.
445	230	282
475	"	235
515	"	188
565	"	141
665	"	94
940	"	47

* Four main poles and two interpoles.

CORE–LOSS TEST (SERIES MOTOR)

RPM	SERIES-FIELD AMP.	PER CENT FULL-LOAD AMP.	VOLTS ACROSS ARMATURE	ARM. AMP.	WATTS LOSS (CORE LOSS AND FRICTION)
445	282	150	197	8.6	1695
475	235	125	202	8.5	1720
515	188	100	210	8.2	1720
565	141	75	216	7.8	1685
665	94	50	229	7.4	1695
940	47	25	234	7.3	1710

It should be noted that the core-loss data were taken at the same speeds and for the same field currents as were used in the speed-regulation test. In the latter test, the series field was separately excited and the machine was operated at no load.

The tabulation for the calculation of the efficiency follows the outlines previously given and is covered in Table III. It should be noted that these computations assume that the core loss and friction are the same under load condition as determined from the no-load core-loss test. This assumption is in error since armature reactions in the series motor cause a considerable increase in the *actual* core loss above the no-load core loss. The AIEE Standards

TABLE III. EFFICIENCY OF A 50-HORSEPOWER, 230-VOLT, 188-AMPERE,
4–2 POLE, 500-RPM SERIES MOTOR

% FULL-LOAD CURRENT	25%	50%	75%	100%	125%	150%
Armature current	47	94	141	188	235	282
Line volts	230	230	230	230	230	230
Arm. $I_a^2 R_a$	155⎫					
Series field I^2R_s	61⎬	985	2220	3940	6160	8975
Com. pole-field I^2R_c	30⎭					
Brush-contact loss	94	188	282	376	470	564
Core loss						
Windage and bearing friction	1710	1695	1685	1720	1720	1695
Brush-friction loss						
Total losses	2050	2868	4187	6036	8350	11134
Input	10810	21610	32410	43240	54050	64800
Output	8760	18742	28223	37204	45700	53666
Efficiency	81	86.7	86.7	86.1	84.5	82.8
Horsepower	11.75	25.1	37.8	50.0	61.2	71.9
Torque	65.7	198	351	510	675	847

provide for this increase of core loss in series railway motors by calling it **stray-load loss** and giving it the following conventional values:

INPUT IN PER CENT OF 1-HOUR RATING	STRAY-LOAD LOSS AS PERCENT OF NO-LOAD CORE LOSS
200	65
150	45
100	30
75	25
50	23
25 and under	22

The test data and the calculated results are plotted in the curves of Fig. 7.

Economic Importance of Efficiency. In considering the subject of efficiency of an electrical machine, it is natural to assume that the most desirable machine is

the one having the highest efficiency. This assumption may be correct or it may be wrong, depending on the economic conditions involved.

A consumer uses an electrical motor for driving a machine in his shop. The total cost for driving this machine per year includes (1) the cost of electrical energy for driving the motor; (2) the interest, taxes, and depreciation on the motor; and, (3) any charges for repairs on the motor. Obviously, the best motor to use for this service would be that one which would give the lowest annual cost for all of the factors

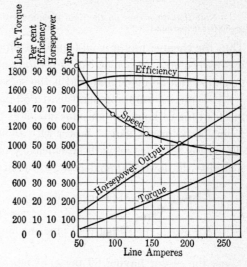

Fig. 7. Curves for a 50-Horsepower, 230 Volt, 500 Rpm Inclosed Series Motor.

involved. The motor with a higher efficiency will reduce the cost of the energy required and it may be a better constructed motor, and hence require less expenditure for repairs. However, this motor with higher efficiency will cost more to build, and hence will carry a higher charge for interest, taxes, and depreciation. If the saving in the cost of energy is greater than the increase in fixed charges, this motor with higher efficiency is more economical; but if the increase in fixed charges is greater than the saving in energy cost, then a less efficient and cheaper motor should be used for this service.

As an illustration of the above, let it be assumed that a ¼-horsepower, direct-current motor as a part of a domestic washing machine costs the customer $25 and has an efficiency of 40 per cent. A motor having double this efficiency (80 per cent) could be placed on this machine at a customer cost of $40. But would this change be advisable? Let it also be assumed that the machine is to be used 3 hours per week and for 52 weeks per year with an electric energy cost of 5 cents per kilowatt hour. The $25 motor will take 465 watts and cost per year for energy $3 \times 52 \times 0.465 \times 0.05 = \$3.63$. Likewise, the $40 motor will cost for energy $3 \times 52 \times 0.233 \times 0.05 = \$1.82$. Thus the higher efficiency motor would represent a saving of $\$3.63 - \$1.82 = \$1.81$ for energy.

However, the $40 motor represents an additional investment of $15 and the additional fixed charges on this investment might be calculated as follows:

Depreciation, 10 per cent on $15	$1.50
Interest, 3[a] per cent	.45
Taxes and insurance, 2 per cent	.30
TOTAL	$2.25

[a] Note that 3 per cent on the total is equivalent to the average of 6 per cent on the depreciated investment.

Thus the cheaper motor would show an annual saving of 44 cents. In addition, it is well to note *the commercial importance* of the fact that many more washing machines can be made and sold if the selling price is reduced by $15.00.

A municipal pumping plant uses a 50-horsepower motor which operates at full load for 24 hours per day for 365 days per year on a flat energy charge of 1 cent per kilowatt hour. A motor with an efficiency of 89 per cent can be purchased for $450 or one with an efficiency of 90 per cent for $600. Which one will give the lowest annual cost to the city?

$$\text{Kilowatts for 90 per cent efficient motor} = \frac{(50 \times 0.746)}{0.9} = 41.44$$

$$\text{Kilowatts for 89 per cent efficient motor} = \frac{(50 \times 0.746)}{0.89} = 41.91$$

Thus, the motor having 89 per cent efficiency will require an input of 0.47 kilowatt more than the other. This extra ½ kilowatt will cost annually

$$0.47 \times 24 \times 365 \times 0.01 = \$41.18.$$

The increased cost of the motor having 90 per cent efficiency is $150. The annual fixed charges on this investment for the city would be about 10 per cent of $150, or $15. Thus, the more efficient motor would represent an annual saving of ($41.18 − 15.00), or $26.18.

PROBLEMS

1. A 230-volt motor has a full-load rating of 10 hp. If the stray-power losses are 700 watts and the electrical losses 803 watts at full load, calculate the mechanical efficiency, the efficiency of conversion, and the overall efficiency.

2. A 30-kw, 250-volt shunt generator has the following losses at full load:

Windage and friction	550 watts
Brush friction	250 "
Core loss	715 "
Field $I_f{}^2R_f$ loss	205 "
Armature $I_a{}^2R_a$ loss	1500 "
Brush-contact loss	248 "

Calculate the electrical efficiency and the efficiency of conversion of this generator at full load. Use ASA Standard C-50 page 234 for stray load loss.

At what load will the efficiency of this machine be a maximum?

3. Develop the formula for the load at which the efficiency of a motor is maximum (similar to development of equation 10).

4. A 15-kw generator has constant losses of 1200 watts. At full load, the variable losses are 1200 watts; at 75 per cent, 650 watts; at 50 per cent load, 325 watts; at 25 per cent load, 100 watts. Calculate the all-day efficiency of this generator for the following conditions of loading: full load, 2 hours; 75 per cent load, 4 hours; 50 per cent load, 10 hours; 25 per cent load, 8 hours.

5. Assume that the machine in Prob. 4 has been redesigned so that the constant losses are 900 watts, the variable losses at 100 per cent load, 1600 watts; at 75 per cent load, 900 watts; at 50 per cent load, 400 watts: at 25 per cent, 100 watts. Calculate the all-day efficiency for the condition of loading in Prob. 4.

6. A generator delivers an output of 100 kw for 6 hours at an efficiency of 90 per cent; 60 kw for 10 hours at 86 per cent, and 12 kw for 8 hours at 30 per cent. What is the all-day efficiency of this generator? Use ASA C-50 for stray load loss.

7. A 25-hp, 240-volt, 6-pole, 750-rpm shunt motor has an armature resistance of 0.169 ohm at 25 C. If the full-load field current is 2.3 amp, the core losses 920 watts, and all frictional losses 390 watts, calculate the efficiency of the motor at 25, 50, 75, 100, and 125 per cent of the armature current, based on an assumption that the efficiency at full load is 85 per cent. Determine the proper current rating of the motor and the proper efficiency for this armature current.

8. Calculate the efficiency of the generator in Prob. 2 on the basis of the following: Terminal voltage held constant at 250 volts by variation of the field rheostat; core loss varies as the square of the internal or generated voltage. Use AIEE rule for brush drop and ASA C-50 for stray load loss.

$$R_a \text{ at } 75 \text{ C} = 0.1 \text{ ohm}$$
$$R_f \text{ at } 75 \text{ C} = 12.8 \text{ ohms}$$
$$I_f \text{ at } 25\% \text{ load} = 3.6 \text{ amp}$$
$$I_f \text{ at } 50\% \text{ load} = 3.75 \text{ amp}$$
$$I_f \text{ at } 75\% \text{ load} = 3.87 \text{ amp}$$
$$I_f \text{ at } 100\% \text{ load} = 4.0 \text{ amp}$$
$$I_f \text{ at } 125\% \text{ load} = 4.15 \text{ amp}$$

9. A 15-kw, 250-volt, flat-compound generator has the following resistances at 25 C: $R_a = 0.11$ ohm, $R_s = 0.01$ ohm; $R_c = 0.011$ ohm; $R_f = 55.0$ ohms; core loss at full load = 350 watts (varies as the square of the generated emf); brush friction = 140 watts; windage and bearing friction = 295 watts; I_f (hot) = 2.5 amp. Calculate efficiency at 25 per cent, 50 per cent, 75 per cent, and full load. Assume brush shunts, AIEE rule for brush loss and ASA C-50 for stray load loss.

10. A 50-kw, 600-volt, flat-compound generator runs at 600 rpm and has an armature resistance of 0.210 ohm, a series-field resistance of 0.022 ohm, an interpole-field resistance of 0.013 ohm, and shunt field 250 ohm at 25 C. At no load, the shunt-field current is 1.6 amp, frictional losses 900 watts, and the core loss 1615 watts. Calculate the efficiency of this generator at 25, 50, 75, 100, and 125 per cent load on the assumption that the core losses vary as the square of the generated emf. Assume long shunt and ASA C-50 for stray load loss.

11. The following data are taken upon a 25-hp series hoist motor:

SPEED–REGULATION TEST

VOLTS	ARMATURE AMPERES	RPM
240	141	900
240	118	970
240	94	1030
240	71	1130
240	48	1335
240	25	1890

CORE–LOSS TEST

VOLTS ACROSS ARMATURE	ARMATURE AMPERES	RPM	
198	4.5	900	
203	4.4	970	Series field
212	4.2	1030	amperes same
218	3.9	1130	as armature
231	3.7	1335	current above.
236	3.6	1890	

If the combined resistance of armature, series field, and interpole field is 0.24 ohm at 75 C, calculate the conventional efficiency of this motor for the load current at which test was made. Can you explain the relation of the voltages shown for the load and no-load tests? Neglect stray-load loss.

12. A 1000-kw generator is to be installed in a powerhouse and operated at full load for 12 hours out of each day and 360 days per year. The cost of placing electrical energy on the switchboard is ½ cent per kilowatt-hour for this plant. A generator with an efficiency of 92.3 per cent costs $500 more than one having an efficiency of 92.1 per cent. Which is the more economical to purchase, assuming unknown factors balanced? Depreciation rate 5 per cent; interest on money, 6 per cent; insurance, 1 per cent; taxes, 2 per cent.

13. Assume in Prob. 12 that machines were used 24 hours per day. Compare the machines as to their desirability.

CHAPTER XIII

Testing of Dynamos

Object of Tests. The objects of tests of electrical apparatus are (*a*) to detect defects in design, materials, and workmanship, and (*b*) to ascertain whether or not the machine meets the guarantees as to *speed or voltage regulation, temperature rise,* and *efficiency.*

Modern research is constantly producing new materials and new discoveries, which the designing engineer is embodying in new apparatus. Castings may contain blowholes not apparent on the exterior but which change their magnetic properties. Insulating materials may contain hidden defects which impair their dielectric strength. Much of the labor in electrical factories is on a piece-rate basis, so that the urge of earning higher compensation by faster work at times results in ill-fitting and improper assembly. Practically all electrical machines are guaranteed to operate under stated load conditions with a temperature rise not to exceed recognized safe standards. Likewise, the efficiency of the machine is guaranteed to meet certain specifications. In order to build the machine at a profit, the designing engineer will make the flux density in the magnetic circuit and the current density in the windings as high as possible and still expect to keep the machine within the limits set by the guarantees. Because of these things, a careful test of new machines is necessary before shipment is made from the factory. Also, it may be desirable to check the operation of machines which have been in use for some time.

General Preparation for Testing. A new machine coming from the assembly floor should be carefully checked and adjusted before it is operated for test. One of the most important requirements is that the proper grade and amount of *oil be placed in the bearings.* This is a general requirement which applies to all machines, both new and old.

New machines should be tested for *polarity* (that is, if one field pole is north, the next one should be south, and so on alternately around the field structure). This test should be made by passing a small fraction (say 5 per cent) of the normal current through the field winding and then testing each pole by means of a compass. If normal current be used, it is likely that the powerful magnetic fields would reverse the polarity of the compass, and hence give an erroneous test.

In order to secure good commutation and minimum brush losses, it is essential that the brushes fit the commutator and have a smooth surface. Brushes on new machines and on some old machines do not fulfill this requirement and must b ground or "sanded." Sanding of the brushes is accomplished by holding sandpaper on the commutator so as to fit the contour of the commutator while relative motion of the sand paper is produced either manually by sliding the sandpaper under the brushes, or mechanically by rotating the armature by some outside source of power. Sanding by hand is a tedious, dirty job, but must be resorted to on many large machines. After the brushes are sanded, the final polish is given them by rotating the machine for two or more hours with brushes down on the commutator.

Brushes must be placed in the correct electrical neutral position if good commutation is to be secured. The emf generated in an armature coil is a minimum when it is passing a line approximately midway between two adjacent main poles, but, due to the throw of the coil, the corresponding commutator bars are opposite the pole centers and the brushes should be set in this position before proceeding with the more accurate determination of the true neutral position. There are several methods for locating the neutral position, one of them being the "kick neutral" method.

The **kick neutral** method of determining the proper brush position is based on the principle that breaking the current flowing in the main field winding of

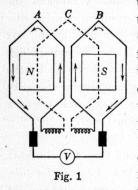

Fig. 1

the machine will induce a voltage in certain turns on the armature. Thus, in Fig. 1, let an armature coil (A) in the commutating zone be located above a north field pole in a symmetrical position so as to link all of the flux issuing from that pole. Then when the field current is broken, an emf will be induced in this coil in the direction shown. For another coil (B) similarly placed under an adjacent south pole, an equal emf (assuming same flux per pole) will be induced in the opposite direction to that of the first coil. For a coil (C) midway between the two, there will be no change in flux linkages when the field is broken, and hence no induced emf. For all coils located between coil A opposite the north pole and the coil C in the mid-position, there will be an emf of varying magnitude, but in the same direction. Likewise, those coils between the coil B opposite the south pole and the coil C in the mid-position will have induced emf's of similar magnitude but opposite in sign. Keeping in mind the effect of adjacent poles, it is apparent that if the terminals of a low-reading voltmeter (V) be connected to commutator bars approximately a pole pitch apart corresponding to conductors located midway between poles, no deflection will be obtained on breaking the field current. These commutator bars are in the correct neutral position, and the brushes should be set so that the center lines of their faces coincide with the positions thus determined.

The procedure in finding this location is as follows: With the machine at standstill, all its brushes are raised and one on each arm replaced by a special brush of the same cross section as the standard so that it fits the holder snugly. This special brush should be beveled practically to a knife edge parallel to the shaft and in the center of its face. It will therefore make a line contact with a commutator bar when in place. Leads from opposite brush arms are connected to a suitable voltmeter, having preferably a 0–1, 0–15-volt scale, so that the deflection may readily be adapted to the value obtained. The connection, however, must always be made to the higher scale first and only changed to the lower one when it is certain that the deflection will be within its range. The shunt-field circuit should be arranged for separate excitation and connected to any convenient source of direct-current power. For opening and closing the circuit, a knife switch with an auxiliary quick-break jaw should be used, if possible, so that the rate of breaking the circuit, and therefore the inductive effect, will then be the same for each trial. The rocker ring is shifted until opening or closing the circuit gives a zero or at least a minimum deflection.

Another method for locating the neutral consists in setting the brushes at such a position that when the machine is being operated as a motor, it runs under load at the *same speed* forward and backward (field reversed). This method is preferred in the case of small commutating pole machines.

Resistance Measurements. Exact resistance measurements are required on all parts of electric machines to check the design calculations, to detect faulty assembly, and to calculate the efficiency of the machine. The fall of potential method using a suitable voltmeter and ammeter and Ohm's law in the form $R = V/I$ may be used for the measurement of the higher resistances, such as that of the shunt field. When this method is used, three or more readings should be taken at a fraction of normal current value, and the average of these readings used. The calculation may be checked by a measurement on a Wheatstone bridge. The fall of potential method may be used satisfactorily for the measurement of the resistance of armatures, series fields, commutating fields (interpoles), and compensating fields of small machines. For such measurements instruments should be selected of such capacity that the deflections are reasonably large in order to reduce the error of observation. To avoid heating the winding appreciably and thus cause the resistance determinations to be inaccurate, it is well to limit the current to not more than 25 to 50 per cent of the rating of the winding. In using the voltmeter-ammeter method, care must be taken to avoid including the resistances of the leads and contacts. This can be done by carrying separate leads to the voltmeter from the machine terminals. The resistance of the armature is taken with all brushes on the commutator. These brushes should be properly sanded and worn in to normal operating condition. Current should be circulated through the armature and the potential drop should be measured across separate leads which contact points on the commutator midway underneath brushes on adjacent brush arms. For large-capacity machines which have very low resistances in armature and all series fields, a Kelvin bridge should be used for resistance measurements. The theory of the Kelvin bridge may be found in any text on electrical measurements. The temperature at which the resistance of any winding is measured should always be recorded at the time readings are taken.

Methods of Determining Losses. The losses of a direct-current commutating machine may be determined by the **running-light test** or by the **separate motor drive** (oftentimes called the **belted method**).

Two other special methods, one the retardation method adaptable to machines of large inertia such as water-wheel generators, and a second the calorimeter method suitable for high-speed machines such as turbine generators, will not be treated in this text. For information covering the latter methods, see ASA Standard C-50.

Running-Light Test. The running-light test is performed, as the name implies, by running the machine (motor or generator) as a motor at no load. If the machine operates at normal voltage and speed, the entire input to the machine will consist of the constant losses plus a small variable loss. The principal losses at no load are the core losses, bearing friction and windage, brush friction, field-copper losses, and a small I^2R or copper loss in the armature, series field, etc. Knowing the resistance of the armature series circuit, it is easy to subtract the series I^2R loss and obtain the constant losses. Thus, let us suppose that a 125-volt machine which is running light at normal voltage and speed takes a line current of 5 amperes, field current 1 ampere, and that the measured resistance of armature brushes and brush contact is 0.3 ohm. Then the input is $125 \times 5 = 625$ watts, and the field loss is $125 \times 1 = 125$ watts. The core loss and the friction losses are $625 - 125 - 4^2 \times 0.3 = 495.2$ watts. This method of determining losses is satisfactory where it is not desired to separate the core and friction losses. It is used chiefly in the cases of small machines where these losses may be considered constant at all loads and a single determination of their total is all that is necessary. Core and friction losses may be separated by retardation tests but the separate motor drive explained in the next paragraph is always to be preferred.

Separate Motor Drive. In this method the machine under test is separately excited and driven at its rated speed by a small shunt motor, preferably of the commutating-pole type. The shunt motor used to drive the machine under test should be of such a size that the friction losses to be measured are not less than $\frac{1}{4}$ load, preferably over $\frac{1}{2}$ load on the driving motor, and that the total losses at the maximum voltage do not exceed $1\frac{1}{4}$ load. This permits the motor to operate on the flat part of its efficiency curve so that, for ordinary tests, any change of its efficiency may be neglected. The machines may be direct-connected by a coupling or by a belt. The former is to be preferred since all losses due to a belt are charged to the machine under test. The driving motor should not operate at more than 15 per cent above its rated speed. If the belt connection is used, its losses should be reduced to a minimum by selecting an endless canvas belt* as small as possible, yet capable, without excessive tension, of transmitting the maximum power required without slipping.

The driving motor and the machine under test are connected as shown in Fig. 2. The machines should be permitted to run idle for some time until the brush and bearing friction have become constant. For all tests, hold the speed of the driving motor constant by varying the voltage impressed across the armature and hold the motor field current constant. This precaution tends to prevent any change in core losses of the driving motor. With the motor disconnected from the machine under test and running at the speed

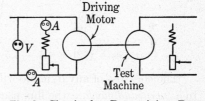

Fig. 2. Circuit for Determining Dynamo Losses by Separate Motor Drive.

corresponding to the full-load speed of machine being tested, take a reading of its armature and field amperes. This will give the data for the constant losses of the driving motor. Raise all brushes from the commutator, leave the field unexcited, and connect the machine under test to the driving motor. A second set of readings will give the data for the bearing friction and windage of the machine under test. Now with the brushes lowered on the commutator, a third set of readings of the motor input will give the data for the brush friction. Next, the field may be excited so as to give one-fifth normal voltage, then increased by steps up to 25 per cent above normal voltage. Readings taken at these points will give the data for the core loss.

The application of the method of separate motor drive will be illustrated by an example using a 10-horsepower, 230-volt motor under test, and a $1\frac{1}{2}$-horsepower, 120-volt shunt motor for the separate drive. When operating alone at normal speed, the reading for the driving motor (armature circuit 1 ohm) was

Volts	Armature Amperes	Field Amperes
120	1.0	0.25

giving as the constant losses of this motor exclusive of field loss

$$120 \times 1 - 1^2 \times 1 - 119 \text{ watts.}$$

* Do not use a laced belt.

The machine under test unexcited and with brushes lifted was connected to the driving motor with readings

Volts	Armature Amperes	Field Amperes
120	1.7	0.25

This gives the bearing friction and windage

$$= (120 \times 1.7 - \overline{1.7}^2 \times 1) - 119 = 82 \text{ watts.}$$

When the brushes are lowered and the field unexcited, the driving-motor readings are

Volts	Armature Amperes	Field Amperes
120	1.9	0.25

Brush-friction loss $= (120 \times 1.9 - \overline{1.9}^2 \times 1) - 119 - 82 = 23.4 \text{ watts.}$

With normal excitation on the field

Volts	Armature Amperes	Field Amperes
121	4.5	0.25

Core loss $= (121 \times 4.5 - \overline{4.5}^2 \times 1) - 119 - 82 - 23.4 = 300 \text{ watts.}$

The core loss of any dynamo will vary with the flux entering the armature. In a *compound machine* the flux usually rises with load due to the action of the series field. Hence it is customary to measure the core loss for several values of field excitation within the operating range of the machine. These values of core loss are usually plotted against values of generated voltage (no load). The curve gives the necessary core loss data for calculating the efficiency of the machine.

On account of the wide range of speeds inherent in *series motors*, it is impractical to measure their losses by separate drive as in other types of rotating apparatus. The standard method followed is to run the motor under load and determine its speed and input current for various loads (torques). With these data available, the field of the motor is *separately excited* so as to produce the normal field flux corresponding to the load currents previously determined. For each of these values of series-field current, a potential is impressed across the armature (motor running light) sufficient to operate the motor at the same speed as in the load test first made. Under these conditions, the input into the armature is equal to the sum of the core and friction losses (plus a negligible I^2R_a loss in the armature). If it is desired to separate these losses, the friction loss corresponding to any point may be determined by measuring the input to the motor when operating with normal connections at a voltage sufficiently low to give the speed required. This input gives approximately the correct friction loss because the core losses vary as some higher power (1.6 to 2.0) of the armature flux and the line current required to overcome no-load friction and windage loss is very small, so that the core loss produced is negligible. The core loss is evidently the difference between the sum of the core and friction losses as determined together, and the corresponding friction losses determined independently. However, this core loss is somewhat less than the actual core loss under load because the armature reactions distort the field flux and increase the core loss.

Methods of Loading Machines. In determining efficiency by the *directly measured* method, means must be provided for loading the machines. In the case of motors, this may be accomplished by means of the (*a*) prony brake, (*b*) electric dynamometer, or (*c*) calibrated generator.

The prony brake is a friction device with a lever arm which clamps on a water-cooled pulley as shown in Fig. 3. Readings are taken of the pull in pounds on the scale and the speed in rpm. The horsepower is calculated by the formula:

$$\text{Horsepower} = \frac{2\pi \times \text{length of arm} \times \text{pull in pounds} \times \text{rpm}}{33,000}.$$

The prony-brake method of loading may be used for testing small and fractional horsepower motors but it is not recommended for larger machines. The objections to this method are that it is rather difficult to get uniform friction and steady indications of the pull on the brake arm, and all of the output energy is transformed into heat and wasted.

The cord-and-pulley method is another form of brake friction load. A cord attached to a spring scale is wrapped loosely around the brake pulley (in rotation) to provide friction.

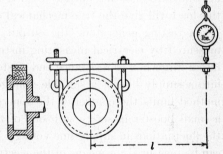

Fig. 3. Prony Brake for Testing Motors.

The magnitude of the load is controlled by the number of wrappings. To obtain accurate results, the following conditions must be fulfilled:

1. The cord should be in proper alignment (vertical) with the scales so that there is no error due to a nonrecording component of the force on the cord.

2. No force must be exerted on the free end of the cord unless the magnitude of the force is known and a correction made.

The electric dynamometer accomplishes the same result as the prony brake and in a similar way, with the advantages that the energy need not be wasted, the load is more uniform, and the load is more easily controlled. The electric dynamometer generally consists of a totally enclosed dynamo having an extended shaft which is supported by bearings in a cradle or yoke. Thus the dynamo is supported entirely by the yoke and is free to rock about the bearings in that cradle or yoke (see Fig. 4). A lever arm is fastened to the frame of the dynamo, and a scale is attached to this lever arm to measure the thrust of the counter torque on this lever arm. If this machine is loaded as a generator, the mechanical power input to the dynamometer is measured by the same formula as for the prony brake.

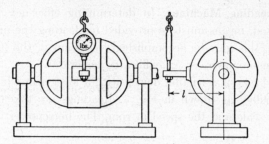

Fig. 4. Electric Dynamometer for Testing Motors.

A generator may be used to measure the mechanical output of a motor, provided that the efficiency of this generator has been carefully determined at all loads. The generator output will be accurately measured with electrical instruments, and this output divided by the efficiency of the generator for this load will give the true mechanical output of the motor under test.

In testing generators, the output can always be easily and accurately measured by electrical measuring instruments. The output can be delivered into a water box or resistance and wasted as heat, or it may be delivered back into a supply line of a suitable voltage and become useful. Since the latter method limits the control of the generator voltage, it is customary to insert a small booster in series with one of the generator leads to compensate for the fluctuations in supply-line voltage. The mechanical input to the generator can be measured by means of the electric dynamometer operated as a motor; or the mechanical input can be measured by using a calibrated motor for driving the generator.

Feed-Back Tests. The efficiency of all large machines and many of medium and small size may be determined by the method of measuring the losses. Yet, even for these machines, it is necessary to determine the speed regulation in the case of a motor or voltage regulation of a generator under load and to determine the actual temperature rise of the machine under continuous full-load operation. A direct method of load test always involves a waste of power, it may require special apparatus for loading, and the machine may be beyond the capacity of the power plant. Because of these objections to direct-load tests, special "feed-back" or "pump-back" tests have been evolved. In these tests, two like machines are directly coupled or belted together and arranged so that one acts as a motor and the other as a generator. Thus the one acting as the motor drives the generator mechanically and the output of the generator is fed back into the motor. The only power necessary for the test is that required to supply the losses in the two machines. These losses may be supplied either electrically or mechanically, or part of them electrically and the balance mechanically.

The Electrical-Loss-Supply Feed-Back Circuit (Kapp's Method). This circuit is commonly used by electrical manufacturers and is shown in Fig. 5. The voltage of the supply line should be the rated voltage of the machines. If it is not or if it varies widely, the correct voltage may be obtained by inserting a series booster (generator) at B. In order to operate the machines, machine M will be started from the supply line as a motor and brought up to normal speed. Next, the field of G is adjusted so that the generator builds up a voltage *equal* in magnitude and *opposed* (positive to positive) to the line voltage. Then the switch S may be closed, so that the machines are connected together electrically as well as mechanically. If machine M is to be operated as a motor,

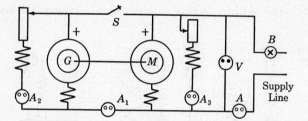

Fig. 5. Electrical-Loss-Supply Feed-Back Circuit.

its series field should be connected so that it will operate as a cumulative-compound motor.

Now, by the proper manipulation of the field rheostats of the machines, M may be made to act as a motor driving G as a generator, which, in turn, "pumps" or "feeds back" current to operate M. Thus, if the field of M is weakened, its counter emf will fall below the supply-line potential and current will flow through its armature in the direction from $+$ to $-$. This flow of current will develop an increased torque and the speed of M and G will rise. The increase of speed of G generates a higher emf in G, thus tending to supply the increased current drawn by M. If the field of G is strengthened, G will generate a higher emf and tend to deliver more current, but this added electrical load on G puts an added mechanical load on M, which, in turn, takes the additional current output of G. Thus any unbalance in the generated voltage of M and G causes a circulating current to flow between the two machines. This circulating current produces an additional $I^2 R_a$ loss in the armatures of the two machines and also an additional core loss due to armature reactions.

These additional losses plus the field I^2R_f losses and the windage and friction losses must be *supplied electrically* from the supply line. This fact gives rise to the term **electrical-loss-supply feed-back circuit.**

In this test, the input to the motor is the supply voltage V times the sum of the currents $A + A_1$. These can be adjusted to be the exact rated input to the motor and, with normal speed, this gives a correct full load on the motor. *Thus, with this method, the speed-regulation test, a commutation test, and a normal heat test of the motor can be made.*

Since all of the losses for the two machines are supplied electrically by the supply line, one might conclude that the efficiency of these like machines could be determined by assessing one half of the power supplied (losses) to each machine. Such a conclusion would be in error because (a) the field current, and hence the field copper loss of the two machines, is different; (b) the core loss varies with the generated emf and will be greater in the generator where the generated emf is $V + I_gR_a$ compared to $V - I_mR_a$ for the motor; and (c) the current in the armature of the motor is $A + A_1 - A_3$, which is larger than the generator current $(A_1 + A_2)$, so that the motor has larger armature copper losses. Also, if the machine acting as a motor is carrying full load, the other

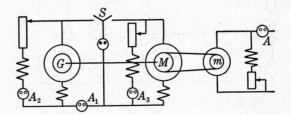

Fig. 6. Mechanical-Loss-Supply Feed-Back Circuit.

like machine will be underloaded because the motor is supplying the rotational losses for both machines. Thus this test is entirely unsuited to furnish any data for separating the losses of the machines or for determining the over-all efficiency of either machine.

The Mechanical-Loss-Supply Feed-Back Circuit (Hopkinson's Method). This circuit is sometimes used on the test floors of electrical manufacturers and is illustrated in Fig. 6. An auxiliary motor (m) is used to drive the machines at their normal rated speed and to supply mechanically the losses in the machines. For operation, the field of each machine is adjusted so that the machine builds up to rated voltage when driven at normal speed. With the voltages properly opposed, the switch S may be closed and the field rheostats adjusted so that G acting as a generator delivers its full rated armature current to motor M. The explanation of the production of this circulating load current is the same as has been given in the preceding article. *This test lends itself very* *well to the determination of the voltage regulation, the temperature rise, and the adjustment of the commutation of a generator* because the normal rating of speed, terminal voltage, and load current can be maintained without overloading the other like machine.

This test, like the previous one, cannot be used for a correct determination of the individual losses or of the efficiency of the machines. However, the *difference* in the magnitude of the individual losses in the two machines is less than in the former method. This follows because all mechanical losses (core loss and friction losses) are supplied directly and mechanically and not through a conversion of electrical to mechanical power in that machine which acts as a motor. The armature-copper losses are more nearly equal since the generator armature current $I_G = (A_1 + A_2)$ is now greater but more nearly equal to the motor armature current $I_M = (A_1 - A_3)$. The field-copper losses are greater in the generator but also differ by a smaller amount than in the first method because the rotational losses are supplied directly by the driving motor. Likewise, the core losses are greater in the machine acting as a generator because it has a stronger field.

This test is particularly suitable where the machine voltage differs from the test supply voltage.

The Blondel Opposition-Test Circuit. It has been shown that neither the electrical-loss-supply feed-back circuit nor the mechanical-loss-supply feed-back

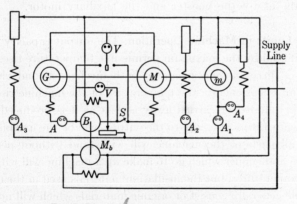

Fig. 7. Blondel Opposition-Test Circuit.

circuit will furnish data suitable for the accurate determination of individual dynamo losses and efficiency, or for the uniform loading of *both* machines for a heat test. A slight modification of the circuit of Fig. 6 will accomplish all of these things, and is even better than the conventional method of determining the efficiency because it takes into account the stray-load losses. This modified circuit suggested by Blondel is shown in Fig. 7. In this circuit, the shunt fields of both machines are separately excited and a booster (generator) B has been inserted in series with the armatures of the two machines under test.

To determine the individual losses of identical machines, M and G are brought up to normal speed with their fields not excited. The increased power taken by the auxiliary motor over its no-load input less its increased $I_a^2 R_a$ loss will represent the correct windage and friction of the two like machines. Next, with S still open, the fields of M and G are excited until they are generating normal no-load voltage. The no-load field-copper loss including field rheostat loss in each case will be the particular field current times the rated voltage of the machine. The no-load core loss of the two machines will be the increase in the output of the auxiliary motor over its previous output. A series of core-loss determinations for different values of field excitation can be made. Next, the switch S is closed, and the booster field regulated until the desired circu-lating current flows through the armatures of the two machines. The terminal voltage of the booster times the circulating current gives the combined arma-ture-copper losses of the two identical machines for that load. Thus, knowing the individual losses of the machines for any load, *the efficiency can be readily and correctly calculated.*

This circuit makes it possible to make a heat test with both machines op-erating under identical conditions of speed, generated emf, armature current, and field strength.

This circuit is rarely used in practice because of the additional complica-tion due to the use of the booster and the auxiliary motor.

Temperature Limits in Machine Operation. The output capacity of electrical machines is limited by the maximum permissible temperature rise. Since all of the losses of a direct-current machine, both mechanical and electrical, are transformed into heat energy, the temperature of the machine rises until this heat energy is radiated or carried away as fast as it is produced. Hence the limit to the temperature rise, and to the output, will be the maximum temper-ature which all parts of the machine will withstand without permanent in-jury. The iron and copper which go to make up a machine will withstand rela-tively high temperatures, but the insulation materials used in the construction of the machine generally consist of organic materials which will not withstand high temperatures.

Classes of Insulating Materials. The AIEE standardization rules list three classes of insulation materials used in the construction of direct-current ma-chines, as follows:

Class O insulation consists of cotton, silk, paper, and similar organic materials when neither impregnated nor immersed in oil.

Class A insulation consists of cotton, silk, paper, and similar organic materials when impregnated* or immersed in oil; also enamel as applied to conductors.

Class B insulation consists of inorganic materials such as mica and asbestos in built-up form combined with binding substances. If Class A material is used in small quantities in conjunction for structural purposes only, the combined material may be considered as Class B, provided the electrical and mechanical properties of the insulated winding are not impaired by the application of the temperature permitted for Class B material. (The word "impair" is here used in the sense of causing any change which could disqualify the insulating material for continuous service.) For example, micanite is constructed of small pieces of overlapping mica cemented together with shellac and built up to any desired thickness. Micanite is used for commutator-bar insulation and for slot insulation. In either application, a high temperature might destroy the shellac but the mica would be held in place mechanically so that its insulating properties would not be affected.

A fourth class of insulation *not* used in the construction of direct-current machines is Class C. It consists of inorganic materials, mica, asbestos, porcelain, etc.

The maximum ultimate temperature which Class O materials will withstand without being impaired is 90 C; for Class A it is 105 C; and for Class B it is about 125 C to 150 C.

A new insulation varnish known as **silicone** (silicon base) was developed during World War II. It will withstand very high temperatures and is likely to find application in commercial machines in the postwar era.

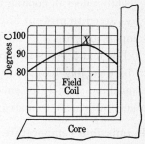

Fig. 8. Temperature Gradient in a Field Coil.

Hot-Spot Temperature. The maximum temperature within the field structure on a machine will probably occur at some point within the winding. Thus Fig. 8 shows a probable temperature gradient within the field coil on a direct-current machine. The lowest temperature occurs on the air-cooled surface where a thermometer would ordinarily be placed. The inside of the coil next to the core shows a somewhat higher temperature because the core is heated on four sides and must conduct the heat to the yoke or frame for dissipation. The highest temperature or "hot spot" of the winding occurs at the point X,

---

* Impregnated cotton, paper, or silk; an insulation is considered to be "impregnated" when a suitable substance replaces the air between its fibers, even if this substance does not completely fill the spaces between the insulated conductors. The impregnating substance, in order to be considered suitable, must have good insulating properties; must entirely cover the fibers and render them adherent to each other and to the conductor; must not produce interstices within itself as a consequence of evaporation of the solvent or through any other cause; must not flow during the operation of the machine at full working load or at the temperature limit specified; must not unduly deteriorate under prolonged action of heat.

and this is the limiting temperature for this part of the machine. In armatures, the hot spot will occur between the upper and lower coil edges in the slot.

Cooling Medium Temperature. As stated above, the output capacity is limited by the permissible temperature rise. Hence, with the upper temperature limit fixed as given above, the permissible temperature rise will be fixed by the temperature of the medium in which the machine operates. This reference temperature is called the **cooling medium temperature** and is defined in the AIEE Standards Rule 3000 as "the temperature of the air or water which, coming into contact with the heated parts of a machine, carries off their heat." A machine operating outdoors in the frigid zone might have a cooling medium temperature of 50° F (10 C), while if the same machine were to operate near the equator the maximum cooling medium temperature would probably be 120° F (49 C). Thus there exists a difference in permissible temperature rise of 39 C in these extremes of climate.

Differences in cooling medium temperature in different countries have always acted to prevent any international standardization covering permissible temperature rise.

For many years American electrical engineers have assumed a maximum or base cooling temperature of 40 C (104 F). This is the highest temperature a machine is likely to encounter when operating in the southern states or as a generator near to a steam engine or turbine.

Permissible Temperature Rise. Present-day direct-current machines use Class A insulation with some Class B. The Class A has a safe temperature limit of 105 C. Subtracting the base temperature of 40 C and allowing for a 15 C difference between the hot-spot temperature and the surface temperature, there remains a permissible temperature rise of 50 C for those parts of a machine using Class A insulation. For other classes of insulation and for constructions where the difference between hot-spot temperature and the measured surface is other than the 15 C assumed, the permissible temperature rise of exposed parts will vary from 50 C. Table I shown on the following page is taken from the American Standards Association bulletin ASA C-50. Reference to this table shows that the limiting temperature rise for the armature windings, field windings, and the iron parts of *totally inclosed* machines is higher than for open types. This is true since the reduction of the cooling effect of air ventilation in an inclosed machine brings all parts nearer to the same temperature and lowers the difference between the hot-spot temperature and the surface temperatures.

Methods of Measuring Temperature Rise. Three methods of temperature measurement are recognized as standard:

1. Direct measurement by thermometer.

TABLE I

THE TEMPERATURE RISES IN DEGREES CENTIGRADE IN THIS TABLE APPLY TO THE SEVERAL CLASSES OF MACHINES AS GIVEN AT HEADS OF THE RESPECTIVE COLUMNS	GENERATORS (INCLUDING THOSE FOR ELECTROLYTIC SERVICE) AND GENERAL-PURPOSE MOTORS[a]	TOTALLY ENCLOSED, AND TOTALLY ENCLOSED FAN-COOLED, MOTORS		GENERATORS HAVING A NOMINAL RATING		GENERATORS HAVING A 25 PER CENT OVERLOAD				MOTORS AND GENERATORS OTHER THAN COLUMNS 1 TO 9 INCLUSIVE	
				At end of 2-hr overload		At continuous load		At end of 2-hr overload			
Item	Col. 1 Class A insulation	Col. 2 Class A insulation	Col. 3 Class B insulation	Col. 4 Class A insulation	Col. 5 Class B insulation	Col. 6 Class A insulation	Col. 7 Class B insulation	Col. 8 Class A insulation	Col. 9 Class B insulation	Col. 10 Class A insulation	Col. 11 Class B insulation
1. Armature windings, wire field windings and all windings other than 2.	40	55	75	55	75	40	60	55	75	50	70
2. Single-layer field windings with exposed uninsulated surfaces and bare copper windings.	50	65	85	65	85	50	70	65	85	60	80
3. Cores and mechanical parts in contact with or adjacent to insulation.	40	65	85	55	75	40	60	55	75	50	70
4. Commutators and collector rings.[b]	55[c]	65	85	65	85	55	70	65	85	65	85
5. Miscellaneous parts (such as brush-holders, brushes, pole tips, etc.) may attain such temperatures as will not injure the machine in any respect.											

[a] These low temperature rises are provided to allow a greater factor of safety where the load conditions are unknown. No other temperature rating or temperature guarantee is given in conjunction with the general-purpose rating.

[b] The class of insulation refers to insulation affected by the heat from the commutator which insulation is employed in the construction of the commutator or is adjacent thereto.

[c] The limiting observable temperature rise for commutators of generators for electrolytic service shall be 50 C.

2. Temperature computed from change in resistance of the winding itself.

3. Temperature determined from embedded resistance coils or thermo-couples.

Mercury thermometers are generally used and should be placed so that the eye is higher than the bulb. In order that the surrounding air may not influence the reading of a thermometer,* the bulbs of thermometers used for taking temperature shall be covered by felt pads cemented to the machine, by oil putty, or by cotton waste. Dimensions of felt pad for use with large machines shall be $1\frac{1}{2}$ inches by 2 inches by $\frac{1}{8}$ inch thick. The use of smaller pads on smaller machines is permissible. The pad should be attached to the surface where the temperature is desired by means of a good grade of fish glue.

The average temperature rise of any part of a machine can be conveniently determined from its change in resistance.

Thus,
$$\frac{R_{\text{(at end of test)}}}{R_{\text{(at beginning)}}} = \frac{234.5 + t_{\text{(final)}}}{234.5 + t_{\text{(initial)}}}.$$

The average temperature rise determined from the change in resistance will be higher than the reading of the thermometer placed on the surface and lower than the hot-spot temperature.

The hot-spot temperature may be obtained by means of thermocouples or resistance units embedded within the winding of the coil. The thermocouple consists of a junction of two dissimilar pieces of metal which will produce a small emf approximately proportional to the difference in temperature be-tween the junction and the other ends of the pieces which are kept at a known temperature. This emf can be measured by a potentiometer and with the calibration of the thermocouple known, the temperature at the junction is known. A resistance coil having a high temperature coefficient will change its resistance directly with its temperature. This change of resistance may be measured by a Wheatstone bridge and the temperature calculated.

The first method of temperature measurement is the simplest and is gen-erally used in testing work. This method gives a continuous indication of the temperature of the machine part where it is located, but it cannot be applied to rotating parts of the machine while in motion and it does not indicate di-rectly the hot-spot temperatures. The information given by the thermometer reading is nearly always supplemented and checked by computations from the change of resistance of the electric circuits of the machine. These computations give average temperatures only and do not tell anything about the temperature of bearings, frame, etc.

Hot-spot temperature indications are especially valuable on large and costly machines which are operated close to their maximum capacity and maximum temperature for long periods of time. Thermocouples and other hot-

* ASA C-50.

spot indicators are embedded in those parts of the machine which are likely to be subject to a maximum high temperature which could cause damage to the machine. Hot-spot indicators are often associated with an alarm-signal system so as to notify station attendants when a dangerously high temperature is reached by any vital part of a machine.

Heat Tests. Heat tests or "heat runs" are made on all large, medium-sized, and nonstock machines produced in the factories. This test is to assure that the machine meets the guarantees covering temperature rise. The direct-current commutating pole machine is prepared for this test by placing mercury thermometers on the following parts: bearings, frame, one or two coils of the shunt, series, commutating, and compensating fields, and one terminal of the above mentioned fields. Three or four thermometers for giving the room (ambient) temperature are placed about 6 to 10 feet from the machine and are carefully protected from drafts. The cold resistance of all machine parts is carefully measured. The machine may be loaded by any one of the means explained on pages 253–256, but the usual way, where practical, is that of the electrical-loss-supply feed-back circuit. If the machine is intended for continuous operation, it is started up under full load and all thermometers read at periodic intervals of usually 1 hour. When the temperature of all parts ceases to rise for two consecutive readings, the machine is shut down and the hot resistance of all parts is measured. Immediately after the machine comes to rest, thermometers are placed on the armature (both teeth and slots) and the commutator to obtain the maximum temperature reached by these parts. The readings of the thermometers so placed must be taken very rapidly until the temperatures cease to rise because no additional heat is being produced inside the machine and all parts are cooling. The average temperature rise calculated from the hot and cold resistance is used to check the thermometer readings and the data of the two show how well the machine operates within its temperature guarantees.

Insulation Tests. Insulation tests are made to demonstrate the probable ability of the insulating medium to fulfill its functions during the continued commercial operation of the apparatus of which it is a part. This ability depends upon the character of the insulating material used, upon its mechanical application, and upon its condition as regards moisture, freedom from dust, or other foreign matter. Tests of insulation are made in two ways.

1. *Insulation resistance test (ohmic resistance to ground).*
2. *Dielectric test (high-potential test).*

The insulation resistance between the windings and frame may afford a useful indication whether or not a machine is in suitable condition for the application of the dielectric and other tests. It is likely to be the first test applied to a new machine, a new installation, or to a machine which has been standing idle for a period of time. A high value of insulation resistance is not by itself proof that the insulation does not have cracks or other faults which may cause breakdown upon application of voltage. Thus it is in no way a substitute for a dielectric test.

The insulation resistance is subject to wide variation with temperature, humidity, and cleanliness of the parts. When the insulation resistance of a machine falls, it can, in most cases of good design and where no defect exists, be brought up to a proper value by cleaning, with a suitable solvent, if necessary, and by drying.

It is difficult to set down any definite rule for the proper value of the insulation resistance of a machine since it varies greatly with the type, size, voltage rating, and kind of insulating material used. The following formula indicates the order of the value of insulation resistance which may be expected in a clean dry machine at approximately 75 C.

$$\text{Insulation resistance in megohms} = \frac{E}{P + 1000}$$

where
$$E = \text{rated terminal voltage}$$
$$P = \text{rated kilowatts}$$

Note: For fractional-horsepower motors, disregard the formula and use 1.0 megohm for the minimum value acceptable.

Insulation resistance may be measured by an instrument such as a megger, ohmmeter, megohmmeter, or by means of a high-voltage voltmeter. In applying the latter method a high-voltage direct-current voltmeter (500–750-volt range) and a 500-volt supply circuit are connected as shown in Fig. 9. Readings are taken with the switch in positions a and b,

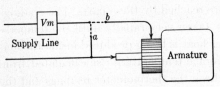

Fig. 9. Circuit for Measuring Insulation Resistance.

giving voltages V_a and V_b. In a series circuit the resistances are directly proportional to the voltage drop across them; hence

$$\text{Insulation resistance} = \frac{V_a - V_b}{V_b} R_{\text{(voltmeter)}} \tag{1}$$

from which the insulation resistance can be calculated.

The test for dielectric strength or the high potential test is a standard test for all kinds of electrical apparatus. The test voltage is applied successively between each electric circuit and all other electric circuits and metal parts grounded. The standard test voltage for all machines shall be an alternating voltage whose root-mean-square, or effective value, is twice the rated voltage of the machine, plus 1000 volts. An exception to this rule is made for machines for use on circuits of 25 volts or lower, such as electric machines used in automobiles and machines used in low-voltage battery circuits, where a test voltage of 500 volts shall be used.

Tests and Location of Grounds, Open Circuits, and Short Circuits. The common faults on direct-current machines are grounds, open circuits, and short circuits. A **ground** is a conductive connection between a coil and the frame or iron core of the machine. A ground is indicated by the insulation test just explained. The circuit of Fig. 9 with the switch in position b may be used for such a test and a wide deflection of the voltmeter indicates a ground. An **open circuit,** as the name implies, is a break in a circuit which should be continuous. It is detected by a voltmeter in series with a source of supply connected to the two terminals of the circuit to be tested. Nondeflection of the voltmeter indicates an open circuit. A short-circuit means a shunt or a conductive bridge across a normal circuit. If the test shows the presence of a fault on an armature, it is desirable to locate the defective coil so that it may be repaired or replaced.

A ground may be located by the circuits shown in Fig. 10. A storage battery in series with a current-limiting resistance is connected to two brushes a and b. A test lead c is connected through a milli-voltmeter to the frame of the machine. The lead c is moved around the commutator so as to test each commutator segment. If a ground exists, a bar will be encountered which will give a minimum' or zero deflection. This bar is connected to the grounded coil. The armature should be rotated by steps of 1 pole pitch so that the test may cover the entire periphery of the commutator.

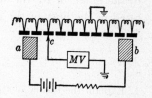

Fig. 10. Circuit for Locating a Ground in an Armature.

A short circuit or an open circuit on an armature can be located by passing approximately normal current through the regular brushes and making a bar-to-bar test with a low-reading voltmeter as indicated in Fig. 11. In the case of an open circuit between a pair of brushes, the voltmeter will show zero for all segments except the pair connected to this open coil. This pair would give a large deflection. In the case of a short circuit, all good coils will give a certain uniform deflection of the voltmeter but the one shorted will give a very low or perhaps zero deflection. The armature must be rotated the span of a pair of brushes (pole pitch) several times in order to apply the test to all of the coils on the machine.

In the factory and the repair shop, short circuits are located by means of a device commonly called a **growler** (so named because of the growling sound it produces). A "growler" (Fig. 12) consists of a coil placed on an iron core C to which is attached two movable jaws A and B. When in use, the armature is placed between the two jaws and alternating current is passed through the coil. The iron laminations of the armature complete the magnetic circuit and the coils on the armature complete the circuits for a transformer. If any coil on the armature is short-circuited, it will have a heavy short-circuit current induced in it. This current will increase the input current to the growler coil

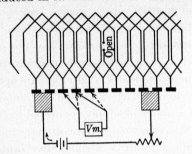

Fig. 11. Connections to Locate Open- or Short-Circuits in Armature Windings.

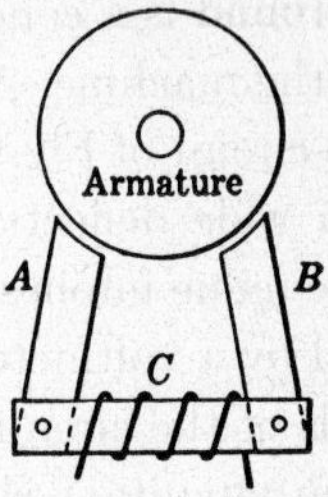

Fig. 12. Device for locating Short Circuits in an Armature.

and will change the tone of the "growl." Either of these signs indicates a short circuit. This short-circuit current through the armature coil will cause its temperature to rise quickly so that the coil can be located by its hot feeling to the hand, or by the smoking of the insulation. The armature must be rotated in the jaws of the growler in order to test all of the coils.

PROBLEMS

1. Explain the theory of the "kick neutral" method of determining the proper brush position when applied to a machine having a wave winding.

2. A shunt motor is rated at 230 volts, 1200 rpm, and has an armature resistance of 0.25 ohm. When running at no load and rated speed, it draws a line current of 5.2 amp and a field current of 2.05 amp. Calculate its field loss and its core loss and friction (stray power).

3. An auxiliary motor is rated at 115 volts, 10 amp, 1000 rpm, and has an armature resistance of 0.6 ohm. It was used to drive a flat-compound generator rated at 230 volts and 975 rpm, to determine the separate losses. The following data were taken:

AUXILIARY MOTOR				MOTOR UNDER TEST		
Volts across armature	Field amperes	Armature amperes	Speed	Volts armature	Field current	Speed
112	1.0	2.5	975	0	0	0
114	1.0	3.3	975	0 Brushes raised	0	975
114	1.0	3.45	975	0 Brushes lowered	0	975
116	1.0	5.2	975	230	1.8[a]	975

[a] Separately excited.

Calculate the windage and friction, brush friction, and the core loss of the machine under test. Use $2I_a$ for brush loss.

4. A compound motor is loaded by a prony brake having a lever arm with its point of attachment to a spring balance 3 ft 6 in. horizontally from the center line of the motor shaft. If the motor has a speed of 762 rpm and the balance registers 13 lb-12 oz, (net) what is the horsepower output of the motor? If the motor is taking 27.3 amp at 225 volts, what is its efficiency for this load?

5. A 2-hp, 125-volt, shunt motor is loaded by a pulley and rope. The pulley has a diameter of 8 in. and the rope a diameter of $\frac{1}{4}$ in. The following readings are taken simultaneously: line volts, 125; line current, 16 amp; speed, 1750 rpm; spring scale, 17.5 lb (net). Calculate the horsepower output and the motor efficiency at this load.

6. A 10-hp, 230-volt, compound motor is direct-connected to a dynamometer serving as a generator and load for the motor. The torque arm on the dynamometer is 18 in. long. Calculate the horsepower output and the motor efficiency for the following conditions of load: line volts, 230; line amperes, 37; 1155 rpm; pull on spring balance, 28.6 lb (net); dynamometer volts, 210; dynamometer output amperes, 28.

7. Two like generators are tested by the electrical-loss-supply feed-back circuit and the following readings are taken: line volts, 220; generator armature current, 60 amp; generator field current, 2.5 amp; motor armature current, 74 amp; motor field current, 1.5 amp; supply line input, 18. amp; and armature resistance at 75 C = 0.15 ohm excluding brushes. Calculate as far as possible the individual losses and the efficiency of these machines from the data given. Point out the errors in the method.

8. The machines of Prob. 7 are connected in accordance with the mechanical-loss-supply feed-back circuit and the following data taken: generator field current, 2.3 amp; generator armature current, 72 amp; motor armature current, 68 amp; motor field current, 1.7 amp., line volts 220.

	I_a	V	I_f	n
Auxiliary motor alone	3	111.5	1.2	1200
Auxiliary motor connected but fields of set unexcited	9.2	114.5	1.2	1200
Auxiliary motor connected and fields of set excited	41	120	1.2	1200
Auxiliary motor $r_a = 0.2$ ohm, excluding brushes				

Make calculations as in Prob. 7.

9. The machines of Prob. 7 are connected according to the Blondel circuit and the following readings are taken: generator terminal volts, 220; field currents, each 2 amp; and the booster supplies 70 amp at 25 volts. The auxiliary motor driving the M-G set has a *net* power output of 720 watts when the M-G fields are not excited and the switch between them is open. The net power output of this motor rises to 1540 watts when operated with the M-G fields excited but the switch open. Lastly, the net power output rises to 1550 watts with the switch closed, so that 70 amperes circulate through the M-G armatures. Make same calculations as for Prob. 7.

10. A dynamo has been at rest for several hours in a room having a constant ambient temperature of 20 C. The measured cold resistance of the windings is as follows: shunt field, 48.3 ohms; series field, 0.031 ohm; armature, 0.092 ohm. The machine is started and operated at full load until the temperatures as indicated by thermometers on the windings become constant. The machine is stopped and the hot resistance of the windings is found to be as follows: shunt field, 57.0 ohms; series field, 0.036 ohm; armature, 0.105 ohm. Compute the average rise in temperature of each part.

11. An insulation resistance test was made between the commutator and the shaft of a dynamo. A line potential of 510 volts was impressed across the voltmeter and the insulation resistance in series. The voltmeter (resistance 37,500 ohms) indicated 10 volts. What was the insulation resistance of the armature in megohms?

CHAPTER XIV

Special Direct-Current Machines and Applications

It was shown in Chap. V that armature reactions present difficulties in the design and in the operation of direct-current machines. It is of interest to note that in a few machines armature reaction may be utilized to produce desirable characteristics in generators. Three such machines are the third-brush generator, the Rosenberg generator, and the amplidyne generator.

The Third-Brush Generator. The third-brush generator was used for many years for charging the storage battery on automobiles. For this service, a generator should charge the battery at the proper rate for all speeds from 10 miles an hour up to a maximum, or through an operating range as high as 10 to 1. The simple circuit of the third-brush generator is given in Fig. 1. This schematic circuit shows a bipolar generator having two main brushes in the usual position and an auxiliary brush (b) commonly called a **third brush** placed under one pole and approximately half way between the main brushes. The shunt field is excited by the current taken from one main brush (+) and the third brush (b). The field is designed to operate on the low voltage which will be delivered to it. When the generator comes up to a speed corresponding

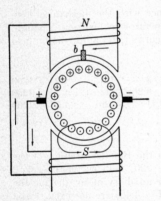

Fig. 1. Circuit for Third Brush Generator.

to a car speed of approximately 10 miles per hour, it builds up to a potential of 8 volts with approximately one half this value across the shunt field. At this point a 6-volt storage battery is connected across the generator by an automatic relay and a charging current of, say, 10 amperes is delivered. This charging current flowing through the armature produces cross-magnetizing armature reaction, which distorts the flux under the poles. This distortion (see flux path under south pole) will be in such a direction as to weaken the flux under the leading pole tips. Since the voltage impressed across the field is generated by the flux cut between + brush and b brush (the flux under the weakened pole tip), the armature reaction lowers the potential across the field and thereby limits the output of the generator. The generator is designed purposely to have a relatively weak field (small number of ampere-turns) and a strong armature reaction (large number of cross-magnetizing ampere-turns), so that the armature reaction will be very effective in controlling the output current.

A second limiting factor results because the third brush is connected through the commutator to an armature coil which is cutting a strong field. The emf generated in this coil will cause a short-circuit current to circulate through the coil and the brush. This short-circuit current will oppose the action which produces it and thus will aid the cross-magnetizing armature reaction in distorting the field and in limiting the current output of the generator.

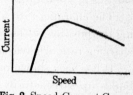

Fig. 2. Speed-Current Curve for a Third-Brush Generator.

As the speed of the car increases above 10 miles per hour, the tendency for the generator having a constant field would be to produce a voltage proportional to that speed and a current output proportional to the generated voltage. In the case of the third-brush generator, any increase in current output is accompanied by greater field distortion due to increased cross-magnetizing armature reaction. This distortion reduces the flux under the leading pole tips, lowers the field current, and decreases the total flux per pole; thus it limits the charging current. For a constant-resistance load the current will increase continuously with the speed, though at a decreasing rate. But for the storage-battery load the current-speed characteristic rises rapidly with speed to reach a maximum, after which the current falls off with the continued increase in speed, as shown in Fig. 2.

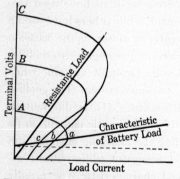

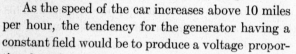

Fig. 3. External Characteristics of a Third-Brush Generator.

One method of explaining the peculiar current-speed characteristic uses the graphical construction of Fig. 3 following the methods outlined in Chap. VIII. Curves A, B, C show approximately the external characteristics of a third-brush generator for three speeds A, B, and C. Line *ca* is the characteristic of the battery. The points of equilibrium for the load for the three speeds A, B, and C would be the intersection of characteristic of the load and the external characteristics at *a*, *b*, and *c*, respectively. Thus the charging current will decrease with the rise in speed. These curves of Fig. 3 also show that the current output increases with the speed for a resistance load.

The current-speed characteristic of the third-brush generator is favorable for the automobile battery because, for city driving at moderate speeds and frequent stops, the battery is getting the maximum charging rate, while for country driving at high speeds and few stops, the charging rate is reduced.

The effect of temperature changes in the third-brush generator is such as to improve its operating characteristics. Thus in the winter and at any time when the generator is cold, the resistance of the field is a minimum, thus giving a stronger field current and higher charging rate. This higher initial charging rate is very desirable in the winter when the drain on the battery for starting a cold motor is a maximum.

The charging rate for the third-brush generator can be changed by shifting the position of the third brush. A clockwise shift in Fig. 1 will increase the charging rate, whereas a counterclockwise movement will decrease the rate.

It has been shown in an earlier chapter that a self-excited generator, which builds up satisfactorily, will also build up if the direction of rotation be reversed and if the leads from the brushes to the field be interchanged. This same statement holds for the third-brush generator. In this case, however, the external characteristic of the machine for constant speed is changed to one similar to that of an over-compound generator. This change in characteristic follows because the reversal of rotation reverses the polarity of the generated voltage and the direction of the armature current. The reversal of the armature current changes the armature reaction under the poles so that the field is now connected to the brushes covering the pole section having increasing flux with load.

Automobile Electric System. Since the year 1912, there have been many electric starting and charging systems developed for automobiles. Battery potentials of 6, 12, and 18 volts have been used. Some systems have used two units consisting of an individual motor and generator, while others have used a single unit or machine which served both as generator or motor, as the occasion required. Since 1926, all American manufacturers of passenger automobiles and light trucks have standardized on the 6-volt, two-unit system, while busses and auto coaches have adopted a 12-volt, two-unit system. The generators used on the two-unit systems have been of three kinds, (1) the differential-compound generator, (2) a shunt generator with an automatic control on its field which used vibrating contacts for controlling the charging current, and (3) the third-brush generator. The first type of generator (differential-compound) was fairly satisfactory. Its current-speed characteristic rose rapidly and then flattened out, but with a continual slow rise in terminal potential instead of an actual decrease as in the case of the third-brush generator. An accidental reversal of current through the differential generator might reverse the residual magnetism, and hence the polarity of generator when started again. The vibrating contacts on the second type of generating unit gave contact troubles when it was first tried about 1915 and hence it was abandoned at that time. The third-brush generator was introduced about 1920 and was so successful that its application on new cars was continued for a score of years.

About 1932 the voltage regulator using vibrating contacts was tried again and the earlier difficulties were overcome, with subsequent experience so satisfactory that this type of system was universally adopted on American cars and trucks by the year 1940. The reason for the universal adoption of this system lies in the superior battery-charging characteristics of the constant-potential system using the vibrating type of voltage and current relays. An automobile battery which is nearly discharged because it has been standing idle for a long time, because of excessive drain through the use of the starter, or because of lights, radio, or fan which were not turned off, should be charged at a relatively high rate as soon as the car is put in service. This high rate of charge is not injurious to a discharged battery and it serves to prepare the battery quickly for future service. Again, a battery which is fully charged on long drives should have the charging current reduced to a low rate to prevent damage from gassing. The third-brush generator will not give automatically this desirable range of charging rate and will overcharge the battery on long trips because its regulation is designed to protect the generator rather than the battery.

The ideal arrangement for charging the battery is a constant-potential system having a potential equal to the voltage of the battery when fully charged. Such a system will charge the battery at a very high rate when it is discharged and then taper the charging rate gradually to zero for the state of full charge. The manner in which this taper charge is accomplished within the battery is illustrated in the family of characteristic curves of a 6-volt battery for a varying specific gravity (Fig. 4). Assuming that the potential is maintained at 7.5 volts, it will be noted that for a specific gravity of 1.160 (a low state of charge) the charging current will be at the rate of 35 amperes. Likewise, for a specific gravity of 1.250 the charging rate is reduced to 15 amperes, and for a specific gravity of 1.280 the charging rate will fall below 3.0 amperes.

Since 1930 there has been a continuous increase in the electric power requirements in the passenger automobile. This increase has been brought about by the use of headlights of larger wattage, by the additions of radios, car heaters with electric blowers, and fans for defrosting windshields. This added load has made it necessary to double the output capacity of the car generator during the decade beginning in 1930. The higher capacity in the automobile generator has been secured by forced air ventilation within the generator, by making the generator longer, and by increasing the weight of iron and the size of wire and weight of copper.

Both the change in the electric loads in cars and the change to the constant potential system have required a larger capacity generator. As stated previously, the constant potential gives a large charging current to a discharged battery. This rate of charge may rise to 150 or more amperes. Obviously, it would be uneconomical to build an auto generator capable of producing such a large current, and a compromise maximum charging rate of approximately 35 amperes (6-volt system) has been chosen for American cars. The output current has been limited to the maximum safe value by the use of a current-regulating relay.

The constant-potential system used on modern automobiles is provided by a combination of relays which control the shunt generator used for charging the battery. Three relays are required with each performing a different but

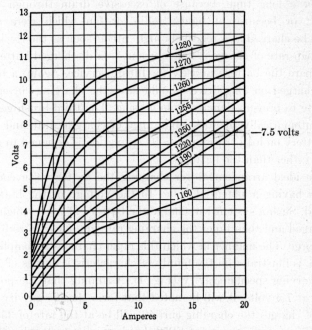

Fig. 4. Volt-Ampere Charging Characteristics for an Automobile Storage Battery Covering a Range of Hydrometer Readings. Hydrometer Reading = 1000 × Specific Gravity.

necessary function. These relays are known as the **circuit-breaker relay,** the **voltage-regulator relay,** and the **current-regulator relay.**

The circuit-breaker or "cutout" relay serves to protect both the generator and battery by connecting them when the generator is running at a speed sufficient for charging duty and disconnecting them and preventing the battery for discharging into the generator at other times. The circuit for the "cutout" relay is shown in Fig. 5. A single electromagnet with movable armature and one make contact is wound with two coils, one of many turns of fine wire (shunt coil) and one of few turns of large wire (series coil). The shunt coil is connected directly across the armature of the generator and the spring tension on the armature of the relay is adjusted so that when the generator voltage rises to 6.3 to 6.7 volts the armature pulls up and its contacts close the circuit to the storage battery. The charging current now flowing through the series coil adds to the mmf of the shunt coil, thus holding the armature firmly in position. When the generator is stopped and its generated emf falls, the battery discharges current into the generator and reverses the direction of flow through the series current coil on the electromagnet. This reversed current deenergizes the electromagnet so that its armature is released and the circuit between the battery and generator is opened. This "cutout" relay has been standard equipment for all types of automobile electric systems from 1915 to date. This type of relay has also been used on d-c farm-lighting plants using storage batteries.

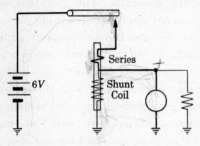
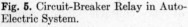
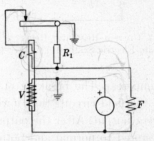

Fig. 5. Circuit-Breaker Relay in Auto-Electric System.

Fig. 6. Voltage-Regulator Relay in Auto-Electric System.

The *voltage-regulation relay* is designed to control the shunt field of the automobile generator so as to hold the output voltage at approximately 7.5 volts. The circuit for this relay (Fig. 6) is similar to that of the "cutoff" relay in that the electromagnet has two coils, one, V, of many turns of the shunt type and the other, C, a series coil of few turns of large wire. The shunt coil V is connected directly across the armature of the generator while the series coil is in series with the shunt field of the generator. The mmf of these coils is additive and is designed so that for proper spring tension on the armature the armature will be pulled down when the generated voltage exceeds 7.5 volts. The downward movement of the armature opens the contacts and the short circuit around the resistance R_1. In other words, the resistance R_1 is inserted into the field circuit. The field current falls and the generated voltage falls. A double action now takes place in the electromagnet. First, the opening of the contacts reduces the current in series coil C to zero and produces a small quick reduction in the magnetic strength of the electromagnet. Simultaneously, the lowering of the generated voltage reduces the current in coil V and thus further weakens the strength of the electromagnet. As a result of this double action, the armature of the electromagnet and its contacts are quickly restored to normal. Then the current is reestablished in C and raised in V until the armature is pulled down and the cycle is repeated. Thus the voltage regulator vibrates very rapidly and short intervals of time or "breaks" are introduced into the field circuit so that the voltage holds close to 7.5 volts. The field circuit is never broken completely since R_1 is inserted in the breaks, and arcing at the vibrating contacts is reduced to a minimum.

The *current-regulating relay* serves to limit the current output of the automobile generator to a safe value so it will not be damaged by overheating when the battery is nearly discharged. The circuit for the current relay is given in Fig. 7. A single-series coil is placed on the magnetic core and the single-relay contact short-circuits a resistance R_2 placed in the circuit of the shunt field of the generator. The operation of the device is rather simple and obvious. When the springs on the armature are properly adjusted, the armature will pull down for a current which constitutes an overload (approximately 35 amperes). The breaking of the contact around R_2 inserts this resistance into the field circuit, thus lowering the generated voltage and reducing the current output. After the output current is sufficiently reduced the armature is restored to normal and both the field current and load current rise again until the cycle is repeated. The current-relay contacts vibrate rapidly like the voltage regulator whenever the current output tends to be high, due to a discharged state of the battery.

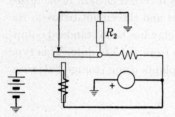

Fig. 7. Current Regulator Relay in Auto-Electric System.

The three relays just described have been used in automobile electric systems in three combinations. First the "cutoff" relay has been used alone

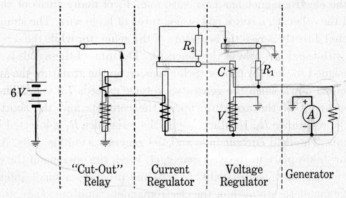

Fig. 8. Three-Unit Voltage-Current Regulator System for Automobiles.

with differential-compound and third-brush generators. Second, the cutoff relay and the voltage-regulator relay have been used with third-brush generators. In this combination the current-limiting characteristic of the third-brush generator made the use of the current-regulating relay unnecessary. The third combination used univesrally today combines the three units with a shunt generator as shown in the circuit diagram of Fig. 8. The student should experience little difficulty in following the operation of this circuit after covering the action of the individual relays in the preceding paragraphs. The combination of these units in the typical voltage-current regulating relay is pictured in Fig. 9. A typical shunt generator now in use is illustrated in Fig. 10.

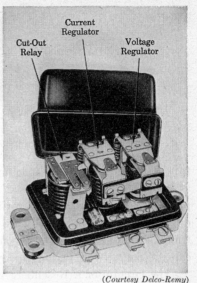

(*Courtesy Delco-Remy*)

Fig. 9. Three-Unit Regulator for Automobiles.

The function of the starting motor is to "crank" the automobile engine. A motor of the series type meets the high torque requirements for this service. An automobile starting motor is shown in Fig. 11. A typical electric circuit for an automobile is shown in Fig. 12. This circuit uses one wire for each individual load and the frame of the car marked "ground" serves as the common return for all individual circuits. The actual circuit of the different makes of American cars usually varies from year to year. In many cars the

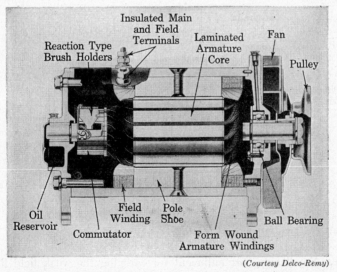

(*Courtesy Delco-Remy*)

Fig. 10. Cross Section of d-c Generator for Automobiles.

circuits for "sealed-beam" headlights and horns have been closed by relays to reduce the drop in potential in contacts and conductors.

The Rosenberg Generator. This is a second type of generator which utilizes armature reactions to produce desirable operating characteristics. Like the

Fig. 11. Series Starting Motor for Automobiles.

third-brush generator, this machine delivers approximately a constant current at all speeds above a required minimum, and, in addition, this machine possesses the property of generating the same polarity of emf regardless of its direction of rotation. These two features made this machine well suited for train-lighting storage-battery systems using the car-axle drive, since railway cars are operated at varying speeds and in both directions.

The circuits of a Rosenberg generator connected for charging a storage battery are given in Fig. 13. The bipolar fields have small cores and heavy

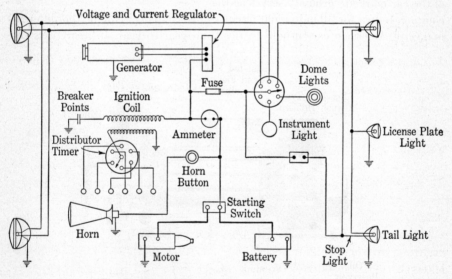

Fig. 12. Typical Electric Circuit for an Automobile.

pole shoes. Small cores are sufficient for carrying the weak field flux which passes throughout the magnetic circuit, while heavy pole shoes are needed to carry a heavy cross flux due to armature reaction. Two brushes, B and B', placed in the usual position for commutation, are short-circuited. A second pair of brushes, b and b', make connection through the commutator with inductors under the centers of the pole faces (opposite the large slots cut in the pole faces). The slots in the pole face offer a high reluctance to the field flux (f) at that region on the armature covered by the brushes bb'. This reduces the reactance voltage in the coils while they are being commutated by the brushes bb'. The generator is excited by a shunt field which is connected directly to the storage battery.

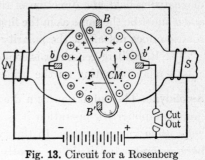

Fig. 13. Circuit for a Rosenberg Generator.

Assuming a clockwise rotation, the operation of the Rosenberg generator is as follows: The shunt field produces a field crossing the armature from left to right and indicated by the arrow f. This field f induces in the armature inductors emf's indicated by the crosses and dots in the circles representing armature inductors. Since the brushes BB' short-circuit the resultant emf's, a large short-circuit current will flow through the armature inductors in the same direction as the induced emf. This short-circuit current will produce a powerful cross-magnetizing field from top to bottom, as indicated by CM. This cross field returns through the heavy section of the pole shoe. The inductors rotating with the armature cut this cross field CM and induce emf's having a direction shown by the inner circle of crosses and dots. The resultant of the emf's in the individual inductors is the correct direction to deliver current at the brushes bb'. The load or charging current is taken from the brushes bb'.

The constant-current feature of the machine follows directly from the preceding statements. The load current flowing out of bb' will produce a cross-magnetizing armature reaction or field from right to left or in the direction of the arrow F. This field is directly opposed to the original field f produced by the main shunt-field winding. Thus, at a full-load current output from the brushes bb', the opposing field F will "buck" and will reduce the field due to the main field. The resultant field from left to right is reduced in value and this reduction, in turn, reduces the short-circuited current and the cross field. The weakened cross field lowers the emf across the brushes bb', and hence lowers the delivered charging current. When the speed of the generator increases, the generator naturally tends to increase its charging rate, but the cycle of reactions just explained will always act to limit such increase in output.

Changing the rotation to the counterclockwise direction will reverse the direction of emf's induced in the inductors due to the main field f. The resulting short-circuit current will flow in the opposite direction, and the cross-magnetizing field will have a direction from bottom to top and opposite to the direction of the arrow shown. However, the inductors on the armature are now moving in the opposite direction, and as they cut a reversed cross-magnetizing field, the direction of the emf's and the polarity of the brushes b and b' must be the same as in the first case. Thus, changing the direction of the rotation does not affect the polarity of the delivered voltage.

The Rosenberg generator is connected and disconnected from its load by a cutout relay operating on the principle described in the preceding article.

Amplidyne. The amplidyne is a d-c generator which functions as a high-gain power amplifier. In operation it is analogous to the electronic amplifier circuits using vacuum tubes. In theory of operation it is similar to the Rosenberg generator but it differs greatly from that machine both in construction and in function. The amplidyne is probably the most important development

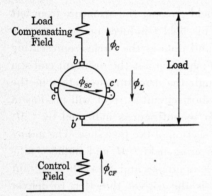

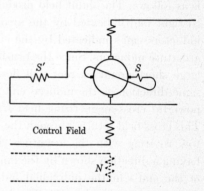

Fig. 14. Basic Fields in an Amplidyne.   **Fig. 15.** Auxiliary Fields in an Amplidyne.

made in the field of d-c machinery during the first half of the twentieth century.

The theory of action of the amplidyne is depicted in Fig. 14. An input or control power is applied to a shunt-field winding known as the **control field.** The excitation of this winding produces the field flux ϕ_{CF} which cuts the inductors of the revolving armature and induces an emf across the brushes cc'. If the brushes cc' are short-circuited, a relatively large short-circuit current will flow in the armature inductors and produce an armature cross field ϕ_{sc} in the direction indicated. This will be a relatively strong cross field (armature reaction) which will be cut by the revolving inductors and thereby furnish an emf across the brushes bb'. The output or load for the generator is taken from brushes bb'. Any load current from bb' flowing through the armature inductors will produce a field ϕ_L which will oppose the control field (demagnetizing action) and tend to weaken the flux of the control field. To neutralize this demagnetizing action, a load compensating field ϕ_c is placed on the same poles as the control field and carries the load current in such a direction as to oppose ϕ_L. With this compensation correctly effected, the output of the generator should respond to changes of input in the control field and with a high degree of amplification.

The amplifying action of the amplidyne may be increased further by the addition of either the field S or S' shown in Fig. 15. These fields are placed on poles which produce flux along the same direction as the armature cross field ϕ_{CF}. Field S is a series field in the short-circuit path while S' is a shunt field connected across brushes bb'. While both types of fields S and S' could be used on the same machine, there is no need for such combined use. The output of the amplidyne is controlled by one or more factors. Each factor involved requires a separate winding or control field. One factor may be a constant and its field is known as a **neutralizing, standard,** or **reference field.** A minimum of two and a maximum of six control fields are used on amplidynes. A second control or neutralizing field is shown as N on Fig. 15.

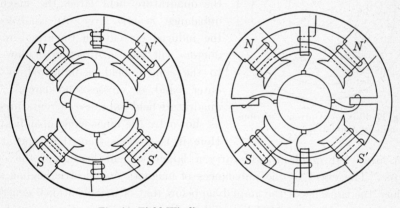

Fig. 16. Field Windings on an Amplidyne.

Most amplidynes are effectively two-pole generators though the actual machine has four segmental poles, as shown in Fig. 16. Segmental poles N and N' and similarly S and S' act as one pole. The control fields are wound on the individual poles and then connected so that N and N' serve as one north-pole structure. The compensating or load fields may be wound on the individual poles, as shown in the left side of Fig. 16, or as a single winding surrounding two segmental poles as in the right side of the figure. Commutating poles and windings are provided to give good commutation at the load brushes. In the left side of Fig. 16 the commutating field is provided entirely by a separate winding, while in the right side of the figure a part of the commutating field is provided by the compensating winding. When commutating poles are used in the quadrature or short-circuit axis they are connected as shown in the right side of Fig. 16. Their effect may be to improve commutation or to increase amplification, depending upon the required output characteristics. In order to improve transient performance, reduce residual magnetism, and assure a greater uniformity of design, a laminated frame and pole structure of special grade of iron is used.

The use of quadrature fields in the amplidyne causes an unbalance in the magnetic and the electric loading of the machine. This is shown in Fig. 17 where the combinations NN' and SS' represent the two poles due to the control fields. The combination of poles NS and $N'S'$ carry the flux due to the quadrature field produced by the armature short-circuit current. The direction of the flux paths in the field poles resulting from the control field is shown by the dotted arrows and that for the quadrature field by the full-line arrows. Obviously, poles N and S' must carry more flux than poles N' and S. Since the control field is of small magnitude and the quadrature field large, the magnetic unbalance is not large. An analysis of the induced currents in the armature inductors will show a direction of flow due to the control field as indicated by the outer band of crosses and circles. The quadrature field will cause currents directed as shown by the inner circle of indicators. Here it is obvious that the upper right and lower left quadrant will carry a larger current load than the other sectors. The effect of the unbalances of magnetic and electric loading is to reduce the capacity of the amplidyne below that of a conventional generator of equal size. In practice the amplidyne is approximately 25 per cent larger than a conventional machine of the same output rating. However, the efficiency is usually higher than that of the conventional machine because refinements in design give lower losses.

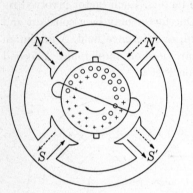

Fig. 17. Flux and Current Distribution in an Amplidyne.

The amplification factor of the amplidyne is defined as the ratio of volt-amperes output to the volt-amperes input to the control field. The amplification is produced in two stages, first from the control field to the quadrature field, and, second, from the quadrature field to the output. Amplifications varying from 100 to 100,000 are possible though the usual practicable range is of the order of 5000 to 10,000. Amplification can be gained at the expense of time or rate of response. If amplification is carried too far the response may be too slow to be useful, especially in the control of sudden changes in machines. The amplification factor increases with the size of the amplidyne because the required control watts do not increase as fast as the output watts. The important things to know in selecting or designing an amplidyne are the amplification factor and the rate of response. The rate of response decreases slightly as the size of the machine increases. The average rate of the rise of voltage in the output is of the order of 2000 volts per second.

The applications of amplidynes are legion. They may be
used as regulators. Thus, an amplidyne may be used directly as
an exciter for a generator or it
may be used as an exciter for a
second conventional exciter for a
generator. In either capacity it
may serve as a combined exciter
and regulator. More often the
amplidyne is used to control the
starting, acceleration, deceleration, and speed of motors. Its
greatest value lies in its ability

(Courtesy General Electric Company)

Fig. 18. Amplidyne.

to combine various functions in a complicated control system. A commercial amplidyne is illustrated in Fig. 18.

Multiple-Field Exciters. Small multifield d-c generators have found many applications in industrial control since 1940. These applications arise from the fact that any d-c generator is an electro-mechanical power amplifier. Such amplification arises from the well-known manner in which the variations of the field of a generator controls the power output of the armature. The re-quirements for good control are (1) large magnitude of amplification (ratio of load output to field power input), and (2) a rapid time response to change of signal input to the field. Those requirements can be met by making certain changes in the design of the d-c generator.

The saturation curve and several field resistance lines for the typical d-c generator are shown in Fig. 19. For a field resistance of R_2 the no-load gen-

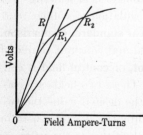

Fig. 19. Field Resistance Lines.

erated voltage will rise to R_2, the intersection of the saturation curve and the field-resistance line. For other values of field resistance other steady-state values of generated voltage may be found. There is some value for the field resistance for which the field-resistance line will coincide with the lower linear portion of the saturation curve. In Fig. 19 this is shown by the line OR. Since line OR does not intersect the saturation curve at any point where the lines coincide, the gener-

ated voltage could lie anywhere along this line of intersection and would not change unless disturbed by a change in field strength produced by some outside factor. But it will be very easy to shift the generated voltage up or down along this line by a change in field produced by a second control or signal winding of a few turns placed on the poles of the generator. Thus the control generator should have at least two separate fields, one designed to produce a field-resistance line coinciding with the linear part of the saturation curve and the second a light field for receiving the control change or signal.

In order to obtain best results in control, the following points should be observed in the design of the control generator. First, the main field should be designed so that with suitable external resistor the resistance line may be made to coincide with the saturation curve. Second, the cross section of magnetic circuit will be made relatively large so that the saturation curve will be linear throughout the voltage range for which the generator must operate. Third, the iron used for the field should have a low hysteresis loss and the inductance of all parts of the circuit should be low so that a quick response to all current changes may be obtained.

The basic and essential adjustment of the control generator, the coinciding of saturation curve and field-resistance line, is brought about by a self-excited field. This self-excitation may be secured by the use of a series field as shown in part 1 of Fig. 20, or a shunt field as of part 2 of the same figure. The first basic circuit is used in a commercial machine known as the **Rototrol,** while the latter circuit is used in a similar machine under the name **Regulex.** In either case, the "resistor" is adjusted to give proper operation for the applications involved. In both circuits operation requires the introduction of the signal through the separate "control" field. For some applications a single control-field winding may suffice, but usually two or more control-field windings will be needed. When the multifield exciter is used for regulation of voltage, current, or speed, two fields are needed. One field known as **standard, comparison, reference,** or **pattern field** is connected to some fixed and constant source of potential. The second field known as the **signal, pilot,** or **control field** is connected to the varying unit which is to be regulated. These two fields are connected in opposition so that when the variable has the desired value the two fields neutralize each other and the voltage generated by the control generator is stationary. When the varying unit moves up or down it throws the reference and signal fields out of balance in such a direction as to cause a change in the generated voltage of the control generator which in turn instantly corrects the shift. In some applications all fields may be of the signal or control type, being

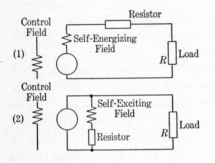

Fig. 20. Circuits for Multifield Exciters.

connected to different varying factors and giving a composite change in the control generator output.

The most numerous applications of the multiple-field exciters are on Ward Leonard systems for controlling speed, acceleration, deceleration, or torque of large motors. They may also be used where control is based on tension (paper, wire, etc.) or the "position" of some unit in an industrial application. These machines, like the amplidyne, can be used to control anything which is convertible into volts, amperes, or watts.

Multiple-field exciters usually control the shunt field of other exciters or generators. For this

(*Courtesy Allis Chalmers Company*)

Fig. 21. Regulex.

purpose their capacity is relatively small and may lie in the range from 0.5 to 2.0 kilowatts. A typical multiple-field exciter is shown in Fig. 21.

Control Applications. The basic circuits for the application of amplidynes and multiple-field exciters to the regulation of voltage, current, and speed are shown in Fig. 22. In each circuit of this figure the amplidyne, Rototrol, or Regulex is represented by the circle E and two adjacent control fields. In each case the comparison or reference field is connected to the constant source from a battery. In part 1 the signal or pilot field varies as the voltage of the generator G; in part 2 the signal field varies as the current output of the generator G; and in part 3 the speed of the motor M determines the voltage output of the direct-connected magneto m, which in turn excites the signal field. Thus circuit 1 regulates voltage, circuit 2 current, and circuit 3 speed.

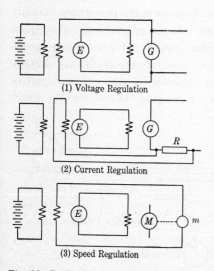

(1) Voltage Regulation

(2) Current Regulation

(3) Speed Regulation

Fig. 22. Basic Circuits for Regulation Using Multiple-Field Exciters.

Boosters. A booster is a generator which is connected in series with a circuit so that its electromotive force is added to that of the circuit. A booster may be a series, shunt, or a compound generator, depending on the particular application. Separately excited shunt and compound generators are frequently used as boosters in experimental and testing work to take care of line voltage fluctuations and thus maintain a constant voltage. They are also used in series with the line to give "special" voltages.

Boosters formerly found their most important applications in electric-railway work. One of the first applications in this field was that of the series

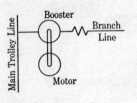

Fig. 23. Use of a Series Booster.

booster. The series booster consisted of a series generator which was connected in series with the trolley (positive) wire to compensate for the IR drops in the trolley, as illustrated in Fig. 23. The series booster may be located at the powerhouse with a separate booster for each feeder (trolley) circuit, or it may be located some distance from the powerhouse, or at a point where a long branch line is tapped off from the main line, as shown in the illustration. The field of the series booster should operate at a low flux density so that the iron will always remain below the knee of the saturation curve. This will cause the machine to "boost" directly in proportion to the load and to the IR drop. Also, if the load is subject to quick changes, the entire field circuit of the booster should be laminated to eliminate any sluggishness in the fields due to induced eddy currents. The series booster finds very little, if any, application in railway service today.

The current from a street-railway system returns to the powerhouse mainly through the tracks, but a part of it may flow into the ground and follow along water mains, gas mains, and telephone cable sheaths. Wherever this return current leaves such mains or cables, it causes electrolysis, which may destroy the pipe or cable in a few months or years. In order to reduce the amount of this leakage return current and to mitigate damaging electrolysis, the street

railway system may install negative boosters. The negative booster, like the series booster, is a series generator which is connected in series with a feeder (conductor) which leads from the negative bus out for some distance, where it is connected to the track (Fig. 24). The action of the booster is negative (that is, it makes the point on the track

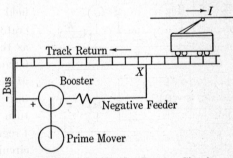

Fig. 24. Negative Feeder-Booster Circuit.

to which it is connected at a lower potential). This action serves to "draw" part of the return current through the feeder and thus reduces the leakage current to the ground. The negative booster also raises the potential across the cars.

If the negative feeder were not connected to the point X on the tracks, all of the return current at the point X would have to return to the negative bus (ground) either through the rails or through some other parallel path. Any current returning through the rails would mean that there would be a fall of potential between X and the negative bus. Such a fall of potential would tend to cause current to leak off from the rails and return by parallel paths through gas mains, water pipes, or telephone cables. The action of the negative booster in mitigating electrolysis can be understood readily by assuming that the terminal voltage of the booster is just equal to the voltage drop in the negative feeder. Then X would be at the same potential as the negative bus and no ground currents could exist between X and the negative bus. In practice, the potential of the negative booster would not be so large as suggested, but large enough to prevent much leakage current through ground returns.

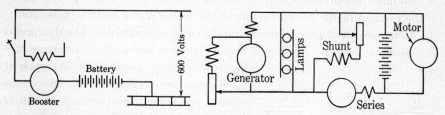

Fig. 25. Battery Booster Circuit for Electric Railway.

Fig. 26. Constant-Current Booster Circuit.

Electric-railway systems have sometimes used storage batteries for emergency service and to help to carry the peak loads. Such storage batteries are connected in parallel with the railway power lines. In order to control the charge and discharge of the battery, it has been customary to place a booster in series with the battery, as shown in Fig. 25. During periods of light load, the booster is separately excited so as to add to the line voltage and cause the battery to be charged. During the peak-load periods, the electromotive force of the booster is reversed, so that it helps the battery to discharge. The control of the booster used for this service may be manual or automatic.

There are a few cases of isolated power plants, such as in hotels, where the load consists of both lights and elevator motors. The load due to the elevator motors is very heavy and also irregular. This tends to produce voltage fluctuations which are objectionable for lighting, and the heavy demands require a large generating capacity. A storage battery and a constant current booster (Fig. 26) may be used to care for the load fluctuations and to maintain constant voltage at the lights. The booster has a shunt and a series-field winding which are connected in opposition magnetically. When there is no elevator-motor load, the shunt winding on the booster predominates, the booster adds to the line voltage, and the battery is charged. When the elevator motor draws a heavy current, the series field predominates, the booster opposes the line voltage, and the battery carries most of the motor load. Thus, with the proper number of turns on the shunt and series field, the current output from the main generator will be nearly constant and independent of the motor load.

Dynamotor. It is frequently desirable to change direct current from one voltage to another. This change is usually accomplished by a motor-generator set which consists of two machines directly connected by a belt or coupling. One of these machines, which has a voltage rating equal to that of the supply line, will be operated as a motor from the supply line. The other machine acting as a generator should have a voltage rating within the range of the desired voltage. The voltage produced by the generator can be controlled through the manipulation of its field rheostat and it is independent of the voltage of the supply line. The disadvantages of the motor-generator set are (1) the high cost of two machines involved, and (2) the low efficiency. The efficiency of the set is the product of the individual efficiencies of the motor and the generator.

A change of voltage can also be produced by a dynamotor. The dynamotor is a machine having a single field-frame structure and a single armature having two separate windings placed upon it. Each armature winding has its own commutator — one being placed on each end of the shaft, as shown in Fig. 27. Since each armature winding cuts the same field, the electromotive force induced per inductor will be the same for either winding. For the same type of winding (lap or wave), the emf induced across the brushes will be directly proportional to the number of inductors on the winding. For Fig. 27, $V_1/V_2 = Z_1/Z_2$, if the IR drops in the windings are neglected. Assuming 100 per cent efficiency, the power input would be equal to the power output, and we would have

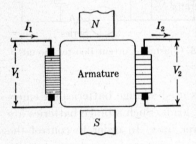

Fig. 27. Dynamotor Circuit.

$$V_1 I_1 = V_2 I_2, \quad \frac{V_1}{V_2} = \frac{I_2}{I_1}, \text{ and } \frac{I_2}{I_1} = \frac{N_1}{N_2}.$$

The advantages of the dynamotor over a motor-generator set are that (1) it is lower in first cost, and (2) it has a much higher efficiency. The higher efficiency results from the fact that the total windage and friction loss, core loss, and field loss are the same as for only one machine of the motor-generator set. The disadvantage of the dynamotor is that the delivered voltage is fixed by the supply-line voltage and the armature IR drops, and cannot be controlled.

Dynamotors have been used on railway cars to give 110-volt service from 550-volt lines. Recently a large number of dynamotors have been used for producing B battery voltages for radio receivers and transmitters, 32-volt farm-lighting systems, and 24-volt airplane systems. A typical dynamotor for this service is illustrated in Fig. 28.

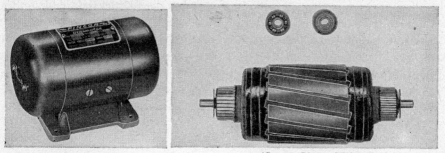

(Courtesy Pioneer GEN-E-Motor Corporation)

Fig. 28. Dynamotor and Parts for Airplane Service.

Direct-Current Airplane System. Important developments were made in d-c equipment and systems for airplanes during World War II. In prewar practice d-c generators were often of small capacity, wind-powered, and mounted outside the plane. For wartime service the generators were driven directly from the airplane motors and the size of the generating equipment was greatly increased to supply electric energy for lights, to power the controls of the plane, to energize communication and direction-finding equipment, and often to operate the gunfire control for turrets. The design of the new d-c machines and equipment required that first consideration be given *to holding the weight to a minimum,* and, second, to giving the greatest *reliability and flexibility* consistent with military needs.

The reduction in weight of d-c generators for airplanes has been accomplished by (1) operation at very high speeds, (2) working all magnetic and electric circuits at high flux and current densities, (3) operation at high temperatures, and (4) by using forced air cooling. The maximum of reliability and flexibility of the electric system has been attained by using several generators and several storage batteries operating in parallel and by using parallel feeder circuits within the plane itself.

(Courtesy General Electric Company)

Fig. 29. Aircraft Generator, 6 Kilowatts, 30 Volts.

The d-c generators used on airplanes are of high-speed shunt-wound type resembling somewhat the generators used on automobiles. Since they must function under varying speeds and with heavy loading, interpoles and a compensating winding are commonly used. A typical aircraft generator is illustrated in

Fig. 29. This machine has the following continuous rating: 3000/8000 rpm, 6 kilowatts, 30 volts d-c, 200 amperes without injurious heating with cooling air not exceeding 30 C (86 F) supplied to the air inlet (left of figure) by a 2-inch diameter tube at a total pressure (static plus velocity) which is at least 6 inches of water higher than the pressure at the outlet. The shunt field carries a maximum of 8 amperes at 3000 rpm and a minimum of 1.1 amperes at 8000 rpm. The weight of this generator is 47 pounds, which is slightly under 8 pounds per kilowatt of capacity. This generator has a diameter of 6 inches and a length of 13.5 inches. A cross-section view showing some of the winding

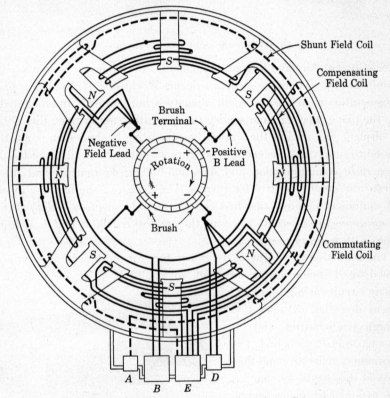

Fig. 30. Circuits and Construction of Aircraft d-c Generator.

and construction features of this remarkable little generator is shown in Fig. 30. It will be noted that the machine has four main poles and four interpoles. One other d-c generator used in war planes has a full-load continuous rating of 300 amperes and a capacity of 9.0 kilowatts.

    The aircraft d-c electric system employs one or more storage batteries, and hence its generators require a cutoff relay and a voltage regulator for the same reasons that they are required on the automobile electric system. The cutoff relay used with the aircraft generator must open circuits carrying currents up to 200 to 500 amperes or more. Hence a special design for such large current interruption is necessary. These designs consist of a combination of a cutoff relay and a heavy current contactor wherein the first relay merely controls the coil for the contactor. The combination weighs about 2.5 pounds and generally is called a **reverse-current relay.**

The voltage regulator for the aircraft generator must operate for a higher voltage and a larger field current so that the vibrating type of relay used for automobile systems is not suitable. Voltage regulators for aircraft generators are of two somewhat different types. One type operates on the same principle as the voltage regulator described on page 150. The other type uses an electromagnet to vary the pressure on a pile of carbon disks and thereby vary the field current to hold the voltage constant. The latter type is illustrated in Fig. 31.

Several electric systems, both direct current and alternating current, have been proposed and tried for aircraft service. Of these systems the 27-volt d-c system proved to be the most acceptable up till the end of World War II. Different systems may be developed and adopted for peacetime aircraft service. The advantages of the 27-volt d-c system are (1) low voltage not dangerous to human life, (2) low voltage gives less commutation trouble at varying altitudes and temperatures, (3) storage battery for this low voltage is not too heavy, (4)

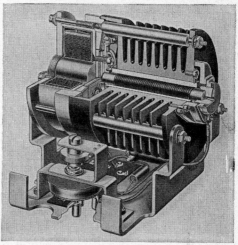

(Reproduced with permission of Bendix Aviation Corporation)

Fig. 31. Voltage Regulator for Aircraft Generator.

electric lights and many pieces of equipment are more rugged when designed for this voltage, (5) breakdown of electric insulation less likely at low voltage, (6) fault currents less damaging at lower voltages, and (7) this system permits simple circuits and equipment for the use of several generators in parallel.

The storage batteries for this d-c system are 24-volt normal. While in operation the voltage of the system is likely to fluctuate between 24 and 28 volts so the system is variously referred to as 24, 26, 27, and 28-volt. On a small noncombat plane a single generator may supply sufficient electric energy for service but on some fighters and all bombers two, four, or six generators operating in parallel may be desirable to provide sufficient reserve capacity. Frequently a separate auxiliary engine-generator plant is provided for emergencies and for operating plane equipment when grounded.

The parallel operation of several d-c aircraft generators running at different speeds represents an interesting problem. Successful operation has been accomplished by the circuit given in Fig. 32. The voltage of each of the four generators shown in the figure is controlled by a separate voltage regulator. Each regulator may be adjusted to perform within the limits of ± 2 per cent but that would permit a possible 4 per cent difference between two machines, which could result in a rather large unbalance of loads. To reduce this load unbalance, two things are done. First, a low resistance S is placed in the negative lead of each generator. This resistance has a value such that it will give a potential drop (RI) of 0.5 volt when the generator is delivering full-load

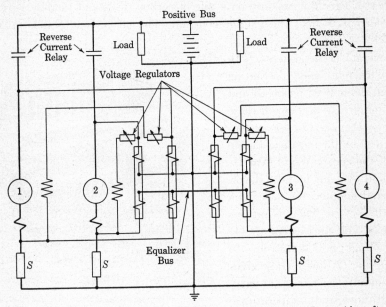

Fig. 32. Circuit for Parallel Operation of 4 d-c Generators on Large Aircraft.

current. Second, the potential at the top of each resistance S is applied to one side of a neutralizing coil on the voltage regulator for the corresponding generator, while the other ends of the neutralizing coil are connected to a common line called the **equalizer bus.** This equalizer bus is analogous to the equalizer bus used for parallel operation of compound generators but it functions in a different manner. If the four generators on Fig. 32 were carrying equal loads the potential drop across all resistors S would be equal and no difference in potential would exist across any of the neutralizer coils on the voltage regulators. Now assume that the total load becomes unbalanced so that generator No. 1 is carrying one half the total load with the other three generators each carrying one sixth of the total load, then the potential drop across S on machine No. 1 will be three times as great as on Nos. 2, 3, and 4. This difference of potential will cause a current to divide into three equal parts and flow up in the neutralizing coils of regulators for machines Nos. 2, 3, and 4, to the equalizer bus and thence down through the neutralizing winding on voltage regulator for machine No. 1. The relatively large unbalanced current in regulator No. 1 will immediately act to reduce the voltage of generator No. 1, while the reversed current through the regulators of the other machine will raise their voltage and bring about a new and approximately equal division of the load. Thus whenever any unequal division of the load occurs, currents are set up in the windings of the neutralizing windings which tend to restore the balance. Obviously, the exact division of load among the generators operating in parallel depends upon the adjustment and the amount of variation of the individual voltage regulators. If one or more of the generators is cut out of service and the corresponding coil S is left connected to the neutralizing winding, the system will continue to divide the load among the remaining generators. However, the voltage of the system will be lowered because of the equalizing current which will flow to the "dead" coil S. If S is opened when the corresponding generator is disconnected from the system, the generators remaining in service will divide the total load uniformly and maintain the proper voltage.

Train-Lighting Systems. Electric systems based on the 32-volt storage battery have been standard on railway passenger cars since the introduction of electric lighting on railroads. The addition of an air-conditioning load with the introduction of streamlined trains in 1933 has led to plans and some use of higher d-c voltages for passenger car service. However, there is good reason to expect that the basic d-c system using a storage battery with individual charging equipment on each car will continue for some time in the future.

The storage battery on each car is charged by a d-c generator driven from the car axle on that car. Like the automobile generator, the railway car generator must operate at varying speeds, hold approximate a constant voltage, and must limit its current output. In addition, this generator must operate automatically for either direction of rotation. Obviously, voltage and current regulation can be secured by methods previously considered. The same polarity for either direction of rotation has been secured by three methods. In some earlier equipment the Rosenberg generator described on page 276 was used. The same polarity regardless of the direction of rotation and current limitation are inherent characteristics of this generator. Voltage regulation was secured by an external regulating circuit and device.

A second method of maintaining polarity has been the use of a brush-shifting device. Friction between brushes and commutator is used to activate a brush rocker arm. The brushes move through the angle of the brush span so that upon reversal of direction of rotation the positive brush moves to the position previously occupied by the negative brush.

The third method of maintaining polarity has used a reversing switch associated with the shaft of the generator. This reversing switch is engaged only at low speeds and serves (1) to operate a double-pole, double-throw switch which reverses the connections to the armature, or (2) serves to reverse the connections to the shunt field or controls relays which perform the same function. Other methods for maintaining polarity have been suggested but those suggested above are the ones which have been employed.

The lighting and air-conditioning load on a passenger car requires the use of a generator of about 20 kilowatts for operating the power equipment and keeping the batteries charged. Shunt generators with interpoles are employed. A speed of 4000 rpm is considered maximum for generators of this size. A 20-kilowatt, 37.5-volt generator designed for a maximum speed of 2500 rpm and weighing 1165 pounds is shown in Fig. 33. The battery to be used with this generator will have a probable rating of 32 volts, 1100 ampere-hours, and weigh about 4200 pounds. The operation of the system will require the use of an overload relay, reverse current relay, and voltage and current regulator relays. These relays will operate on the principles previously covered for similar devices though the construction will be heavier to handle the magnitude of current and power involved.

(*Courtesy General Electric Company*)

Fig. 33. Generator for Railway Coach Service, 20 Kilowatts and 37.5 Volts.

The loads placed on the generator and battery usually consist of incandescent lamps, motors for operating compressors and fans in air conditioning, and a d-c to a-c conversion unit for supplying a small amount of alternating current for electric razors.

At the end of World War II one American railroad was trying out a 110-volt d-c system and two others had adopted a 64-volt (75-volt generator) d-c system. There were indications that the trend would be for the 64-volt d-c system to replace the 32-volt type. The trend was toward increased use of alternating current for fluorescent lighting and other uses. This latter trend would require d-c to a-c conversion equipment of larger capacity. Another definite trend was toward having the d-c generator operated either by car axle drive or by a direct-connected, three-phase, alternating-current motor. The function of the a-c motor was to use a-c supply lines to charge the battery or operate the air-conditioning equipment when passenger cars and Pullman sleeping cars are waiting in yards to be switched on an incoming train.

Electric Drive for Motor Buses. Many modern motor buses for urban operation use electric transmission of power from engine to wheels. Early systems for electric drive used one d-c generator and two motors for individual drive at each rear wheel. Present-day practice is to use only one electric motor to drive through a standard rear axle and differential. The power plant consists of a gasoline or Diesel engine direct-connected to a d-c shunt generator with inter-poles. A 125-horsepower, Diesel-electric unit is illustrated in Fig. 34. The generator uses forced air cooling, has one bearing, and the armature replaced the flywheel of the ordinary combustion engine. An auxiliary shunt generator for charging the storage battery is mounted on the main generator and driven by a V-belt from its shaft. The complete power unit may be placed at the front or the rear of the motor bus. The electric motor for driving the bus is of the

(Courtesy General Electric Company)

Fig. 34. Motor Bus Power Unit.

series type with interpoles, and is direct-connected to a standard axle differ-ential with a single reduction gear. This motor weighs about 900 pounds and the complete weight of the electric transmission unit consisting of generator, motor, and controls is 1750 pounds (for a 20,000-lb bus).

The starting and speed control for the electric drive of the motor bus is rather simple. Aside from the operation of the brakes and the bus in reverse, the entire operation is controlled by the foot accelerator. A typical circuit diagram for the control of a gas-electric motor bus is given in Fig. 35. Begin-ning with the motor bus stationary and the engine idling, the emf of the generator will be low, the holding relay contacts HR will be open, leaving the motor disconnected from the generators. To start the bus the operator presses the foot accelerator slightly. This action (1) increases the gas feed to the carburetor, and (2) closes the accelerating switch. The first action causes the engine to speed up while the second connects the battery to the shunt field. Actually the battery current divides in two parallel paths, one through the shunt-field resistor and the other through the armature and shunt field. The magnetizing and accelerating action of the battery current through the generator field is called the **teaser field.** The teaser field plus the increased rpm causes (1) the generator emf to rise, (2) the holding relay to close the circuit to the motor, and (3) the motor to develop full torque. It should be noted that the rising emf of the generator is added to the battery potential to increase the field current of the generator. As the motor bus picks up speed the operator presses the foot accelerator lower, feeding more gas, and raising the generated emf as the counter emf of the motor rises. As soon as generator voltage rises to a predetermined point where it will operate self-excited, the teaser relay operates and disconnects the battery at the TR contacts. The teaser relay has two windings, one TR_1 in series with the armature load currents, and another TR_2 in series with the shunt field. The two coils are additive serving to cut out the teaser field on acceleration and reestablish the teaser field after deceleration. When climbing long or steep grades the "foot switch" is depressed to insert additional resistance in the shunt-field circuit. This reduces the generated emf and permits the engine to run at a higher speed and the electric motor at a lower speed, giving a "low" in transmission.

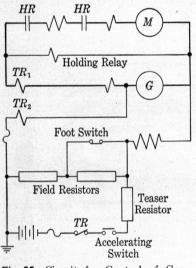

Fig. 35. Circuit for Control of Gas-Electric Motor Bus.

The electric transmission for the motor bus is free from "jerks" and gives smooth, fast, acceleration which utilizes the maximum output of the engine at all running speeds. The efficiency of the electric transmission is 80 per cent or higher for all speeds above 20 miles per hour.

Diesel-Electric Locomotives. At the beginning of the twentieth century a few sections of American transcontinental railroads and many short-line interurban roads were electrified. Current discussion at that time pointed toward the electrification of all rail transportation systems. However, the rise of automobile and bus transportation and the general economic condition of the railroads prevented any extension of railroad electrification using trolley transmission of electric power. About 1930, improvements in the Diesel engine made possible the portable electric power plant carried on the locomotive. Since the early thirties the streamlined train powered by Diesel-electric loco-motives has been replacing the steam locomotive for both long-haul and switching service. The advantages of Diesel-electric power for traction are (1) high thermal efficiency of Diesel engines; (2) simple, smooth, speed reduc-tion of the d-c generator-motor electric transmission system; (3) excellent high torque and approximately constant power characteristics of series motors; (4) higher train speeds for normal engine speeds; and (5) lower maintenance and operating costs. Many different kinds of equipment and different circuits are used by the locomotive manufacturers. In general, the locomotive will have one or two direct-connected, Diesel-engine-generator power plants to

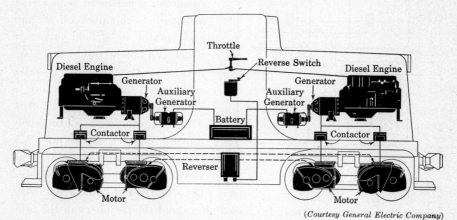

(*Courtesy General Electric Company*)

Fig. 36. Equipment and Circuits on a Diesel-Electric Switching Locomotive.

supply power to individual series traction motors geared to each pair of driv-ing wheels on the trucks. The generator fields are separately excited by auxil-iary exciter-generators. A storage battery charged by an auxiliary generator supplies power for cranking Diesels, for lighting, and for other functions on the locomotive. The top speed of travel is controlled (1) by a throttle which con-trols the speed of the Diesel engine, (2) by changes in generator field, and (3) where designed by changes in motor series-parallel circuits. Reversal of direc-tion of travel can be attained through a reversal of either the generator or motor fields. The location of equipment and the circuits involved on a typical Diesel-electric switching locomotive are shown in Fig. 36.

Ship-Propulsion Equipment. Most large ocean-going ships use alternating current for ship propulsion. Some small ships and tugs use direct-current systems for propulsion. Diesel engine or turbine-generator d-c plants supply power to one or more separately excited shunt-type motors direct-connected to the driving propellers. The control system is the Ward Leonard type using a separate exciter with all controls located in the pilot house.

Acyclic Dynamo. The student may have wondered if it is possible to construct a direct-current dynamo so that its inductors are always cutting flux in the same direction. With such an arrangement, the generated emf and the current flow would be steady and in the same direction at all times, which would eliminate the need of a commutator and would avoid the difficulties arising from reactance voltage. A machine which embodies these features is called an **acyclic dynamo** (also known as a **homopolar** or a **unipolar dynamo**).

The construction of a simple homopolar dynamo is illustrated in the cross-sectional view of Fig. 37. The armature has only one inductor, which consists of

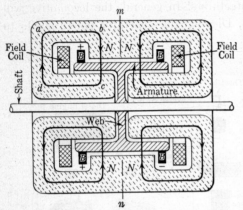

a hollow brass cylinder supported by a central web. This combination resembles a flat-faced pulley. The armature is mounted on a shaft and rotates in a field structure which is a hollow torus. The magnetic circuit through all cross sections of the field structure is illustrated by the flux path *abcd*. Thus the armature is continuously moving under a north pole *NN* (flux coming from outside to inside), and a constant emf is induced between the two ends of the cylin-

Fig. 37. Construction of an Acyclic Dynamo.

drical armature. Brushes may be placed all around the periphery of the armature, as shown at *BBBB*. The flux is produced by two circular field coils which are mounted concentric with the armature shaft. The field frame of the machine must be divided in some way to make it possible to assemble it.

Since the armature of this machine has only one inductor, its emf is low (about 3 volts) but the current output may be large, reaching possibly thousands of amperes. Thus this simple form of machine is essentially a low-voltage and high-current generator. The Westinghouse Electric & Manufacturing Company designed a homopolar generator of this type for meter testing in 1896. Two such machines having a rating of 3 volts, 6000 amperes, and 1500 rpm were built and have been giving satisfactory service since that date. When the two machines are placed in parallel, they will give a maximum current of 20,000 amperes for intermittent service.*

Acyclic generators are used today for supplying current of large magnitude in the Sperry rail flaw-detector cars. These cars are leased to American railroads for detecting concealed cracks and defects in the rails on their systems,

---

* For a very interesting account of the history and design of this type of machine, the reader is referred to the article on *Development of a successful direct-current, 2000-kw unipolar generator*, in Electrical Engineering Papers by B. G. Lamme.

so that preventive measures may be taken to reduce the possibility of wrecks. An acyclic generator built by the Chandeysson Electric Company for use in the Sperry test car is shown in Fig. 38. These units are used in pairs. Each unit has a rating of 3 volts, 4500 amperes, and 1200 rpm.

(*Courtesy Chandeysson Electric Company*)

Fig. 38. Homopolar Generator for a Flaw-Detector Test Car.

Another interesting principle is embodied in the construction of the motor element in the Sangamo mercury type of watt-hour meter and ampere-hour meter. As illustrated in Fig. 39, the armature consists of a flat-toothed copper disk D which floats in a bath of mercury H. The disk is cut at each side by the field of the electromagnet M and its return circuit M_1. Current enters into the mercury at the lug C_1, passes through the copper disk D, and out through the mercury to lug C_2. Part of the current flows around through the mercury bath, but the largest part passes through the lower resistance of the copper disk. Current flowing through this copper disk in the field of the electromagnet is urged out of this field. The action under each pole of the electromagnet will be in opposite directions, so that the disk will rotate in a clockwise direction as viewed from above. Like the simple homopolar generator, this motor element has only one armature conductor.

The circuits of Fig. 39 for the watt-hour meter show that the flux produced by the magnet M is proportional to the line potential, and that the load current flows through the copper disk, so that the torque produced is proportional to the product of volts and amperes.

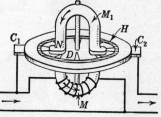

Fig. 39. Mercury-Type Watt-hour Meter.

Arc-Welding Generators. Electric arc welding has become of great importance in recent years. Castings and forged machine parts are being replaced by structural steel welded electrically. In structural-steel bridges and buildings, the use of rivets is being supplanted by electrically welded joints.

Direct current has certain advantages over alternating current for electric welding, and the common practice is to use metallic electrodes with about 20

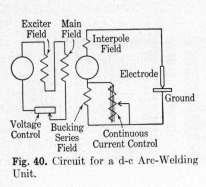

Fig. 40. Circuit for a d-c Arc-Welding Unit.

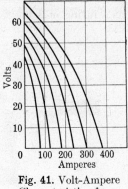
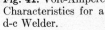

Fig. 41. Volt-Ampere Characteristics for a d-c Welder.

volts across the arc. The current required for the arc depends upon the size of the work and the diameter of the electrode. If the usual line voltage of 110 or 220 volts is used for arc welding, much energy must be lost in a series resistance

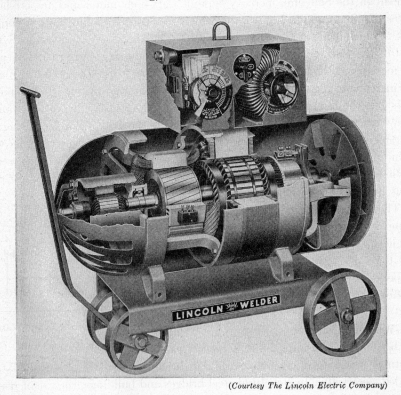

(*Courtesy The Lincoln Electric Company*)

Fig. 42. Portable Arc-Welding Set.

in order to reduce the voltage across the arc to 20 volts. Hence it has been customary to use special motor-generator sets for producing direct current for arc-welding purposes. The generators of these sets which are designed to supply current for one operator are usually of the differential-compound type and have a separately excited main field. One circuit for such a generator is given in Fig. 40. Separate excitation is necessary because the terminal voltage of the machine when in service may vary from 70 volts down to near zero. Under such conditions, a self-excited field would be too sluggish in building up after the arc was struck. Separate excitation is supplied by a small direct-connected exciter. Shunt, series, and compound types of exciters have been successfully used. The magnetic-field circuit of the generator is laminated throughout to care for the quick flux changes induced by the series field. A choke coil or inductance coil which is called a **stabilizer** or **reactor** may be placed in the arc circuit to smooth out fluctuations in the arc current due to the manipulations of the operator. The "bucking" series field of the differential generator tends to give a constant power input into the arc because the voltage falls with the increase of arc current, which gives approximately a constant value of volts times amperes, or watts. The volt-ampere characteristic of this form of generator is given in Fig. 41. The different curves apply to different adjustments of the controls. A portable arc-welding set is illustrated in Fig. 42 and its circuit in Fig. 40.

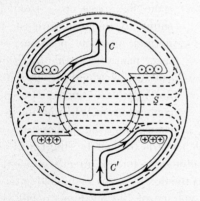
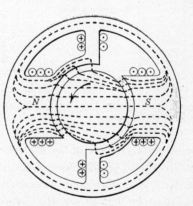

Fig. 43. Flux at no Load on a Divertor Pole Generator.

Fig. 44. Flux under Load on a Divertor Pole Generator.

The Divertor-Pole Generator. This is an interesting development in direct-current machines and consists of a shunt-wound interpole generator in which a magnetic shunt is placed between each interpole and an adjacent main pole having the same polarity. The actual structure used is produced by making the shunt-field core, the interpole core, and the magnetic shunt out of unit punchings, as illustrated in Figures 43 and 44.

The principle of the operation of this machine is very interesting. At no load, there is no current in the interpole winding and the field produced by the shunt field causes the major part of the main pole flux to pass from the north pole across the armature to the south pole in the usual manner, as shown in Fig. 43. However, a part of the main pole flux does not enter the armature, but is diverted around through the shunt and returns through the interpole core. Hence the interpole and the magnetic shunt is termed a **divertor pole.** The amount of flux which is diverted is limited by the saturation of the shunt and the divertor-pole core. As the load comes on the generator, current flows through the series divertor-pole winding and this current produces a magneto-motive force which opposes the diverted or leakage flux which returns through the divertor pole. Hence the diverted flux decreases in value and the flux from the main pole which enters the armature increases. By proper design of the cross section of the shunt and divertor pole, the increase of flux entering the armature from the main pole may be made to counteract the armature reac-tion and the speed decrease of the driving motor, and to offset the $I_a R_a$ drop in the armature as the load comes on. With this balance, the distribution of the flux at full load will be as shown in Fig. 44. Here the magnetomotive force

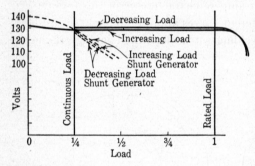

Fig. 45. Constant Voltage Characteristic of a Divertor Pole Generator.

of the interpole just balances that of the shunt field, so that no flux passes through the divertor pole. The flux distribution is such that some flux does cross from the shunt to the armature at the normal interpole position. This flux neutralizes the reactance voltage, as would the flux from an interpole, and gives good commutation. When an overload comes on the generator, the magnetomotive force of the divertor pole exceeds that of the shunt field and thus the excess or difference of the magnetomotive force is directly opposed to the shunt field. This opposition decreases the flux from the main field entering the armature and causes the terminal voltage of the machine to fall very rapidly. These various factors serve to give this generator the external char-acteristic of the type illustrated in Fig. 45. This characteristic resembles that of a flat-compound generator, but is superior to it because the curve is a *flat* straight line and because the generator is *self-protecting* on an overload.

The divertor-pole generator is especially adapted for charging the storage batteries which supply the power for operating circuit breakers in powerhouses and substations. The motor-generator set floats on the supply line on one side and on the battery on the other, thus keeping the battery charged without any attention from the station attendant. Compound generators are not suitable for this service, because, if the power supply is removed, the generator operates as a differential motor from the battery and will probably be unstable and open its breakers. If a station attendant is not present to restart the motor-generator set, the batteries will become discharged and fail to function. Shunt generators have been used for this service in the past, but their external characteristic is drooping, so that they are not well suited for charging the batteries at a rate proportional to their state of discharge.

When a storage battery is discharged, its terminal voltage is low and it can be safely charged at a high rate. As a storage battery approaches a state of charge, its terminal emf rises and it should be charged at a slow rate to prevent "gassing." The shunt generator has a lowered terminal voltage at full load and a higher voltage at light load; hence it would tend to charge a storage battery at a constant rate. The divertor-pole generator with its flat external characteristic will charge at a high rate when the battery is discharged and then taper off the current flow as the battery comes up to charge.

The Direct-Current Watt-hour Meter. The **watt-hour meter** is an instrument for measuring *electrical energy*. Electrical energy is the product of power (watts) and time and is commonly expressed in watt-hours or kilowatt-hours. Kilowatt hours in a direct-current system are equal to volts × amperes × hours divided by 1000. The load on any electrical system generally varies with time; hence a watt-hour meter must be an integrating device for adding the instantaneous increments of energy consumed in the system. If an electric motor can be made to run at a

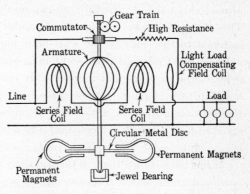

Fig. 46. Circuit of a d-c Watt-hour Meter.

speed proportional to the power taken at each instant by the load with which it is associated, then the total revolutions of the motor will be proportional to the electrical energy consumed. The direct-current watt-hour meter in general use is a device based on this principle.

The direct-current watt-hour meter has a circuit and a principle of operation similar to that of a shunt motor. However, it differs from the shunt motor in three ways, as illustrated in Fig. 46. First, the armature has a high resistance, takes but little current, and is connected directly across the line. Second, the field coils of the watt-hour meter have a low resistance and are connected in series with the load. In the third place, the watt-hour meter does not contain any iron in its magnetic circuit, either in the field or the armature. Each of these differences is important in the operation of the watt-hour meter. The armature (moving element) circuit is constantly connected across the line and the current through the armature inductors will be proportional to the line potential *in volts*. With no load on the system, there is no current in the field coils which are in series with the load, and hence there is no torque developed in the motor. However, when a load is placed on the system, this load current passes through the series coils and produces a field which is directly proportional to the load current in *amperes*. Thus, the torque developed in the motor will be directly proportional to volts times amperes. This follows from the fundamental torque equation of a motor ($T = K_2 I \phi$), since K_2 is a constant, I is proportional to line potential, and ϕ is proportional to the load current.

For any given torque developed in a motor, the resulting speed will depend on the load or counter torque on the motor. If a constant torque (brake) were applied, the motor would never start until the developed torque reached this constant value. For light loads on a watt-hour meter, a low counter torque is desired, and for heavier loads a larger counter torque. Thus, if the speed is to be proportional to the load (power), the counter torque must be directly proportional to the speed. Such a counter torque can be produced by the magnetic brake (eddy current generator) shown on the lower part of the shaft in Fig. 46. This magnetic brake consists of a circular metal disk (copper or aluminum) fastened to the shaft of the watt-hour meter so that it rotates between the poles of two C-shaped permanent magnets. The rotation of the disk cuts the fields of the magnets and induces eddy currents in the disk. These eddy currents, in turn, react with these same fields and produce a magnetic drag upon the rotation of the disk. This counter torque or drag, like the driving torque, is equal to $K\phi I$ where K is a constant and ϕ produced by the permanent magnets is constant, and I, the eddy current, varies directly with the speed.

It has been shown that, in theory, the watt-hour meter runs at a speed proportional to the load it is measuring. In practice, however, this instrument has bearing friction which acts as a counter torque all of the time in addition to any counter torque developed in the magnetic brake. At full load, this friction has very little influence on the accuracy of the instrument but, at light loads, its effect may be relatively large; in fact, so large that the meter would not run at all at very light loads. In order to compensate for this light-load friction, a coil having a few turns of wire is connected in series with the armature and is placed in a position parallel to the series coil. This coil carries the same current as the armature and thus produces a constant torque of a value almost sufficient to overcome the friction of the bearings and commutator. This **light-load compensation,** as it is called, places the watt-hour meter "on the mark" and ready to go at all times.

The shaft of the watt-hour meter usually has a worm at the top which meshes with a reducing-gear train. The last gears of this reducing-gear train are connected to the pointers on the dial. A dial is shown in Fig. 47. There are four or more pointers on the dial having a speed ratio of 1 to 10 to 100 to 1000, etc. The dial should be read right to left and the digits set down in that same order. The first dial to the right usually indicates kilowatt-hours. The reading in Fig. 47 is 3111.

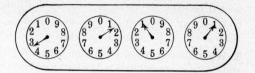

Fig. 47. Watt-Hour Meter Dial Register.

The correct registration of the watt-hour meter is very important because the monthly bill for the energy consumed is based on its reading. Overregistration means that the customer is overcharged, while underregistration means that the public utility is underpaid. A watt-hour meter originally accurate in its registration may become in error due to friction in its bearings, to friction in the commutator, to excess voltage on the system, and to weakened permanent magnets. The so-called full-load adjustment of the meter is made by shifting the permanent magnets toward or away from the center of the disk. A shift toward the center of the disk reduces the radius of the point where the permanent-magnet flux cuts the disk. And for the same rpm of the disk, this gives a smaller eddy current, thus reducing the counterforce. At the same time, the reduced radius further lowers the counter torque (force times radius). In like manner, the light-load adjustment is made by shifting the compensating field coil toward or away from the armature, so that the field flux and the compensating torque on the meter are varied.

The lower end of the shaft of the moving element has a sharp conical point called the **pivot** which rests on a jewel bearing. The upper bearing merely serves as a guide bearing so that the total bearing friction of the instrument is very low.

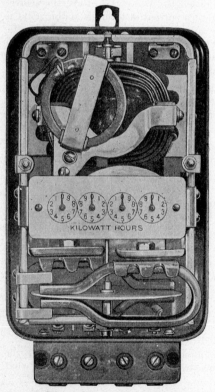

Fig. 48. Direct-Current Watt-Hour Meter.

A general view of a direct-current watt-hour meter is given in Fig. 48. Another type of construction for direct-current watt-hour meters is indicated on page 297.

PROBLEMS

1. What will happen if the field leads on a third-brush generator are accidentally connected between the third brush and the wrong main brush?

2. What will happen if the ungrounded lead to the third-brush generator on an auto-electric system becomes grounded to the frame?

3. What would happen to a differential-compound generator if used on an automobile and the ungrounded lead to the battery became "open"?

4. A shunt generator on a passenger car is delivering 15 amp at 7.5 volts. If the mechanical input to the generator is 0.5 hp, what is the generator efficiency? Can you explain and justify this value of efficiency?

5. Explain the operation of the Rosenberg generator as a motor.

6. The resistance of the control field of an amplidyne is 200 ohms and a current of 10 ma through it produces a current of 2.0 amp at 125 volts at the load brushes. What is the amplification factor?

7. A streetcar line begins at the powerhouse and extends for 4 miles. The rails are of uniform size and uniform resistance per unit of length. At a certain time, the nearest car is 3 miles from the powerhouse and the return current in the rails at this point is 200 amp. At this instant a test shows that the voltage drop from this point back to the negative bus at the powerhouse is 30 volts. What is the probable resistance per mile of the track? Suppose that a simultaneous reading at a point 2 miles from the powerhouse showed a voltage drop of 10 volts. How would you explain the situation?

8. In Fig. 24, the current flowing in the trolley wire is 140 amp, the resistance of the negative feeder is 0.1 ohm, and the booster 0.1 ohm. If the resistance of the track return is 0.25 ohm out to the point where the negative feeder joins the track and the booster emf is 15 volts, calculate the current flowing in the track and in the negative feeder.

9. In Fig. 27, the ratio of the inductors on V_1 to V_2 is 10 to 1, the armature resistance of V_1 is 5.0 ohms and V_2 is 0.1 ohm. The terminal voltage across V_2 is 8 volts when 25 amp are being delivered. Assuming a core loss and friction loss of 40 watts, find V_1 and I_1 for the dynamotor.

10. A dynamotor has an input of 5.8 volts and 9.1 amp. For this condition the output is 3.0 ma at 185 volts. What is the efficiency for this load? Can this value be justified?

11. Discuss the advantages and disadvantages of a shunt motor for a gas-electric drive on a bus.

12. The total flux cutting the armature of an acyclic generator is 5×10^6 maxwells. The armature is 12 in. in diameter and revolves at 1800 rpm. If the effective length of the armature under the poles is $10\frac{1}{2}$ in., what is the emf at the brushes?

13. Suppose the armature of Prob. 12 is held stationary and the field revolved around it at 1800 rpm. What will be the emf between the brushes? Justify your answer.

14. Explain the action of the divertor-pole generator as a motor.

15. A watt-hour meter used for measuring the input of a mill is 2.6 per cent fast. If the meter registers 10,500 kw-hrs in one month on a straight rate of 2 cents per kw-hr, what will be the overcharge?

REFERENCES

Alexanderson, E. F., Edward, M.A., and Bowman, K.K., "The Amplidyne Generator," *General Electric Review*, March 1940.

Mohler, F., "The Amplidyne—A New Tool of Many Uses," *Iron and Steel Engineer*, Sept. 1940.

CHAPTER XV

Rating, Weight, and Cost of Dynamos

Standard Voltage and Speed Ratings of Dynamos. The rated terminal voltage of a dynamo intended for use as a generator is the voltage at *full load* except in the case of *compound generators* where *both the no-load and the full-load voltages* are specified. The *standard* voltage ratings for generators are 4 to 8 volts for electroplating, 8 volts for passenger-car generators, 16 volts for bus, truck, and a few farm-lighting generators, 40 volts for most farm-lighting generators; 125 volts for exciters and some lighting generators; 250 volts for general power purposes; and 600 volts for electric railway service. The standard voltage rating of dynamos intended for use as motors is always lower than that of the corresponding generator because of the line drop or because of the difference between the battery voltage on charge and discharge. The usual standard voltages for motors are 6 volts for use on passenger automobiles; 12 volts for buses and trucks; 32 volts for farm-lighting plants; 115 volts for small general-purpose motors; 230 volts for power applications; and 550 volts for electric railway service.

The rated speed of dynamos used as generators is usually fixed by the type and size of the prime mover. A gas engine or a Diesel engine has a desirable speed range for highest economy, a reciprocating steam engine operates best at a low speed, while a turbine should operate at high speeds. The rated speed of a motor is entirely independent of the speed of its source of power and it is designed to suit the speed of its load. Since the speed of the direct-current motor (shunt and compound) may be adjustable, many motors are designed to have this highly desirable feature. Standard speed ratios for adjustable-speed motors are $1\frac{1}{2}$ to 1, 2 to 1, 3 to 1, and 4 to 1. Practically all constant-speed direct-current motors are designed to have a rated speed such that they may be interchangeable with alternating-current induction motors. The speeds of alternating-current motors are fixed by the frequency of the supply and the number of poles. Thus constant-speed motors are usually rated for full-load speeds of 575, 850, 1150, and 1750 rpm, corresponding to the speeds of alternating-current motors on 60-cycle circuits.

305

Power Ratings of Dynamos. The power-output rating of a dynamo is determined by the permissible temperature rise which was discussed in a preceding chapter. There are several recognized kinds of ratings for machines, such as continuous, short-time, nominal rating of a generator, and continuous with 2-hour, 25 per cent overload rating of a generator. The continuous rating defines the load which can be carried for an unrestricted time without exceeding the temperature limitations. The short-time rating defines the load which can be carried for a specified time without exceeding temperature limitations. Standard periods for short-time ratings are 5, 10, 15, 30, 60, and 120 minutes. The nominal rating of a generator defines the constant load which, having been carried without further measurable increase in temperature rise, may be increased 50 per cent in amperes at a specified voltage for 2 hours without exceeding specified temperature limitations. In the absence of any specifications as to kind of rating, the continuous rating shall be implied for all purposes except for machines carrying traction loads where the nominal rating shall be implied.

It is recognized that the load on general-purpose machines operating under usual service conditions of a cooling medium not exceeding 40 C and an altitude not exceeding 3300 feet, may carry some overload without damage to the machine. The magnitude of such permissible overload is specified as 1.15 times the continuous rating. This factor of 1.15 is called the **service factor.**

The actual load which may be safely placed upon a dynamo will depend upon the conditions surrounding its application. Thus, a motor rated at 10 horsepower might not be used to develop over 7 horsepower if operated in the sun at the equator, while if used in Alaska it might safely carry a load of 12 or more horsepower. Again, a motor operated in a small closed room or any place where the circulation of air is restricted, could not be expected to carry its rated load continuously. A motor used for short periods should be given a different rating than when used for continuous service. Permissible ratings for intermittent service and for enclosed motors will be discussed in a later article.

Influence of Speed on Capacity. The power developed in a dynamo is equal to the product of its generated emf and the current flowing in its armature. The permissible armature current may be assumed to be constant, since it is limited by the temperature rise. The shunt-field current is constant (giving constant field ϕ) for a given speed. Hence it follows that in a shunt dynamo the permissible power output (EI) is directly proportional to the generated emf, which, in turn, is directly proportional to the speed. This gives a linear relation between the capacity and the speed of a dynamo as shown by the full line of Fig. 1. This relationship is very important because it indicates (1), that the capacity of a dynamo of a given size and frame may be increased by raising the operating speed, and (2) it indicates that a smaller, lighter, and less costly dynamo can be built for a given output by raising the operating speed.

The linear relation shown in Fig. 1 has certain limitations. On the one hand, as the operating speed is increased, the fanning and the cooling action on the armature is improved so that an increased armature current may be carried without exceeding safe operating temperatures. This would tend to cause the curve to rise as shown by the dotted line. On the other hand, as the operating speed rises indefinitely, (1) the core losses increase with the magnetic frequency, and (2) the generated voltage will increase to points where additional insulation on the armature inductors is required and thus will necessitate conductors of reduced cross section, lower current-carrying capacity, and greater heat insulation. These factors will reduce

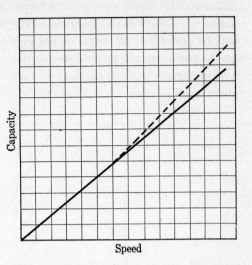

Fig. 1. Relation Between Capacity and Speed of a Dynamo.

the rate of increase of capacity with speed. An excellent example showing the effect of speed on capacity is that of the special aircraft generators described on page 287.

Influence of Speed on Weight. The general influence of speed upon the size and weight of a dynamo of a given power rating was suggested in the preceding article. A rough approximation to the relationship between speed and weight may be secured as follows:

$$\text{Horsepower} = \text{constant} \times \text{speed} \times \text{torque}.$$

The torque developed by a machine may be assumed to be approximately proportional to the weight of the machine. Thus

$$\text{Horsepower} = \text{constant} \times \text{speed} \times \text{weight}$$

and

$$\text{Weight} = \frac{\text{horsepower}}{\text{speed}} \times \text{constant}$$

and for a given capacity

$$\text{Weight} = \frac{\text{constant}}{\text{speed}} \text{ (approx.).} \tag{1}$$

Therefore the above assumption leads to the approximation that, for a given capacity, the weight of a dynamo is inversely proportional to the speed. This deduction is given justification by the three curves of Fig. 2, which were pre-pared from data covering a line of standard machines of a large electrical manu-facturer. The three curves for different machines of 60, 75, and 100 horse-power run nearly parallel and have the inverse trend of weight to speed. It may be noted that all points do not fall on their respective curves. This is not due to a discrepancy in the trend of the curve, but is caused by the fact that a manufacturer's line of machines is built on a series of stock frames, so that a given machine may not be built on the exact size of frame which theoretically

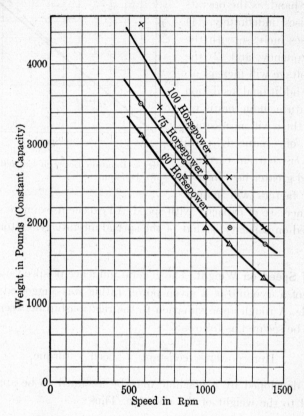

Fig. 2. Influence of Speed on Weight of Dynamos.

would give the best weight per horsepower for the given speed. Designs made on a strictly theoretical basis would probably give points lying on a smooth curve.

Influence of Speed on Cost. The cost of producing any machine is made up of two items, labor and materials. For dynamos which are alike in construction it is reasonable to assume that the *ratio* of the costs for these items may remain nearly constant so that the total cost is proportional to the weight of the finished machine. In accordance with this assumption, cost may be substituted for weight in equation 1, giving

$$\text{Cost} = \frac{\text{constant}}{\text{speed}} \text{ (approx.).} \qquad (2)$$

The truth of this relationship is illustrated by the three curves of Fig. 3 which cover the same line of direct-current machines as the curves of Fig. 2. The re-

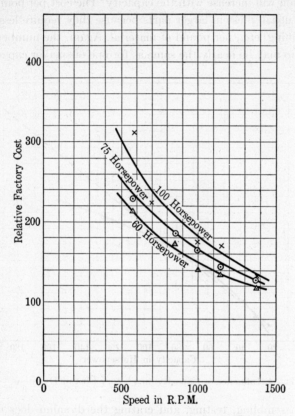

Fig. 3. Influence of Speed on Factory Cost of Dynamos.

tail cost or price of a machine is proportional to the factory cost, so that the purchaser will generally find it more economical to use the highest speed motor which can be satisfactorily adapted to a given application. It should be noted that there are limitations to the speed-cost relationship shown in Fig. 3. An increase of speed beyond reasonable limits will raise the cost of a machine. This follows because the diameter of the armature is limited by centrifugal forces so that when the speed passes a certain point the armature must be made longer, stiffer, and heavier. Reactance voltage will be greater for the longer lengths of inductors and the commutator becomes long and more expensive. The critical speed limit is much lower in machines of large capacity because they are inherently low-speed machines. Thus the cost and the weight of a dynamo may rise when the speed rating exceeds a reasonable limit for the given capacity of the machine.

Influence of Capacity on Cost. The size and weight of a dynamo is expected to increase with its capacity. Likewise, the size and weight of each part used in the construction will increase with the capacity. The cost per pound of weight of material is usually less in larger parts because they require less labor, heat energy, machining, etc., per pound of material. Again, the number of parts in a large dynamo may be nearly the same as for one of smaller capacity, so that

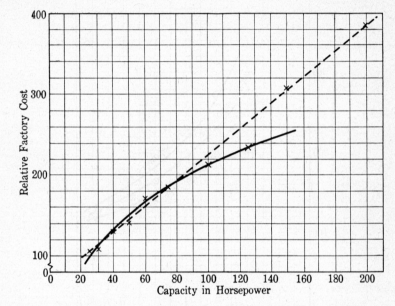

Fig. 4. Influence of Capacity on Factory Cost of Dynamos.

the labor in assembling, testing, and crating the dynamo does not increase directly with its capacity. Thus it is to be expected that the cost of a dynamo will not increase directly as the capacity if the rating in volts and speed is kept constant. The relationship between capacity and factory cost* for a line of constant-speed motors is given in Fig. 4. The cost for the range from 25 to 125 horsepower is shown by the full-line curve and follows the trend which might be anticipated from the preceding considerations. The line of motors covered in this range is similar and all motors have a wave winding. The last two motors in the series (150 and 200 hp) take such a large line current that it is necessary to change to a lap winding with equalizer connections. The extra cost for this

* Factory cost covers the labor, materials, and overhead in the factory and omits selling expense.

change caused the points for these motors to fall far above the curve for the others. Hence the curve for the entire range of sizes would be approximately the straight dotted line as shown.

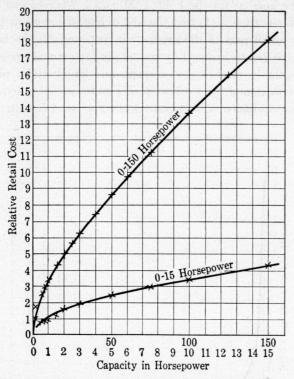

Fig. 5. Influence of Capacity on Retail Cost of Dynamos.

The influence of capacity on cost is further illustrated by the curves in Fig. 5. These curves cover a long line of 230-volt, constant-speed interpole direct-current motors built in another factory. These curves follow the ex-

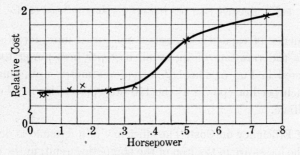

Fig. 6. Influence of Quantity of Production on Cost.

pected trend except for the irregularity at the lower end of the 0 to 15-hp curve. This irregularity is undoubtedly due to the influence of quantity production.

In the case of fractional-horsepower motors, quantity production becomes still more important, as shown by Fig. 6. Here the factory cost of a 1/4-horsepower motor is shown to be less than for the smaller 1/6- and 1/8-horsepower motors and nearly the same as for the 1/30, 1/20, and 1/3-horsepower motors. The reason for this situation is (1) that the cost of material alone in a small motor is but a very small part of the production cost, and (2) the labor cost per machine may be greatly reduced by special production machines and jigs and by special assembly machines, conveyors, and standardized methods. The large-scale production of the 1/4-horsepower motor justifies the maximum use of labor saving equipment and thus gives the low cost per unit.

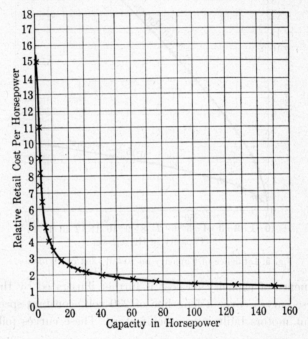

Fig. 7. Relative Cost per Horsepower with Increase of Size.

The influence of capacity on cost is illustrated more forcefully in Fig. 7 which shows the variation of the retail cost per horsepower for the line of motors covered in Fig. 5. The 1/2-horsepower motor costs almost fourteen times as much per horsepower as the 150 horsepower size for the same speed and line voltage.

Influence of Efficiency on Cost. The efficiency of a dynamo is determined by its losses. The losses are in the iron of the magnetic circuit, in the copper windings, and in mechanical friction. The iron losses may be reduced by using higher grade steels or by using more iron and operating at lower flux densities. Copper losses may be reduced by using copper of larger cross section and greater total weight. Bearing friction may be reduced by a change from sleeve to ball bearing. All of these changes suggested to reduce losses and improve efficiency will increase the cost of the machine. Hence, in general, it may be stated that an improvement in efficiency is accompanied by an increase in weight and cost of a dynamo. This statement assumes that the best principles of design are followed.

It is easily possible for a less efficient machine to be more costly than a very efficient one, and there are cases where an improvement in efficiency may be accompanied by a reduction in cost. For example, a dynamo built today like those in general use in 1890 would cost much more than a highly efficient modern dynamo of the same rating.

There is a limit to the improvement in efficiency in any dynamo which is determined by (1) the properties of materials which are available today, and (2) by an increase in windage losses and iron losses as the size of the dynamo is increased.

Most modern dynamos are built with a high efficiency. Exceptions are found in the case of generators for automobiles and aircraft, synchronous motors for electric clocks, and in other highly specialized applications.

Capacity *vs*. Weight. (1) Fractional-horsepower and small dynamos have high inherent losses and a relatively low efficiency, so that their output per pound of weight is lower than in larger machines. (2) The weight of any dynamo is made up of two parts: that due to the active iron and copper circuits, and that necessary for supporting the armature and magnetic circuit in the proper position. It is natural to expect that the weight of the supporting parts may be reduced relatively and that the ratio of the weight of active materials to total weight might be increased with the capacity of the machine. (3) The space factor* of both the iron and copper increase with the size of the machine.

All of the three factors stated in the preceding paragraph enter in to reduce the weight of a dynamo per horsepower, as shown in the curves of Fig. 8 for fractional-horsepower motors. The last two factors are influential in the case of larger machines, as shown by the curves of Fig. 9.

Capacity *vs*. Cycle of Service. The capacity rating given to dynamos is based on continuous load unless otherwise specified. Many types of load are intermittent. The user of a dynamo may wish to know what horsepower or kilowatts will be developed by a machine if the load comes in cycles (that is, to be on for a short interval, then off for another interval of time). The time cycles may be short, as for a few seconds or minutes, or long, covering several minutes or one or two hours. In any case, the best method of determining the proper capacity rating is by means of an actual test following the general pro-

---

* Space factor is the ratio of the effective volume of copper or iron to the total volume including insulation on copper conductors or iron laminations.

cedure outlined in Chap. XIII, Testing of Dynamos. However, a fair approximation can be made by calculation.

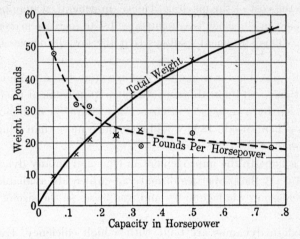

Fig. 8. Relation of Weight to Capacity of Electric Motors.

The heat produced in the armature of a dynamo is proportional to the square of the effective current flowing in it. If the current in the armature varies in accordance with some time cycle, the effective current during the

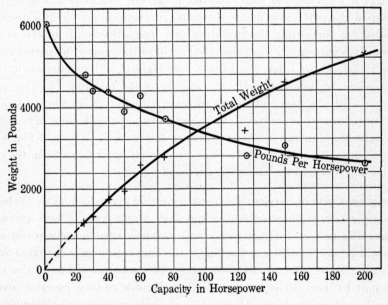

Fig. 9. Relation of Weight to Capacity for Large Motors.

cycle will be proportional to the square root of the average square of all current values during this cycle. For example, let it be assumed that the full-load current for a machine is 10 amperes and that a particular load cycle of 5 amperes for 1 minute, 10 amperes for 1 minute, and 20 amperes for 1 minute, and zero current for 1 minute, is continually repeated. The average square of the current per cycle is

$$\frac{5^2 + 10^2 + 20^2 + 0^2}{4} = 131.25$$

and the square root of this average square is $(131.25)^{1/2}. = 11.43$.

Since the normal current is 10 amperes and the heating proportional to 100, the armature would have 31.25 per cent excess heat generated in it and the machine could not be operated at this cycle continuously. The output by the dynamo during this cycle in ampere-minutes would be

$$5 + 10 + 20 + 0 = 35 \text{ ampere-minutes.}$$

A normal full load on the dynamo for the same time interval would produce

$$4 \times 10 = 40 \text{ ampere-minutes}$$

which shows that the total output on intermittent loads is less than on steady loads for the same temperature rise. Thus, a dynamo operated at double load for one unit interval and running idle for three unit intervals at its normal constant potential will be operating at full-load temperature but will be giving out only one half as much energy as when operating at full load continuously. Thus

$$I \text{ (Effective heating)} = \left(\frac{(2I)^2 + (0)^2}{1 + 3}\right)^{1/2} = I$$
$$(2I) \times 1 \text{ (min.)} = \tfrac{1}{2}I \times 4 \text{ (min.).}$$

The preceding calculations are based on heating in the armature copper alone. The heating for the field coils and the iron parts of the magnetic circuit would not change greatly, so that the resultant temperature rise for intermittent loads would be less than that indicated. *A dynamo constructed for intermittent service should have relatively low copper losses in the armature.*

Capacity *vs*. Ventilation. The load which a dynamo will carry under continuous or intermittent load depends upon the circulation of air over its parts. Large dynamos are generally of the open type, so that air circulates freely to all parts and the natural fanning action of the armature helps to cool the armature and the surrounding field poles and windings (Fig. 10, left). On small motors, the frame and housing restricts the free circulation of air to the armature and fields, and it has become customary to place fans on the armature which produce a forced circulation of air across the armature and fields.

Many applications of dynamos exist in dusty places, in rooms where explosive gases may form, in damp places, outdoors, and even under water. Most of these applications require a totally enclosed motor. In the totally enclosed motor there is no inside ventilation and all heat must be conducted away from the outer surface. The temperatures inside of these machines are more uniform (less difference between hot spots and other parts of the ma-

(*Cut at right Courtesy Century Electric Company*)

Fig. 10. Open Type Motors.

chine). A totally enclosed dynamo may have about one half the capacity rating it would have when operated as an open machine. This relationship is only approximate, depending on the length of frame, distribution of losses, and

Shock-Proof

Totally Enclosed and Dust-Proof

Explosion-Proof

Drip-Proof

(*Courtesy The Reliance Electric & Engineering Company*)

Fig. 11. Types of Enclosure for Motors.

speed. The only reliable method of determining the capacity is by actual test.

Some applications of motors require a semienclosed construction. This construction may be desired for (1) protection of human life, or (2) protection of the machine from mechanical hazards. This type of motor takes in air through small screened openings and forces the air around the armature and out of appropriate openings. Such a motor is illustrated in the upper left-hand view of Fig. 11.

Applications in dusty atmospheres, where high humidity exists, and outdoor installations, require a totally enclosed motor of the type illustrated in the upper right-hand view of Fig. 11. An enclosed explosion-proof motor is shown in the lower left view of Fig. 11 and a dripproof motor in the lower right.

Motor manufacturers have adopted a standardized type of construction for small and medium-sized d-c motors which permit the use of the motor under various external operating conditions by a change of the cover plates on the ventilating openings. The basic construction is shown in the right view of Fig. 10. As illustrated with the cover plates removed, the motor serves as an open-type motor. The addition of suitable cover plates will convert to the semi-enclosed or totally enclosed assemblage as suggested in the top views of Fig. 11. The use of the top cover plates alone gives a dripproof assembly and the addition of special cover plates on the lower opening may result in a splash-proof protection.

PROBLEMS

1. A 5-hp, 125-volt, 900-rpm, shunt motor is connected to a 230-volt source after a resistance has been connected in its field so that the field current I_f has the normal value for 125 volts. Assuming that the mechanical and electrical design of the motor makes it suitable for the new condition, what is the speed and hp rating for the new set of conditions?

2. Why are high-speed generators and motors used on airplanes?

3. A 115-volt, 1-hp (continuous rating) shunt motor is to be used on a duty cycle consisting of one-half load for 5 min followed by 200 per cent load for 5 min, followed by no load for 15 min. Will the motor be overheated?

4. If in Prob. 3 the service factor for rating be taken into account, would it be permissible to reduce the rest period to 10 min?

CHAPTER XVI

Commutation

General. The first experimental dynamos with commutators were built about the middle of the last century. These dynamos were equipped with metal brushes consisting of copper or brass leaves assembled in a bundle. Severe sparking occurred under load at the contact between the brushes and the commutators of these machines, and both the brushes and the commutators were blackened and burned away. It was only through constant and careful adjustment of the brushes that the operators were able to keep the sparking within reasonable limits. With the introduction of the electric street-railway system, the difficulties of commutation were multiplied because the transmission of power for the system required an operating voltage of 500 instead of 110 volts. The early designers held the theory that sparking at the brushes was due to poor contact, with the accompanying high-contact resistance. With this in mind, they sought relief through the use of metals having the lowest possible resistance. Failing to make any improvement in this direction, electric light (arc) carbons were tried for brushes. Immediately the sparking was checked, the commutators which had been made rough and black from much experimenting with metal brushes became polished by the carbons, and the sparking ceased. Thus the old theory about commutation was found faulty, and carbon, a relatively poor conductor of electricity, was proved to be a suitable material for brushes.

However, the discovery of the value of carbon as a brush material did not solve all of the problems of commutation. With the gradual change to higher generated voltages, higher speeds, and an increase in the rated capacity of machines, new problems in commutation arose. Today, commutation remains one of the chief limiting factors in the design, operation, and maintenance of direct-current machines.

Successful commutation is defined as the degree or quality of commutation which does not result in accumulative injury to commutator and brushes that will incapacitate them from carrying their rated current continuously and which does not require undue maintenance attention to enable them to so function.* The judging of commutation in this respect is difficult because of

* AIEE 501.

the difficulties in evaluating observable characteristics of commutation. From the standpoint of the average operator any machine which gives sparkless commutation under all conditions of speed and load may be thought of as having satisfactory commutation. *Ideal commutation is defined as that in which the current density is uniform at all points under the brush for all conditions of load and speed.* The significance of this latter statement will become evident after studying the succeeding articles in this chapter.

The elementary theory of commutation has been treated in the two chapters on Dynamo Principles, and Reactance Voltage and Interpoles. A more complete understanding of commutation involves the following factors:

1. Resistance commutation, or the inherent commutating properties of carbon brushes.

2. Action of interface films or the commutator.

3. The effect of the self-inductance of the coil during commutation.

4. The effect of the mutual inductance of other coils in which current is changing at the time a given coil is undergoing commutation.

5. Rotational or commutation emf's produced within a coil while undergoing commutation.

6. Transient conditions in the machine due to load changes.

7. Mechanical conditions and features of the machine.

Each of these factors in commutation will be treated in detail in the articles which follow, with the aim of giving a satisfactory picture of this phenomenon.

Resistance Commutation. The resistance between a carbon brush and the copper in the commutator is called **contact resistance.** The change in contact resistance between a given commutator bar and the brush during commutation tends to reverse the direction of current automatically. This process can be understood by taking a simple case of commutation and making the following assumptions:

1. The mica insulation between commutator bars has negligible thickness.

2. The brush width equals that of a commutator bar.

3. The instantaneous resistance between the brush and the commutator bar varies inversely as the area of contact.

4. The resistance of the armature coil and leads is neglected.

5. The armature coils have no self- or mutual inductance.

6. The armature coil does not cut any flux due to its motion during the time of commutation.

Resistance commutation under these assumptions is illustrated in Fig. 1 for a coil designated as c. At position 1 and the corresponding time of commutation zero, the coil c is in the proper position for commutation. If we assume a brush current of 100 amperes, the coil c is now carrying the full conductor current of 50 amperes. The resistance between the brush and the bar a is the normal brush-contact resistance R_b. The resistance between the brush and the bar b is infinite. Now, as the commutator moves to the right, the brush will touch the bar b, the resistance to b will fall from infinity to a finite value, and some current will pass from b to the brush. At the same time, the area of contact between the brush and a will decrease, the resistance will increase, and the current will decrease correspondingly. Position 2 of Fig. 1 shows one fourth of brush surface making contact with b and three fourths with a. If the contact resistance is uniform, the currents should divide in the ratio of 1 to 3, or 25 and 75 amperes, respectively. At position 3 of Fig. 1, the area of contact between a and b and the brush are equal, and the current in the coil c becomes zero. As the commutator advances still farther to the right, the area of contact between

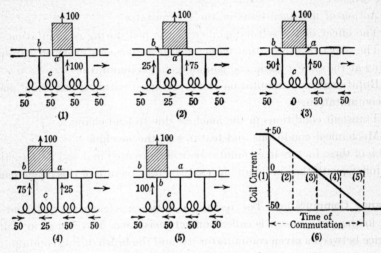

Fig. 1. Resistance Commutation.

the bar b and the brush becomes greater than for a. The increased current from b to the brush must come through the coil c, and thus the reversal of the current in c is being accomplished (position 4). Position 5 of the figure shows the completion of the process of commutation for the coil c and the complete reversal of the conductor current. The change of current with time is shown in part 6 of the figure. Such a straight-line change is called **linear commutation** and represents the ideal form for the reversal of current.

Linear commutation may also exist if the second assumption (that the brush width equals the bar width) is not fulfilled. In Fig. 2, the brush width is made equal to five commutator bars. This change serves to increase the time of commutation and to decrease the rate of current reversal. An analysis similar to the one used in the preceding case shows that linear or straight-line commutation results, since the current density underneath the brush will be constant.

Although linear commutation was easily attained by making certain limiting assumptions, when these assumptions are removed, the commutation tends to become nonlinear. When we drop the assumption (No. 4) that the armature coils have zero resistance, the relation will become nonlinear. This may be shown readily by giving the coils of the last example (Fig. 2) a resistance of 0.003 ohm each. Current through the coils during commutation will produce RI drops in the coils and these drops will unbalance potential drops from bar to brush. Figure 3 is like Fig. 2 except that the coil drops are shown and are added to the normal brush-contact drop. For a normal brush-contact drop of 1 volt, there will be one point or bar under the brush where this drop exists. Assume this point to exist at X. As bars are selected at either side of (X), the bar to brush-contact drop must equal the normal drop plus the RI drop

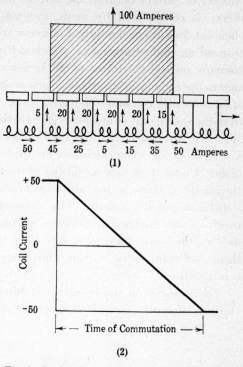

Fig. 2. Resistance Commutation with a Wide Brush.

in the armature coil. Thus it is evident that the drop from brush to bar will vary for different points along the brush arc. If the brush drop varies, it follows that the current density varies and the current change becomes nonlinear.

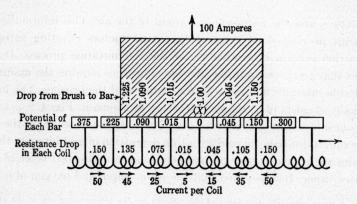

Fig. 3

Theory of Interface Films.* The preceding discussion of resistance commutation leaves the impression that commutation is a simple process. While the transfer of current between the brushes and copper seems simple, the actual theory is complicated by many varying factors of electrical, mechanical, chemical, and physical nature. For many years the problem of current transfer to rotating commutators was attacked from the angle of finding a suitable composition and treatment of the brushes, and to giving proper mechanical care to the commutator surface. Much progress was made in the developments of brushes and commutator maintenance with the result that commutation from the standpoint of brushes seemed satisfactory. With the advent of World War II it was discovered that the brushes on commutating d-c machines had a very short life when carried on an airplane to elevations of 25,000 feet and higher. Under these new conditions of operation brushes which might last for thousands of hours at low altitudes would be worn out in a few hours and sometimes in a few minutes. This discovery has led to extensive research to overcome this unexpected weakness of commutators at high altitudes. Remedies for the newly found difficulty have been discovered and the search for them has contributed to our knowledge of the processes of satisfactory commutation.

The research on the operation of brushes at high altitudes showed conclusively that the unexpected short life of brushes was due to the reduction

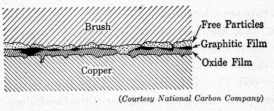

(Courtesy National Carbon Company)

Fig. 4. Interface Film between Brush and Copper.

in the oxygen and the water-vapor content of the air. This information combined with previous knowledge of the many factors effecting satisfactory commutation gives a better picture of the commutation process. It is now apparent that good commutation and life of brushes requires the maintenance of a suitable interface film between the copper and the brushes. The interface film usually consists of a complex structure as shown in Fig. 4.

This film structure consists of a thin layer of copper oxide on the surface of the commutator bars covered by a thin deposition of graphite. On this combined film there exists under normal conditions an adsorbed layer of oxygen and water vapor. It is assumed that the water vapor and oxygen film provide

* For a more complete discussion of this subject see the references given at the end of this chapter.

the boundary lubrication between the brush face and graphite copper oxide layer on the commutator bars. Free particles of dirt or carbon plus air fill the rest of the space between the brush and the copper. There seems to be rather general agreement that the cuprous oxide layer is one of the important constituents in the interface film. Apparently this copper oxide film provides the proper resistance for "resistance commutation." In addition, some investigators believe its presence reduces the wear on the carbon and copper surfaces.

An acceptance of the presence of the copper oxide layer gives one reason why metal brushes on copper failed to give satisfactory commutation. If the metal brush fits the copper commutator perfectly, there will be a seizure due to the atomic forces present (like attraction between Johansson blocks). This seizure will give a high coefficient of friction (loss) and will result in a rapid wear of the surfaces. The copper oxide film is worn off and the helpful effect of "resistance commutation" is absent. When some form of carbon is used for the brushes, the brush surface is highly porous and the brush wears down, depositing a thin film of carbon or graphite on the commutator. The carbon brush and the film of graphite adsorb water vapor giving a sort of lubricated surface having low friction. The lubricated surface plus the beneficial effect of the copper oxide film normally result in good commutation.

The copper oxide film forms naturally in the presence of oxygen and water vapor. At normal temperature a pure copper surface oxidizes slowly but as the temperature rises the process is hastened. A carbon brush bearing on a rotating copper commutator raises the temperature and tears lightly into the copper. The heated and raised fins of copper oxidize rapidly and the burnishing action of the brush proceeds to form a fine copper oxide surface having a chocolate brown color. The friction of the carbon brush does grind off some of the copper oxide continuously but the process of formation of new oxide likewise proceeds continuously so that under normal conditions the copper oxide film is established and maintained.

Several explanations have been offered for the beneficial effects of the water vapor on the graphite film. One covering the lubricating property of the film has been suggested. A second is that the water offers a catalytic action in aiding the oxidization of the copper, while the third suggests that electrolysis resulting from current across the interface film frees oxygen for attacking the copper and forming the desirable copper oxide film.

The graphite in the interface film which comes from the brush serves as a lubricant to reduce mechanical friction and the coefficient of friction between the rubbing surfaces. The particles of carbon in the interspace may act like ball bearings to reduce the friction. If the air in the brush-commutator space becomes ionized, it serves as a conducting path and constitutes an arc which is likely to produce an "electrical wear" on both the brushes and the commutator.

The preceding theory of the action of the interface film makes it easy to understand some examples of poor commutation. Obviously, any condition which destroys the copper oxide film or prevents its maintenance will result in commutating difficulties. Thus in the case of high-altitude operation the absence of a sufficient quantity of oxygen and water vapor destroys the lubricating property of the graphite film, and the brushes soon grind off the existing oxide film and brush dusting (rapid wear of brushes causing carbon dust) results. A remedy for this condition will be given in a subsequent article. At normal altitudes various contaminants in the air may prove very detrimental to commutation by acting upon the copper oxide film. Contaminants which are reducing agents such as vapors of carbon tetrachloride, alcohol, acetone, turpentine, chlorine, sulphur, acid, smoke, and other corrosive fumes reduce the copper oxide film and cause an increase in friction and wear upon the brushes and commutator itself. The only remedy for this condition is to keep the contaminants away from the machines. Other contaminants which are oxidizing agents may have an opposite effect upon the copper oxide film. Thus they accentuate the formation of copper oxide with the result that the film becomes too thick and the resistance too high. This condition may be remedied through the use of a brush which contains an abrasive or polishing material which will hold the copper oxide film to the proper thickness.

Aside from the chemical reactions which destroy the copper oxide film, there are physical causes of wear such as excess pressure of brushes or abrasive action arising from dirt in the surrounding air or excess abrasives in the brush itself.

Properties of Carbon as a Brush Material. There are certain basic properties of carbon which influence its application as a brush material. Some of these properties are resistivity, thermal conductivity, and abrasiveness.

Carbon has a resistivity many times that of copper. Its resistivity is greatly affected by the heat treatment as well as by the ingredients which are added in the formation of brushes. Its high resistivity is its chief advantage as a brush material. Carbon is one of the few solid substances which shows a negative temperature coefficient of resistance. This is one of its disadvantages as a brush material, as any unbalancing of the current through parallel paths formed by brushes on the same stud, or even on other studs in the case of wave windings, will raise the temperature of the overloaded brush, lower its resistance, and still further unbalance the currents.

The thermal conductivity of carbon brushes is far below that of metals. The relative magnitude of heat conduction depends upon the base material of the brush. Electric furnace graphite has a heat conductivity three times that of cast iron but coke base carbon has only 4 per cent conductivity of graphite. Most brushes are a combination of carbon and graphite and have a relatively low heat conduction. This poor conduction of heat is another disadvantage of carbon. When current densities in a brush are badly unbalanced, one portion of the brush heats up more rapidly than other portions, and the low thermal conductivity permits a considerable portion of the heat to accumulate at the spot where it is generated.

The abrasiveness of the brush determines the rate of wear of the commutator surface. Abrasiveness is produced by sharp-edged impurities introduced into the brush or by a grade of carbon which wears off, leaving a face with sharp edges. In early d-c commutating machines abrasive brushes were needed to wear down the hard mica segments. The introduction of undercutting has eliminated this need so that today brushes are nonabrasive or are designed to produce mild "polishing" action.

Criteria of Commutation. The criteria for judging commutation from the standpoint of brush performance depends on the factors of contact drop, brush friction, brush life, and commutator maintenance. Contact drop is the voltage

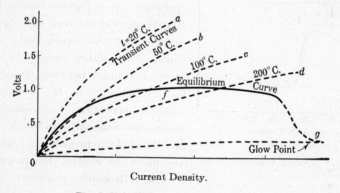

Fig. 5. Volts Drop at a Carbon Brush.

drop between the brush lead and the copper in the commutator bars. The magnitude of this voltage drop equals the sum of the potential differences in the brush itself, and in the interface film consisting of graphite film, loose particles, air space, and the copper oxide film. The temperature, thickness, and general condition of each of these parts will control the resulting contact drop. Thus for the solid carbon of the brush the resistance decreases with a rise in temperature and the temperature in turn will depend on the current density in the various parts of the contact circuit. It is impossible to make any complete analysis of these various factors but a somewhat speculative picture is given in Fig. 5. The dotted curves show how the contact drop in potential changes with the current density for a series of fixed temperatures. The full line or equilibrium curve shows the stable or final values of voltage drop which are likely to exist after a given current density is maintained for a time. The explanation of the shape of this equilibrium curve depends on the decrease of the brush (carbon) resistance with a rise in temperature and the change in resistance of interface film with the rise in current density and temperature. A part of the current from the brush passes through an ionized gaseous film (an arc). The voltage drop across an arc falls as the current rises and other unknown factors probably enter into the picture. The glow point is reached when the temperature becomes so high that the interface film is destroyed and a carbon-to-copper arc is carrying a very intense current. It should be noted that the contact drop is approximately constant over a wide range of current density so the brush contact loss may be assumed to be directly proportional to the currents. The magnitude of the contact drop depends on the composition and treatment of the brush, the brush pressure, and the condition of the commutator surface.

Brush friction is an item of major importance in relation to brush performance affecting the total mechanical energy loss of the machine, the commutator temperature, and the quietness of operation. Since friction results from the relative motion between the commutator surface and the brush face, anything which affects either surface, or the intimacy of contact between these surfaces, has an influence on the friction experienced in operation. Consequently, such things as temperature, brush pressure, and the abrasive properties of the brushes are likely to control the magnitude of friction. Research engineers of brush

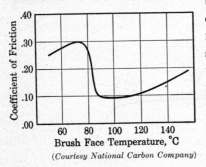

(*Courtesy National Carbon Company*)

Fig. 6. Effect of Brush Temperature on Coefficient of Friction.

manufacturers have discovered new information in some of these things previous to and during the period of World War II. The effect of brush-face temperature on the coefficient of friction for electrographitic brushes is shown in Fig. 6. Tests have shown that the changes in the coefficient of friction as indicated by this curve are due only to the effect of temperature since practically identical curves are obtained whether the brushes are operating with load current or under no-load conditions. The minimum coefficient of friction lies in the neighborhood of 100 C and may vary from 0.09 to 0.12, while the normal maximum at temperatures close to 70 C may vary from 0.26 to 0.32.

The life of brushes is an important factor in commutation. Studies by research engineers show the relationship between brush pressure and the rate of brush wear as illustrated in Fig. 7. The curve proves that brush wear is not necessarily reduced by a lowering of brush pressure. In fact, at pressures appreciably below the recommended optimum range, brush wear increases very rapidly. Electrical causes predominate as the source of brush wear at low pressures. At high pressures, mechanical wear predominates. Obviously, the optimum pressure for the grade of brush tested in Fig. 7 should lie within the range of 2 to 3 pounds per square inch.

The proper criterion of the operation of brushes is their performance in service over a long period of time. For years brush manufacturers have attempted to develop tests which might indicate the future performance of a given brush. These tests have covered such factors as resistivity, hardness, abrasiveness, density, coefficient of friction, and contact drop. All of these tests have failed to give positive assurance of future performance. In recent years another factor, the elastic property of the brush, has been studied and found to be very important in predicting future performance. The reason for the value of this factor probably lies in the importance of the intimate contact between the brush and commutator surface. Since no brush face or commutator surface can be expected to be mechanically perfect,

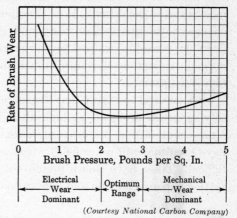

Fig. 7. Effect of Brush Pressure on Brush Wear.

there must be some radial movements between brushes and commutator. Hence it is obvious that the intimacy of contact would depend upon the elastic property of the brush. This elastic property has been termed **commutation factor** and its application to brush testing has added much to the uniformity of brush grades and performance.

Brush Grades. The composition and treatment of the various grades of brushes are designed to fit specific applications. A high contact drop usually requires a hard carbon brush and is employed where low current densities are used. This would apply in the case of the field current brush of a third-brush generator or for small commutating machines having a high voltage per bar. Graphitic and carbon-graphitic brushes are used for the average application requiring a contact drop of about 1 volt and current densities of 40 amperes per square inch. For high current densities and low contact drop graphite brushes impregnated with copper are used. The percentage of copper varies and may be as high as 50 per cent. These metal-graphite brushes are generally used on low voltage applications such as starting motors on automobiles. For applications which require some abrasive action or a mild polishing action, a suitable ingredient is added to the brush to give the desired effect. The selection of the proper grade of brush requires expert knowledge and the advice of the technical staff of the brush manufacturer should always be sought and followed.

The problems of rapid brush wear at high altitudes has been solved through the introduction of various ingredients into the brush. Both organic and inorganic ingredients have been used with a fair measure of success. Metallic halides have proved successful. Among the group of halides, lead iodide has been preferred and applied in service on war aircraft equipment. It was found that lead-iodide treated brushes are able to maintain a perfect film even in the most adverse conditions. It is presumed that in service the lead iodide is changed to an intermediate compound, cuprous iodide, which, being extremely unstable, is readily oxidized to cuprous oxide even in an atmosphere where the normal oxidization of copper would not take place. Thus the copper oxide film is maintained.

It is natural to expect that the successful application of metallic halides in solving brush problems at high altitudes may lead to their use in solving some commutating problems at normal altitudes. Exploratory applications have been made in other fields where commutating conditions are unusually difficult. These have shown promise of success and it is to be expected that further experimentation and application will follow in the postwar era.

Overcommutation and Undercommutation. The effect of the self-inductance or the current inertia of the coil undergoing commutation is to delay the current reversal in the coil during commutation. This will cause a current change known as **undercommutation,** as shown in the upper curve of Fig. 8. Undercommutation produces a rapid current change and a very high current density at the brush tip as the coil approaches the close of the commutating period. If the current reversal is not completed when the bar leaves the brush, sparking at the trailing brush tips is certain to result.

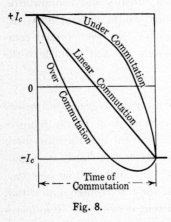

Fig. 8.

The rotational emf produced in a coil undergoing commutation by cutting the interpole field or a pole-tip flux should be in such a direction as to neutralize the effect of self-inductance and to aid the reversal of the current in the coil. If the interpole field is made too strong, the current will reverse too rapidly and **overcommutation** will result. Overcommutation is illustrated by the lower curve of Fig. 8. It may result in an excessive value of the reversed current with a correspondingly high current density at the leading brush tip or both brush tips.

The energy loss due to brush heating is the summation of the instantaneous current squared times the brush contact resistance. The instantaneous value of the power loss at the brush contact is $i^2 r_c$, where i is the instantaneous current flowing across the contact and r_c is the instantaneous value of the contact resistance. The average value of the instantaneous current squared will be greater in the curves shown for undercommutation or overcommutation in Fig. 8 than for linear commutation. Likewise, the average instantaneous resistance, which varies inversely as the contact area (for constant temperature), will be slightly greater for either under- or overcommutation than for linear commutation. If both the average values of the instantaneous current squared and the contact resistance are greater, it would be expected that the average of the product would be greater.

Thus, linear commutation gives the lowest possible heating effect at the brushes, in addition to its value in eliminating sparking.

It is readily conceivable that a small degree of under- or overcommutation might not produce sparking, yet the heating effect at the brushes would be greater than for linear commutation. Thus, sparkless commutation is *not necessarily ideal or perfect* commutation.

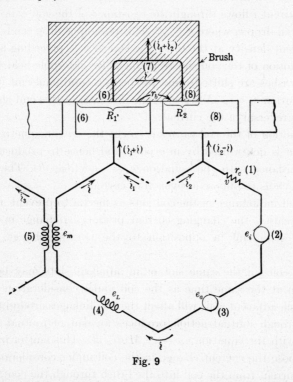

Fig. 9

The Equation of Commutation. From the preceding paragraphs, it is evident that the commutation of a direct-current machine depends on a large number of factors. A study of the relationship and the changing magnitude of these various factors becomes a complex task, yet it has been felt that a picture showing the electrical factors in commutation would be helpful to the student. Such a crude picture has been attempted in Fig. 9. A single armature coil is shown with its commutator bars short-circuited by a brush.

The coil under consideration together with commutator bars to which it is connected and the short-circuiting brush forms a closed circuit. In this closed circuit a circulating current will flow whenever the commutation is unsatisfactory. It should be noted that some current does flow in the coil itself much of the time during the commutation period but it is the *circulating current* or short-circuit current which is important in the present study.

The various potential differences which exist in the closed circuit of Fig. 9 determine the current i which results, and consequently the kind of commutation at any given instant. In accordance with Kirchhoff's laws, the algebraic sum of the potential differences in this closed circuit must be equal to zero at any instant.

The various factors in the circuit of the coil will be taken up in the numerical sequence shown in Fig. 9.

1. The current i flows through the resistance of the coil r_c in the direction of the potential drop v, where $v = ir_c$. This resistance drop tends to prevent a uniform current density at the brush, as shown in a preceding article.

2. The motion of the coil causes it to cut the interpole field (or a pole-tip flux if the brushes are shifted), and produces a rotational emf in accordance with the equation $e_i = - N(d\phi/dt)$. The direction of this emf should be such as to aid the reversal of the current.

3. The motion of the coil causes it to cut the cross-magnetizing armature flux (unless it is neutralized by interpole) and hence to produce a rotational emf, in accordance with the equation $e_a = - N(d\phi_a/dt)$. The direction of this emf is such as to oppose a reversal of current.

4. The self-inductance of the coil acts as inertia to prevent any change of current. In reality, the changing current produces a change in flux linkages which induces an emf in opposition to the current change. Thus, $e_L = - L(di/dt)$.

5. Other coils in the same slot or in adjacent slots may be undergoing commutation at the same time as the coil under consideration. The current change in such adjacent coils will affect the flux linkages around the given coil and thus through mutual action produces an emf of mutual induction, in accordance with the equation $e_M = - M(di_3/dt)$. This emf of mutual induction will oppose the current change in the coil under consideration.

6. The current from the coil into the brush through the contact resistance R_1 gives a fall of potential equal to $R_1(i_1 + i)$.

7. The circulating current i passing through the brush section produces a resistance drop $r_b i$.

8. Current entering the brush through the contact resistance R_2 will produce a resistance drop $R_2(i_2 - i)$, or $(R_2i_2 - R_2i)$.

The mathematical representation of the above eight factors may be written in the form of Kirchhoff's law by considering all factors which aid in the reversal of current as positive and all which retard as negative. Thus, taking the above factors in numerical sequence, we have

$$+r_ci + e_i - e_a - e_L - e_M + R_1(i_1 + i) + r_bi - R_2i_2 + R_2i = 0$$

where r_c = resistance of the coil plus leads

$\quad\;\; i$ = instantaneous circulating current in the coil and brush

$\quad e_i$ = rotational emf due to interpole flux

$\quad e_a$ = rotational emf due to armature cross-magnetizing flux

$\quad e_L$ = emf due to self-inductance of coil (numerical value)

$\quad e_M$ = emf due to mutual inductance (numerical value)

$\quad R_1$ = contact resistance from left segment to brush

$\quad R_2$ = contact resistance from right segment to brush

$\quad r_b$ = internal resistance of brush in path of current i

$\quad i_1$ = instantaneous current from next coil to the right

$\quad i_2$ = instantaneous current from next coil to the left

Rearranging and combining, we find

$$e_i + i(r_c + r_b + R_1 + R_2) + R_1i_1 = e_a + e_L + e_M + R_2i_2. \tag{1}$$

In general, the contact drops at R_1 and R_2 will be very nearly equal, and hence R_1i_1 and R_2i_2 will cancel. The resistance of the coil r_c and the internal resistance of the brush r_b are very low, particularly on machines of large capacity. Thus no serious error will result in omitting these factors. When interpoles are used or when the brushes are shifted to produce good commutation, the armature cross-magnetizing flux is neutralized or otherwise made ineffective. Applying these considerations, we may reduce equation 1 to the form

$$e_i + i(R_1 + R_2) = e_L + e_M. \tag{2}$$

This might be termed the **equation of commutation.** It is exceedingly useful in considering the electrical theory of commutation. The positive factors which will aid in the reversal of current in the coil undergoing commutation are the rotational emf e_i due to the interpole or pole-tip flux, and the contact drops due to the circulating current i. This rotational emf is frequently called the **commutating emf,** since it aids commutation. The negative factors are the emf's of self- and mutual induction. They are usually combined and are known as **reactance voltage.** Thus, equation (2) may be written in the form

$$\text{Commutating emf} + i(R_1 + R_2) = \text{reactance voltage} \tag{3}$$

and
$$i = \frac{\text{reactance voltage} - \text{commutating emf}}{R_1 + R_2}.$$

The latter expression shows how the circulating current i is determined. If the commutating emf can be made to neutralize the reactance voltage, then the circulating current i is zero and excellent commutation will result.

The absence of interpoles or the omission of brush shift reduces the commutating emf to zero. This leaves the double contact drop $i(R_1 + R_2)$ to balance the reactance voltage. Because of the characteristics of carbon, the brush-contact drop rises to a maximum of about 1 volt per contact, so that the expression $i(R_1 + R_2)$ has a limiting value of approximately 2 volts. Thus, in the absence of a commutating emf, a reactance voltage in excess of 2 volts will cause excessive sparking at the brushes.

Self-Inductance of an Armature Coil. Self-inductance is the property of an electric circuit which acts like inertia in opposing a change in the current. Quantitatively, the **self-inductance** of a circuit is defined as the *flux linkages produced per unit of current**.

$$L = N \frac{\phi}{I}. \tag{4}$$

Armature coils in modern dynamos are imbedded in slots in an iron core and the flux which links a coil passes largely through the iron walls of the slot

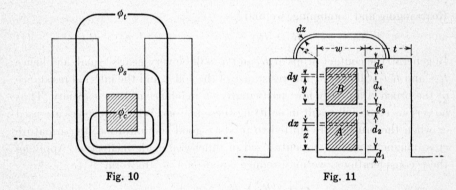

Fig. 10   Fig. 11

surrounding the coil. This flux linking the coil may be divided into five parts, three of which are illustrated in Fig. 10. One part, ϕ_c, passes through the section of the coil and each section of this flux links all of the coil conductor beneath it. A second part of the flux, ϕ_s, passes between the parallel faces of the slot and links all of the turns of the coil. A third part of the flux, ϕ_t, passes between tooth tips and also links all of the turns of the coil. A fourth part of the coil flux (not shown in Fig. 10) links the end turns of the coil. A fifth part existing in the ventilating ducts links the coil, but this part is small and will be neglected.

The equations for slot flux and flux linkages may be derived after making certain assumptions. Thus, Fig. 11 shows a slot containing two coil edges, each

* See page 385.

of which may consist of one conductor or a group of conductors. It will be assumed in this article that all inductors in each coil edge of the slot belong to one coil. The right side of coil A for a full pitch winding will be approximately a pole span away and will be in the top of a duplicate slot in position B, so that the coil edges A and B in Fig. 11 may be regarded as belonging to the same coil. The approximation will be made that all of the drop in magnetic potential occurs in the slot because the reluctance of the iron path is negligible compared to that of the air path across the slot.

Let N = the number of conductors in series per coil edge

$\quad\ I$ = the abamperes per conductor

$\quad w$ = width of slot in centimeters

$\quad\ l$ = length of tooth (cm) parallel to shaft exclusive of ventilating ducts

$\quad d$ = height (cm) of one coil edge

$\quad L$ = flux linkages per abampere

$$\phi = \frac{\text{mmf}}{\Re} = \frac{4\pi NI}{\dfrac{\text{length of path}}{\text{cross-sectional area of path}}} \quad \text{(for air)}.$$

To determine an expression for the self-inductance of a coil for the conditions assumed, it is necessary to determine the flux linkages for all of the flux paths of each coil side separately.

Part a. Flux linkages for coil side A due to flux through that coil (path ϕ_c, Fig. 10). In Fig. 11, let

$$d\phi_c = \text{flux through element } dx$$
$$d\Re = \text{reluctance through element } dx$$
$$d\phi_c = \frac{\text{mmf}}{d\Re}.$$

The conductors of the coil side A effective at x are all of those below the horizontal line through x, or $(x/d_2)N$. The current has been assumed to be one abampere. Hence

$$\text{Mmf at } x \text{ per abampere} = 4\pi \frac{x}{d_2} N$$

$$d\Re = \frac{w}{l\, dx}$$

$$d\phi_c = \frac{4\pi Nlx\, dx}{d_2 w}.$$

Flux linkages at x per abampere have the value $d\phi_c \times$ effective turns, or

$$d\phi_c \frac{x}{d_2} N = \frac{4\pi N^2 lx^2\, dx}{d_2{}^2 w}.$$

Flux linkages for lower coil through coil (from $x = 0$ to $x = d_2$) **have the** value

$$\frac{4\pi N^2 l}{d_2{}^2 w} \int_0^{d_2} x^2 \, dx = \frac{4\pi N^2 l d_2}{3w}.$$

Part *b*. Flux linkages per abampere for lower coil side A due to flux above coil (λ_s, Fig. 10) are given by the equation

$$\lambda_s = \frac{4\pi N^2}{w} (d_3 + d_4 + d_5) l$$

Flux linkages (per abampere) $= 4\pi N^2 \dfrac{(d_3 + d_4 + d_5) l}{w}.$

Part *c*. Flux linkages for the lower coil side A due to the tooth tip flux (ϕ_t, Fig. 10).

The tooth-tip flux cannot be calculated accurately because the path of the tooth-tip flux depends on the air-gap length, position of armature slot, and other factors. The usual approximation is to assume that all flux passes from the face of one tooth to the next adjacent tooth along arcs of radius z and a straight section w, as indicated in Fig. 11. Thus for the tooth-tip flux

Mmf (per abampere) $= 4\pi N$

Reluctance per element $dz = \dfrac{\pi z + w}{l \, dz}$

Permeance $\left(\dfrac{1}{\mathcal{R}}\right)$ per element $dz = \dfrac{l \, dz}{\pi z + w}$

Permeance for path $= l \displaystyle\int_0^t \frac{dz}{\pi z + w} = \frac{l}{\pi} \log_e \frac{\pi t + w}{w}.$

Therefore

Flux linkages (per abampere) $= 4lN^2 \log_e \dfrac{\pi t + w}{w}.$

Flux linkages through the upper coil B due to current in it are the same as for lower coil A in part *a*, since $d_2 = d_4$. Similarly, the flux linkages due to upper coil through height d_5 are equal to

$$4\pi N^2 \frac{d_5 l}{w}$$

and flux linkages due to tooth-tip linkages are the same as for the lower coil, as developed in part *c*.

Combining the above components of flux linkages per abampere for the parts A and B of the coil lying in iron slots gives

Part a   Part c

$$2\left(\frac{4}{3w}\, \pi N^2 l d_2\right) + 2\left(4lN^2 \log_e \frac{\pi t + w}{w}\right)$$

Part b

$$+ \, 4\pi N^2 \frac{(d_3 + d_4 + d_5) l}{w} + 4\pi N^2 \frac{d_5 l}{w}.$$

The self-inductance of an armature coil is defined as the flux linkages per unit current; hence the above expression is that of the self-inductance of the coil AB for a full-pitch winding having a brush arc equal to one commutator bar in width and one coil per slot. Simplifying the above we find that the self-inductance L of an armature coil is

$$L = \frac{4\pi l N^2}{w} \left\{ \frac{2}{3} d_2 + d_3 + d_4 + 2d_5 + \frac{2w}{\pi} \log_e \frac{\pi t + w}{w} \right\} . \qquad (5)$$

The flux due to the end turns should be included in the calculation of the self-inductance of the coil, but the irregular geometry of the adjacent iron parts makes it quite difficult to calculate this flux. Also, the magnitude of this flux is small relative to the part in the slots. Equation 5 involves some rather broad approximations, yet it serves to show how the various factors affect the self-inductance of a coil.

The self-inductance of the coil will depend upon the shape of the slot. Some different slot forms are shown in Fig. 12. A wide slot as illustrated at a reduces the flux across the slot, and therefore reduces the self-inductance of the coil. A narrow deep slot gives a very high self-inductance and makes good commutation difficult. Semienclosed slots as shown at c and d of Fig. 12 are often used in very small motors. Obviously, such slot forms produce relatively higher flux linkages and self-inductance, but they are not particularly objectionable on machines of small capacity.

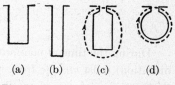

(a)   (b)   (c)   (d)

Fig. 12. Forms of Armature Slots.

Mutual Inductance of Armature Coils. Commutation of armature coils should take place when those coils are in the neutral zone between the pole tips. When any given coil is being commutated in this position, it follows that other coils lying in the same slot or in adjacent slots should likewise be undergoing commutation. The current change in these latter coils produces a change of flux linking the particular coil under consideration. This change in flux linkages gives rise to a mutual inductance between these coils. For the particular case where there are two coil sides per slot (side by side) and a full-pitch winding, the mutual inductance would be approximately equal to the self-inductance. Where the two coil sides are in the top and bottom of the slot, the mutual inductance is somewhat less than the self-inductance. Such high values of mutual inductance may be avoided by short-chording the winding, so that both coil sides in the same slot are not undergoing commutation at exactly the same time. Some mutual effect will exist even if the coil sides are in different slots at the time of commutation.

A brush covering several segments may produce commutation of two or more coils lying in the same slot. The current change in each of these coils will cause a change in the flux linkages with the other coils and thus the mutual inductance will be detrimental to good commutation.

Formulas may be derived for calculating mutual inductance but because of the large number of variables involved, these formulas are inaccurate and of little value.

Reactance Voltage. In considering the subject of commutation, consideration is not generally given separately to either the self or mutual inductance of coils, but to the algebraic sum of the emf's due to self- and mutual inductance, which is called **reactance voltage** and is denoted by symbol RV:

$$RV = L \frac{di}{dt} + M \frac{di_1}{dt}.$$

This expression for the numerical value of the reactance voltage may be simplified by assuming an equivalent value of mutual inductance M_e so that di_1/dt may be equal to di/dt. Thus

$$RV = (L + M_e) \frac{di}{dt}.$$

During the time of commutation, the current in the coil (undergoing commutation) must change from that in one armature path to that in the other, that is, from $+I_c$ to $-I_c$, so that there is a total change of $2I_c$ during this time T_c. Hence the average reactance voltage is

$$(L + M_e) \frac{2I_c}{T_c}. \tag{6}$$

This formula for average reactance voltage may be applied to a specific case as follows. Assume that a coil contains four turns and that the number of flux linkages per turn per ampere is 400. Let the current per conductor be 50 amperes. The brush arc is one-hundredth of the commutator circumference and the armature turns at 1200 rpm. Substituting in equation 6, we find

$$RV = \frac{400 \times 4 \times 2 \times 50}{1/100 \times 1/20 \times 10^8} = 3.2 \text{ volts.}$$

The average reactance voltage of a dynamo will depend upon the number of turns per coil, the width of the brush, the current per armature path, and the speed. From equation 6, it is obvious that the average reactance voltage will vary directly as the current per path (I_c) and as the speed, since the time of commutation T_c is inversely proportional to the speed. The usual problem in armature and commutator design contemplates a fixed speed and number of armature paths, so that the consideration of reactance voltage depends upon the self- and mutual inductance of the coil and the time of commutation as affected by the brush width. These variables will be discussed in the following paragraph.

The expression for the self-inductance of a coil given in equation 5 shows that the self-inductance varies as the square of the number of turns in the coil. A coil having three turns lying in one slot has a certain self-inductance. This concentrated coil of three turns may be divided into three one-turn coils connected to separate commutator bars as shown in parts 1, 2, and 3 of Fig. 13. The self-inductance of the new one-turn coils will be one-ninth as much as for the concentrated three-turn coil. If the three-turn coil had a brush one bar wide and if the one-turn coils have a brush one bar wide (really one-third that of the former), the time of commutation will be reduced to one-third. Hence the average reactance voltage will be determined by a self-inductance of one-ninth and a time of commutation of one-third. This gives a reactance voltage one-third as great as for the three-turn coil. Thus it will follow that if a concentrated coil of N turns lying in one slot be split up into coils of n turns, the resulting reactance voltage will be reduced to n/N of its former value, provided that the coils are commutated by brushes one bar wide, respectively.

For the case of Fig. 13, let it be assumed that a brush is used which covers three commutator bars. Then, between the tips of a brush, there are three

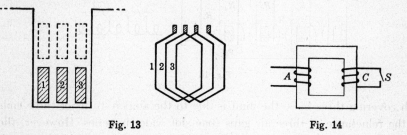

Fig. 13   Fig. 14

turns of the three coils in series and these tend to act like the three turns of a concentrated coil. Thus the flux linkages should be the same in both cases, the current change is the same, and the time of commutation is the same. With all factors affecting reactance voltage the same, it would seem that, for the given assumptions, the reactance voltage for the three-turn concentrated coil and the three one-turn coils should be the same. This assumption is correct, but the actual commutation of the machine will be better in the case having three one-turn coils. This follows because the three turns of the one-turn coils are separated and are short-circuited by the brush. This short-circuit by the brush permits a beneficial mutual action between these coils while they are undergoing commutation. This action is illustrated by Fig. 14, where the coil A has a certain self-inductance due to its flux linkages with the magnetic circuit. If, now, the switch S for the coil C be closed, any change in the flux in the core will induce a current in the coil C which, in accordance with Lenz's law, will oppose the flux change. Hence the flux linkages of the coil A will be reduced and the mutual inductance of the short-circuited coil C has reduced the apparent self-inductance of A. In a similar manner, the three coils of Fig. 13 serve to reduce the apparent self-inductance of that one of their number which is just completing its commutating period.

A brush may be wide enough to connect coils lying in two or more adjacent slots. In this case, the consideration of the resulting reactance voltage becomes more involved. In Fig. 15, coils in three adjacent slots are short-circuited by the brush. These coils may have one or more turns each. The self-inductance of each coil and, in turn, that of the group of short-circuited coils, will depend on the flux change which links each individual coil. The flux change which links each coil may consist of two parts — one part ϕ_s linking the individual slot in which this coil is placed, and a part ϕ_t, which links the group of coils which is short-circuited. If the teeth are sufficiently wide at the top and at the root, the reluctance of the iron path for the slot flux will be negligible. In this case, the total flux linking the coil will be the same whether the brush covers one bar or three bars. For one bar brush width, the mmf is due to the turns of one coil and the reluctance is that due to the air gap of one slot, while for the

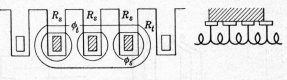

Fig. 15

brush covering three bars, the mmf is due to the ampere-turns of three coils and the reluctance of three air gaps (one slot wide) in series. However, the situation will be different if the teeth are narrow at the roots with corresponding appreciable reluctance in the root portion of the slot flux path. Here the ratio of the mmf to the reluctance will be greater for the three coils considered as a group than for the individual coils. Referring to Fig. 15, we note that R_s represents the reluctance of the air gap in the slot above a coil side and R_t represents the reluctance of the teeth. Hence

$$\text{Reluctance to flux } \phi_s \text{ (encircling one slot)} = R_s + 2R_t$$
$$\text{Reluctance to flux } \phi_t \text{ (encircling three slots)} = 3R_s + 2R_t.$$

Obviously, the relative reluctance to ϕ_t is less than to ϕ_s if R_t has any appreciable magnitude. Thus a component flux ϕ_t will be present which would not exist in the case in which the brush covers only one commutator bar. The tendency is for the wide brush to cause a greater flux change to link each individual coil for the example being considered. The self-inductance of the coil depends directly on the flux change with which it is linked. The self-inductance of the three coils as a group is equal to the sum of the self-inductances of the three coils. The increase in the width of the brush from one to three commutator bars has tripled the time of commutation. The reactance voltage is then determined largely by a tripling of both the self-inductance and the time of commutation, which would give no change in reactance voltage except that produced by the flux increase due to the reluctance of narrow teeth. This apparent increase in reactance voltage may be offset by the beneficial effect to commutation resulting from the mutual action of the short-circuited coils previously explained in this article. The latter action is less effective because the coils lie in separate slots.

The wide brush does not present any problem from the standpoint of reactance voltage and it tends to reduce the length and cost of the commutator, yet it has definite limitations from other angles. A brush short-circuiting several coils prolongs the period during which short-circuited currents may flow in the coils during commutation and thus increases the heating of both the coils and the brushes (unless the current reversal is linear). A wide brush means a wide commutating zone, and hence a longer interpole arc and a wider interpole. The widening of the interpole increases the leakage flux from both the main pole and the interpole. Hence a compromise must be made in choosing a suitable brush arc and brush width.

Rotational EMF. A rotational emf is induced in the inductors of a coil by the motion of the coil during the time of commutation. The flux cut by the motion may be produced by the armature field, by the main field coils, or by the interpole field. The emf induced by cutting the pole-tip flux (main field) and the interpole field is called a **commutating emf,** since it is generally used to aid commutation.

The load current in the coils of the armature produces a cross-magnetizing armature reaction, as explained on page 75. The mmf of this reaction tends to produce a flux at right angles to the main field flux. This cross flux will induce a rotational emf which opposes the reversal of the current in a coil during commutation. This action can be observed from Fig. 16, which represents a bipolar direct-current generator rotating clockwise that has the brushes on the mechanical neutral. The emf's induced by the main field are indicated by the conventional symbols. Any load current result-

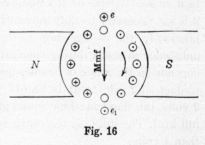

Fig. 16

ing from these emf's will tend to produce a cross field having the direction indicated by the arrow Mmf. The inductors on the line of the mechanical neutral will cut the cross field due to their rotation and induce component emf's having a direction as indicated by the circles e and e_1. Obviously, the direction of these component emf's is such as to tend to continue the flow of current and oppose commutation. The magnitude of this rotational emf is proportional to the load current.

One method of neutralizing reactance voltage is the production of a commutating emf through a shift of the brushes. A proper forward shift of the brushes on a generator or backward on a motor will bring the coil under commutation within a pole-tip flux of the correct sign to aid in commutation. The pole-tip flux depends somewhat on armature reaction and may vary with the load current. Thus, in Fig. 17, the line aa' represents the commutating emf on a shunt machine for the zero to full-load range. The effect of armature reaction is to reduce the commutating emf as the load increases.

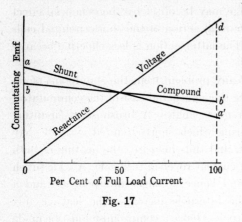

Fig. 17

The average reactance voltage has been shown in equation 6 to be $2I_c(L + M_e)/T_c$. Assuming a constant speed of rotation and a constant permeability of the flux paths, all factors of this equation are constant except I_c. Thus the reactance voltage will vary directly as the load, or as shown by the line od in Fig. 17. The sign of the reactance voltage od is opposite that of the commutating voltage aa'.

A study of the lines aa' and od shows that for the given brush setting the commutating voltage can neutralize the reactance voltage for only one load, namely, that at 50 per cent. For any other load an exact neutralization could be secured by shifting the brushes and thus moving the line aa' up or down until it crosses the line od at a point corresponding to the given load. In general, it is not necessary to shift the brushes with each change in load. As explained previously, the voltage drop at the brush contacts counteracts some voltage unbalance in a coil during commutation. The permissible voltage unbalance depends on the grade of brushes used but is usually of the order of 1 volt per contact, or 2 volts total. In Fig. 17, if the line oa and the line $a'd$ do not exceed 2 volts, the shunt machine would give satisfactory commutation from zero to full load. The full-load reactance voltage would be limited to something less than 4 volts.

A compound machine increases its main field mmf and flux as the load comes on the machine. This increase of mmf tends to offset the cross-magnetizing mmf and helps to maintain the pole-tip flux under changes in load. Line bb' represents the commutating emf for a typical compound dynamo. The slope of the line bb' is inversely proportional to the degree of compounding of the machine. The general statements made concerning the shunt machine apply here equally well. The characteristic bb' will permit a slightly larger reactance voltage for a fixed shift of the brushes than in the case of a shunt machine.

The ideal method of producing a commutating emf to neutralize reactance voltage is by means of interpoles. The interpole is placed on the line of the mechanical neutral and produces a flux which is cut by the rotational motion of the coil while it is undergoing commutation. The interpole winding is in series with the armature and produces a mmf proportional to the load current. Thus the interpole flux and the resulting commutating emf are proportional to the load until the interpole core approaches saturation. It has been shown that both the counter-rotational emf due to cross-magnetizing armature reaction and the reactance voltage vary directly with the load. Thus, within cer-

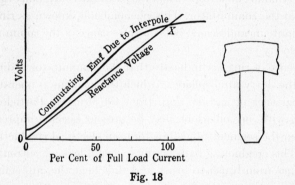

Fig. 18

tain limits, it should be possible for the commutating emf due to interpoles to neutralize both of these voltages which oppose commutation. Figure 18 illustrates how this result may be obtained. The interpole commutating emf has the trend of a typical magnetization curve. The knee in this curve is due to the saturation in the interpole core and to the leakage flux from the interpole to the main field cores. The curvature at the knee is effectively reduced in practice by making a taper at the armature end of the interpole (Fig. 18). This taper causes the interpole tip to become saturated before the main part of the core and it reduces the amount of leakage flux from the interpole.

The knee of the commutating emf curve due to the interpole should not be reached at any load below the maximum steady load at which good commutation is desired.

Brush Sparking. Direct-current dynamos sometimes show sparks at the leading or the trailing tips of the brushes. Such sparking, which is confined to the immediate vicinity of the brushes, is known as **sparking at the brushes** and should not be confused with other luminous phenomena to be considered subsequently. Brush sparking results from (a) poor commutation due to a lack of balance of the several electrical factors of commutation considered in the preceding articles, and (b) from mechanical defects or unbalances in the machine. The mechanical factors affecting commutation will be considered later in this chapter.

The sparks which appear at brushes may vary in size from those which are minute up to those which are relatively large. The color of sparks may vary through the shades of blue, white, or red. The damage produced by the sparking varies with the intensity of the sparks and with the color. Blue sparks are the least harmful and red (colored by the burning of carbon) the most harmful. Sparking tends to burn the carbon brushes, makes them hot, reduces their contact area, and makes them rough or pitted. Sparking likewise overheats the commutator, burns away the copper, and blackens and roughens its surface.

Ring Fire. Dynamos under operation may exhibit continuous rings or streaks of fire around the commutator. This phenomenon, known as **ring fire,** is produced by minute incandescent spots on the surface of the commutator moving at a high velocity.

The presence of ring fire indicates that the commutator is dirty. Dirt may come from the dusty atmosphere in which the machine is operated, or it may consist of particles of carbon worn from the brushes. Particles from either source along with any oil which may be present become impregnated in the mica between the segments and thus form an electrical conducting path from bar to bar. This conducting path permits a small leakage current to pass from bar to bar and from brush to brush and thus heat the impregnated particles of dirt. A few of these particles may be heated to incandescence as they pass beneath a brush and then the leakage current may be sufficient to maintain this glow as they are carried around by the commutator.

Ring fire is not a direct phenomenon of commutation, but by overheating the commutator and brushes it interferes with commutation and may lead to flashing or flashover. It grows progressively worse with time. Ring fire can be remedied by removing the cause (that is, by cleaning the commutator).

Flashing under Steady State. Flashing consists of electric arcs from *bar to bar* on the surface of the commutator. The arcs usually occur on bars approximately midway between the brushes. This phenomenon is distinct from both brush sparking and ring fire.

One or more armature coils are connected to adjacent bars on the armature, depending on the type of winding used. As a coil or series of coils cuts the flux due to the main field poles, an emf is induced in it. If a short-circuit develops within the coil or on the commutator bars to which this coil is connected, a large current will flow. Since the bars are separated by a very thin sheet of micanite, it is reasonable to suppose that a short-circuit consisting of an arc might form between these bars under suitable conditions. Such an arc would be called **flashing.**

Flashing may be started in two ways. The incandescent particles of ring fire produce a small heated and ionized gas region which is very conducive to the formation of an electric arc. In a similar manner, where ring fire is absent, the ionized gas film between the brushes and commutator may be carried along on the surface of the commutator to a point where conditions are favorable for the formation of an electric arc.

The criterion for flashing is not only the presence of an ionized gas but also the proper relation between arc and coil characteristics. The voltage-current characteristics of electric arcs differ widely with electrode material, etc. In general, however, the voltage across the arc varies inversely with the current along a curve like the arc characteristic of Fig. 19. The external characteristic of the load of a single coil under steady state is the straight line representing

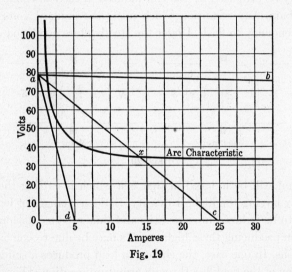

Fig. 19

terminal volts or generated emf minus RI voltage drop plotted against conductor current. Such coil characteristics are represented by the lines ab, ac, and ad. The line ab represents a coil of low resistance and probably a machine of large capacity. The line ac represents a coil of medium resistance and probably a machine of medium capacity. The line ad represents a coil of high resistance placed on a machine of low capacity. If an arc starts on a coil having an external characteristic like ab, it is obvious that an enormous current will flow. Such a heavy arc would probably melt pools of copper on the segments, throw off molten copper, and leave little craters in the copper. Craters thus formed would wear down and roughen the carbon brushes rapidly.

A coil that has the characteristic given by the line ac (Fig. 19) would be less likely to flash and even if it did flash, the arc current would be definitely limited to that corresponding to point x where line ac crosses the arc characteristic. A coil that has the characteristic shown by line ad would never flash.

Flashing does not occur on machines of small capacity because the coil characteristic is always below the arc characteristic. On machines of larger capacity, the formation of arcs may be prevented under steady-state conditions by keeping the bar-to-bar voltage low, so that it does not cross the arc characteristic. However, a low bar-to-bar voltage secured through the use of very narrow segments may not prevent flashing because a flash may develop across a series of narrow segments. As a general rule, the potential distribution along the commutator surface should not exceed 100 volts per inch. Since it takes some time for a flash to develop, an increase in the speed of a machine will reduce its tendency to flash.

Flashing under Transient Loads. A flash or arc across two adjacent commutator bars may be produced by the emf induced in the coil connected to those commutator bars. Any condition which raises the induced volts per coil will increase the tendency to flash. Under the steady-state condition of operation,

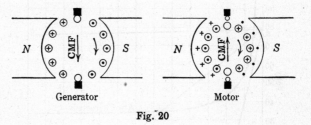

Fig. 20

the highest emf will be induced in that coil which is cutting the part of the main field flux having the highest density. Sudden changes of load will cause higher emf's to be induced in some coils and thus produce flashing. The transient condition producing these higher emf's may be due to one or both of two different actions. In one case, the change in load produces a sudden change in the distribution of the field flux through armature reaction. The rotational emf induced in a certain coil or coils passing through a point of high flux density under a pole tip is suddenly raised and a flash results. This action may be produced by a heavy overload under a steady-state condition. The other cause of flashes due to transients may be understood by considering the induced voltage (transformer action) resulting from sudden changes in cross flux. This action can be studied in Fig. 20 where a bipolar generator is considered to be operating under load and to have a clockwise rotation. The direction of the induced emf's and the current is indicated by the conventional symbols. The direction of the cross-magnetizing field is given as CMF. If the load is suddenly removed from this generator by tripping circuit breakers, the field

CMF tends to fall to zero. This change in flux will induce emf's in the coils on the armature in accordance with Lenz's law. The direction of the emf's will be the same as that of the rotational emf's already present. Hence the effect of this transient load change is to greatly increase the volts induced per bar. A similar method of reasoning shows that a sudden increase in load on a generator will reduce the resultant induced emf per bar. Thus a generator tends to flash when the load is suddenly removed or reduced in magnitude.

In a motor, the direction of current flow in the armature is opposite to that of the induced counter emf. Thus it is reasonable to assume that a motor would tend to flash when a sudden load is applied. In Fig. 20, the bipolar motor has been given the same field polarity and direction of rotation as the generator. The direction of current flow under load (symbols in circles) will be opposite that for the generator, but the counter emf (symbols outside circles) has the same direction as in the generator. A sudden load thrown upon the motor will give a transient increase in the cross flux CMF. In accordance with Lenz's law, the rise in cross flux will induce an emf in the armature inductors in the same direction as the rotational emf already present. Thus a motor has a rise in coil emf and tends to flash with a sudden rise in load. Conversely, a sudden drop in load does not produce flashing in motors of normal design.

It is evident from Fig. 20 that a transient in the cross flux induces the largest emf in those inductors which are near the center of the pole faces. Thus flashing starts with a coil that has sides near the center of the pole face. Under severe transient conditions of load several coils are likely to flash at once. Since the voltage drop across an arc is low, flashes across several bars *on a motor* will raise the voltage per bar across the remaining bars to the point where the flashes will occur progressively across all bars. Such progressive action results in a single arc or short circuit from brush to brush. This latter phenomenon is called a **flashover** and causes protective apparatus to disconnect the machine from the system. The damage done by a flashover depends on the time that the arc persists before being interrupted. Flashing and flashover can be prevented by the use of a compensating winding in the pole faces.

Special Electrical Causes of Poor Commutation. Electrical troubles sometimes develop within an armature and interfere with the normal process of commutation. A short-circuited coil will produce excess heating of that coil and may produce sparking at the brushes. An open circuit in the winding will likewise produce a transient condition in the current flow in the armature paths and thus cause sparking at the brushes. A ground within the armature may also produce sparking if another ground exists somewhere on the distribution system so as to permit a fluctuating current to flow in the grounded circuit. All of these troubles represent an abnormal condition and should be suspected whenever sparking appears suddenly at the brushes under normal load conditions.

Any design of an armature which permits a nonuniform distribution of coils with respect to the commutator bars will interfere with ideal commutation. In a design having six coil sides per slot, there are three coils which are concentrated in single slots on the armature, but the commutator bars for these coils are uniformly distributed around the commutator. A brush setting which gives the proper time of commutation for one of these three coils cannot be correct for the other two. Thus a tendency for sparking exists. In a similar manner, the presence of a dummy coil within the armature gives rise to a nonuniform distribution of armature coils with respect to the commutator-bar distribution and may produce sparking.

Mechanical Aspects of Commutation. The preceding articles of this chapter have emphasized the various electrical factors in securing good commutation. The interpole has been shown to be the most outstanding medium for improving commutation from the electrical standpoint. Of *equal* or even *greater* importance than the electrical considerations, are several mechanical factors. These factors enter into the design, the initial operation, and the later operation of direct-current dynamos. These mechanical factors may be classed as (*a*) selection of the proper brush, (*b*) treatment of commutators, and (*c*) mechanical adjustments for improving commutation.

Treatment of Commutators. Until 1905, practically all direct-current machines used commutators having mica flush with the copper, but about that time undercutting of commutators was tried on railway motors and was found very beneficial. Approximately ten years later, the undercut commutator was applied to industrial machines and today it is standard for all except a few special machines.

Undercutting, also called **commutator slotting** and **commutator grooving,** consists in removing the mica between the commutator bars to a depth of about 1/32 to 3/64 inch below the surface of the commutator. This leaves only the copper in contact with the brushes and permits the use of a soft brush having high conductivity. The advantages of undercutting are the increased life of the commutator and brushes, the elimination of flat spots and sparking due to high mica, a decrease in commutator heating, and a large reduction in friction losses. The friction loss with an abrasive brush operated at a pressure of 2 pounds per square inch on the average machine will be about $2\frac{1}{2}$ per cent of the machine's capacity. On a 100-kilowatt generator operating 10 hours per day, 300 days per year, at a power rate of $1\frac{1}{2}$ cents per kilowatt hour, this friction loss costs $112.50 per year. Most of this expense can be saved by the use of the proper brush on an undercut commutator.

Commutator undercutting may be done with circular milling saws driven by some convenient means or by hand tools, such as broken hack-saw blades or a commutator slotting file. Lubricants should never be used on undercut commutators, as they will hold carbon dust and other dirt in the slots and thus may cause short circuits, ring fire, or flashing.

A commutator wears down with use due to the abrasive action of the brushes, and to sparking and flashing (if present). An undercut commutator may wear down uniformly and may merely need new brushes and further undercutting as time goes by. More often, however, there will be some sparking present which will burn and roughen the commutator with time. If flashing should occur, the commutator may be roughened badly. On a flush mica commutator, the mica may be harder than the copper and then high mica will develop as the copper wears away more rapidly. High mica may cause the brush to jump from mica to bar and thus wear flat places (called **flats**) on the face of the commutator bars. There is some shrinkage of the mica with time and unless the commutator is tightened, a bar may move outward due to centrifugal force and develop a "high bar." Wear in the bearings may permit the commutator to vibrate and to move out of center. This freedom of movement coupled with the abrasive action of the brushes may wear the commutator eccentric. Sparking or the presence of oil, or both, will make a commutator dirty.

The unfavorable mechanical conditions of the commutator suggested above tend to promote brush sparking, ring fire, or flashing. The cure for these conditions is to be found in sanding, stoning, grinding, or turning of the commutator. If the commutator is merely dirty or slightly roughened, it should be cleaned with gasoline and then sanded while being rotated by external means or by its own power. Sanding should be done by placing fine sandpaper under a wooden block formed to fit the curvature of the commutator. *Never use emery cloth for polishing a commutator* since emery powder is a conductor and it may become imbedded in the mica and produce a short circuit.

Ordinary flats on a commutator may be removed by "stoning." A very fine grade of stone cut to fit the commutator is pressed against the rotating commutator and caused to travel slowly parallel to the shaft.

If the commutator is badly worn, it should be turned or ground. This can be done by placing the armature in a lathe or by special equipment attached direct to the frame of the dynamo. A diamond-pointed tool and small cuts should be used for turning a commutator. Grinding is done by means of a rotating grinding stone. If grinding is performed on the machine, the armature may be driven at normal speed and given a commutator surface true for operating conditions. A commutator which is turned should be given a fine polish by grinding or stoning before being put back in service.

Mechanical Adjustments for Improving Commutation. A new machine just assembled in the factory or an old one which has been in use for some years may need certain mechanical adjustments to produce good commutation. Some of these adjustments are considered in the following paragraphs.

Brushes must be set so that commutation of the current in the armature coils occurs at the right time. The rocker arm should be adjusted to give the proper brush setting for electrical neutral while the machine is under load. Occasionally, the spacing of the brush studs is such that it is impossible to place all brush sets in the best position for commutation.

In new machines, the assembly of the main pole cores and interpole core may be such as to produce an unbalance in the field fluxes. Such unbalances cause circulating current in the armature or poor commutation. The same result may happen in old machines where the bearings wear and allow the armature to move out of its original central position. The correction for these troubles is obvious.

Chattering of the brushes is due to a rough and dirty commutator, high mica, high bars, flat spots, incorrect angle of brush, or improper pressure of brush. Chattering causes noise and sparking at the brushes. In general, it can be remedied by cleaning and truing up the commutator, or perhaps by sanding the brushes and adjusting the brush pressure.

Improper brush pressure may produce high contact drop, heating, chattering, unnecessary wear of brushes and commutator, excess friction loss, and poor commutation. For average conditions on undercut commutators, a brush pressure of 2 pounds per square inch is recommended for stationary motors and generators; 2 to 3 pounds for elevator and mill-type motors; 3 to 5 pounds for crane motors; and 4 to 7 pounds for railway motors.

Brushes on machines in service may be badly worn, so that the normal area of contact is reduced, and so that the normal brush tension is reduced. The remedy lies in new brushes or perhaps a sanding of the old ones. Sanding of brushes is accomplished by placing a strip of fine sandpaper (cutting face out) on the commutator underneath the brush. The sandpaper is held close to the commutator and given a circumferential reciprocating motion under the brush until the brush is worn to the form of the commutator surface.

Brushes are separated from each other along the brush stud by the space occupied by the brush holders. If all brushes on one rocker arm are set so that they trail the same path as the next succeeding set and so on for all sets of brushes, the commutator will be worn down in parallel circular grooves with ridges between. This objectionable condition can be prevented by staggering each set of brushes with respect to the adjacent sets, thus assuring a more uniform wear on the commutator.

REFERENCES

Elsey, Howard M., "Treatment of High-Altitude Brushes by Application of Metallic Halides," *Proceedings*, AIEE., Vol. 64, pp. 576–579.

Kalb, E. C., "Maintenance of Good Brush Performance," *Proceedings*, AIEE., Vol. 64, pp. 819–825.

Modern Pyramids, National Carbon Company.

Ramadanoff, D. and Glass, S. C., "High-Altitude Brush Problem," *Proceedings*, AIEE, Vol. 63, pp. 825–830.

Van Brunt, C. and Savage, R. H., "Carbon-Brush Contact Films," *G.E. Review*, Vol. 47, Nos. 7 and 8, and Vol. 48, No. 10.

Units and Fundamental Concepts

Magnets. A magnet is a body which attracts iron, steel, and a few alloys, and which possesses the property of orientation. These properties were first noted in certain pieces of iron ore (Fe_3O_4) which occur in natural formations. Such pieces of iron ore, or natural magnets, were called **lodestones.** Artificial magnets are generally produced by passing an electric current through a coil of wire surrounding a piece of iron or steel. If a hard grade of steel is used, the attracting property continues after the magnetizing current is stopped, and the magnet thus formed is called a **permanent magnet.** If the body in the coil consists of soft iron, the attracting property may be greater in magnitude but exists only during the time of the current flow through the coil. Such a magnet is known as an **electromagnet.**

Poles. The attracting power of a magnet seems to exist in two regions on the body of the magnet. These regions of the magnet which exhibit this power of attraction are called **poles.** Magnetic poles may also be defined as those portions of a magnet toward which the external magnetizing force tends to converge or diverge. (See AIEE & ASA definition 05.25.160)

On short thick bar magnets, the polar regions seem to exist over a considerable portion of the magnet, and hence are called **distributed poles.** In the case of long slender needlelike magnets, the magnetism seems to be concentrated in small regions near the ends of the magnet. Such poles may be called **point poles.** The theoretical point pole does not have any physical reality but the conception is often used in solving some problems and in defining quantities in magnetism.

Either pole of a magnet will attract a piece of unmagnetized iron, yet the two poles exhibit a different polarity. Thus, when a magnet is freely suspended anywhere on the inhabited part of the earth, the poles will orient themselves along a straight line in the general northward and southward direction. One pole of the magnet always seeks the general geographic north, and is called a **north pole.** Conversely, the other pole seeks the geographic south, and is called the **south pole.** It has become conventional to denote the north pole as the *positive* pole and the south pole as the *negative* pole. Experiments have shown that like poles (both north or both south) repel each other, while unlike poles (north and south) attract one another. This indicates that the geographic north pole as indicated by a compass needle is really a south magnetic pole. Poles of a magnet always occur in pairs, and it is impossible to isolate a single pole. However, the conception of the isolated pole is often used in defining magnetic and electromagnetic terms.

Coulomb's Law. In the year 1800, Charles Augustin Coulomb showed experimentally that the force of attraction or repulsion of two magnetic poles in an isotropic medium is proportional to the product of the pole strengths and inversely proportional to the square of the distance between them. The result of this experiment has come to be known as **Coulomb's law.** It is expressed algebraically in the form

$$f = \frac{1}{\mu_0 \mu} \frac{mm'}{d^2} \tag{1}$$

where f is the force, μ_0 the permeability of free space, μ the relative permeability, d the distance between poles, and m and m' are the pole strengths. The permeability of free space μ_0 is necessary in equation 1 to make it adaptable to all kinds of units. The relative permeability, μ, is the ratio of the permeability of the medium in question to that of free space. If the poles are considered to exist in the medium of free space, μ is obviously unity and in any event nondimensional. Under the conditions of the existence of the poles in free space, equation 1 becomes

$$f = \frac{1}{\mu_0} \frac{mm'}{d^2} \tag{2}$$

In the classical system of definitions which is based upon the centimeter, gram, and second (cgs), μ_0 was arbitrarily assigned a value of unity though it is not a simple numeric because it does have dimensions. Hence in the cgs system of magnetic units

$$f = \frac{mm'}{d^2} \tag{3}$$

Another system of units based upon the meter, kilogram, and second, abbreviated mks, has been internationally adopted. This system, while admirably adapted to the electric units, is not quite so convenient when applied to the magnetic units. One difficulty results from the inconvenient size of the units of flux and area. Another trouble accrues from the failure to have any universal agreement upon the method of defining reluctance (see pages 372 and 375). On this account the cgs system will be used to present concepts of certain of the magnetic quantities, and the commonly used systems employed in practical calculations of the magnetic circuit will be employed.

Pole Strength. The unit of pole strength may be determined and defined by reducing all of the quantities in equation 3 to unity. Thus a unit pole in the cgs system is one which will repel an equal and like pole with a force of 1 dyne when they are placed 1 centimeter apart in a vacuum. For nearly all practical purposes this is the same as in air. This unit has no official name and will be called the **cgs unit of pole strength.**

Magnetic Field. A magnetic field is a region in which a pole experiences a force. Thus a compass needle may be used to detect the presence of a magnetic field, since the force exerted on its poles causes the needle to turn and to oscillate before coming to rest in a new position. A magnetic field is a form of *magnetic stress* existing in space. It may be created by the magnetic poles of the earth, by permanent magnets, by electromagnets, or by a coil of wire bearing an electric current.

The *direction of a magnetic field* is arbitrarily defined as the direction in which a *north pole is urged.*

The **magnetizing force** (also called **magnetic intensity,** magnetic force and magnetizing field) at any point in a magnetic field may be defined by the force (dynes) exerted on a unit pole placed at that point. It may also be defined by equations of current flowing in an electric circuit (see equation 19). Magnetizing force is represented by the *symbol H*. The cgs unit of *magnetizing force* is the oersted. It was formerly called the **gilbert-per-centimeter.*** The oersted is defined as the magnetizing force which will act upon a cgs unit pole in air with a force of 1 dyne. The defining equation is

$$H = \frac{f}{m},$$ (4)

$$\text{Oersteds} = \frac{\text{dynes}}{\text{cgs units of pole strength}}$$

A field is called **uniform** over any given area or volume when a pole is acted upon by the same force everywhere in this area or volume. In general, the intensity of a field varies both in magnitude and direction, in which case the field is said to be nonuniform, or variable.

Flux. A magnetic field has been defined as a region in which there exists some form of magnetic stress. This stress produces in the medium of this region "something" which has been termed **flux.** Flux is a collective term and is made up of units called **lines of force,** or **maxwells.** Thus flux may also be considered to be the measure of the quantity of magnetism. The symbol for flux is ϕ. The units of flux cannot be perceived by any of the human senses and they are defined in terms of the surrounding conditions and the magnetic properties of a medium. Thus, if a magnetic stress or magnetizing force of 1 oersted exists in space consisting of air, there will be 1 **maxwell** (or line of force) *in each square centimeter* of area at right angles to the magnetic field. It should not be inferred that the unit of flux is necessarily confined to an area of 1 square centimeter. The unit may occupy hundreds of square centimeters or but a fraction of a unit area, depending on the density of the flux under consideration.

* The name "oersted" was adopted for this unit at the international conference at Oslo (1930) and approved by the American Standards Association in 1941.

The term **line of force** has two different meanings — one quantitative and the other qualitative. Quantitatively speaking, the line of force is the synonym for the *maxwell*. In the qualitative sense, a line of force is a line where a tangent at any point gives the direction of the field at that point. Such a line of force is the path of a free-moving pole. Since there are an infinite number of paths for the flux in a magnetic field, there would be an infinite number of lines of force in the qualitative sense. To avoid confusion in discussions, it is well to use the term **line of force** for *paths of flux* and the term **maxwell** for *the cgs unit of flux*.

The mks unit of flux, called the **weber,** is 100,000,000 (10^8) maxwells.

Flux Density. Flux density is the measure of the number of flux units (maxwells) per unit of area at right angles to the direction of the field. The units of flux density are the *maxwells per square inch* for the English system, maxwells per square centimeter for the cgs system, and webers per square meter for the mks system. The cgs unit has been named the **gauss** and the use of the term **gauss** means *maxwells per square centimeter*. Thus, to speak of 50 gausses means that the space under consideration has a flux density of 50 maxwells per square centimeter.

The symbol of flux density is B. From the definition of flux density it follows that

$$B = \frac{\phi}{A}$$

where the flux density is uniform over the area under consideration. Conversely,

$$\phi = BA. \tag{5}$$

If all of the area A is not at right angles to the direction of the flux, the component of the area perpendicular to the flux must be used. For an area A making an angle θ with the area perpendicular to the field, the flux is

$$\phi = B(\mathrm{A} \cos \theta) = (B \cos \theta)A. \tag{6}$$

If the flux density varies from point to point, we have

$$\phi = \int (B \cos \theta) dA. \tag{7}$$

H vs. B. It has always been difficult for students to distinguish clearly between H and B and their respective units. Magnetizing force H is a certain *magnetic stress* in space which tends to produce flux and magnetism.

B is the *flux density* which results from the magnetizing force H. The actual magnitude of this flux density depends directly upon the magnetizing force H and also upon the nature of the medium in which B is measured. Some materials are more permeable (present less opposition) to the existence of flux than others. For instance, the permeability of air is very low. If a magnetizing force of 1 oersted exists in air, only 1 maxwell per square centimeter or 1 *gauss* of flux density will exist. Thus in air

$$H = B, \text{ numerically.} \tag{8}$$

The permeability of iron to the existence of flux is relatively very high. Thus a magnetizing force of 1 oersted may produce a flux density of 1000 to 1500 gausses in a sample of iron. Therefore it follows that flux density is equal to the magnetizing force H multiplied by a constant of permeability for the medium under consideration:

$$B = \mu H \tag{9}$$

where μ is the relative permeability.

$$\mu = \frac{B}{H} \tag{10}$$

For air μ is unity and equation 9 resolves into the form of equation 8. A more detailed discussion of this subject is given on page 375.

Flux from a Pole. The total flux emanating from a pole may be determined from the previous definitions and equations. Assume a point pole of m cgs units strength placed at the center of a sphere of radius d centimeters. Let a pole of strength m' be placed at the surface of the sphere. Then from equations 8, 4, and 3

$$B = H = \frac{f}{m'} = \frac{mm'/d^2}{m'} = \frac{m}{d^2}. \tag{11}$$

Since the area of the sphere is $4\pi d^2$, we have

$$\phi = BA = \frac{m}{d^2} 4\pi d^2 = 4\pi m. \tag{12}$$

Thus $4\pi m$ maxwells or lines of force emanate from a pole of m cgs units and there are 4π lines per cgs unit pole.

Magnetic Field about a Wire Carrying a Current. A magnetic field encircles a straight wire carrying an electric current. The configuration of such a field about a wire at the center is shown in Fig. 1. The cross in this figure represents the tail of an arrow and is a symbol for the direction of current flow (that is, away from the reader). A north magnetic pole would be urged around the wire in the direction indicated by the arrows. This by definition is the direction of the magnetic field.

A simple rule known as **Ampere's right-hand rule** is very convenient for determining the direction of the magnetic field about a wire carrying current. The rule may be applied as follows. *Grasp the wire in the right hand with the thumb pointing in the direction of current flow and the fingers will point in the direction that the magnetic field encircles the wire.* This rule is one of the simplest and most valuable of all rules for analyzing problems regarding directions of fields, of induced voltages, and of the rotation of direct-current machinery.

Fig. 1. Magnetic Field about a Wire Carrying a Current.

Resultant Field Due to a Straight Wire Carrying a Current in a Magnetic Field. The distribution of the field between the two poles of a magnet is shown in Fig. 2. This distribution is changed to that shown in Fig. 3 when a wire carrying a current is placed in the field. The presence of the wire carrying a current has distorted the field and has lengthened some of the lines of force. These distorted lines of force tend to return to their position of Fig. 2 and thus exert a force upon the wire as indicated by F of Fig. 3. The three following steps may be used for determining the direction of the force on a conductor carrying current in a magnetic field:

1. Use Ampere's right-hand rule to determine the direction of the field about the wire, due to the current it carries.

2. Determine upon which side of the conductor the field is increased and distorted as shown in Fig. 3. The distortion given at I in Fig. 3 occurs where

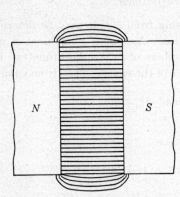

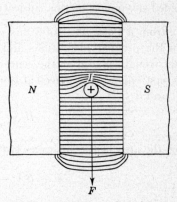

Fig. 2. Lines of Force between Poles of a Magnet.

Fig. 3. Conductor Carrying a Current in a Magnetic Field.

the magnetic fields due to the magnet and the conductor assist. The lower density of the lines of force on the under side of the conductor is caused by the opposition of the two fields.

3. Imagine the lines of force tending to straighten like stretched rubber bands. The direction of the force exerted by such bands will be the same as that due to electromagnetic action.

Another much-used method to find the direction of force on a conductor is known as **Fleming's left-hand rule.** The thumb, forefinger, and middle finger of the left hand are placed mutually at right angles. The forefinger is then pointed in the direction of the magnetic field, and the middle finger in the direction of current flow in the conductor. The thumb will then point in the direction of the force exerted on the conductor.

The above results may be proved by the following more rigid analysis. Using Ampere's right-hand rule, the field about the conductor is found to be upward in direction at the face of the north pole. According to the definition of the direction of a magnetic field, this is the direction in which a north pole is urged. Since the pole is stationary, the conductor is urged downward as indicated by the arrow. A study of Fig. 3 shows that the magnetic field, the wire, and the force are mutually at right angles to each other.

Flux-Linkages. A flux-linkage is produced by 1 maxwell of flux linking or encircling one turn of wire as illustrated in Fig. 4. The total number of flux-linkages (λ) in an electromagnetic circuit is the product of the flux in maxwells by the number of turns with which that flux links. Thus the flux linkages in maxwell turns are

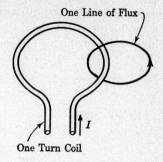

One Line of Flux

$$\lambda = N\phi \qquad (13)$$

If all the flux does not link all of the turns, the total flux-linkages are the sum of the products of the number of maxwells of flux by the number of turns with which the flux considered links. Thus in maxwell turns

One Turn Coil

Fig. 4. One Flux Linkage.

$$\lambda = \phi_1 + \phi_2 + \phi_3 + \phi_4 \ldots \phi_N \qquad (14)$$

where ϕ_1, ϕ_2, etc., represent the number of maxwells that link each single turn respectively of an N-turn coil.

In the mks system the unit of flux-linkage is the weber turn. One weber (10^8 maxwells) linking one turn constitutes a weber turn. Equations 13 and 14 will give flux-linkages in weber turns if flux is expressed in webers.

Strength of a Current. A current of electricity is a direct movement or a transfer of electrons. The conventional direction of an electric current was arbitrarily chosen years before the present theories of electricity were evolved. Unfortunately, the direction chosen was opposite to the actual movement of electrons. However, the concept can be reconciled by the statement that *the conventional direction of current is that direction in which the proton or positive electricity is urged.*

The strength of a current in the cgs electromagnetic system is defined in terms of the force exerted upon a conductor carrying a current in a magnetic field. **Unit cgs current, the abampere,** *exists in a conductor when a force of 1 dyne per centimeter length is exerted on the conductor placed perpendicular to a magnetic field of 1 gauss.* For example, if, in Fig. 3, the flux density of the field is 1 gauss and the force per centimeter length of the conductor is 1 dyne, the current strength is 1 abampere.

Our early scientists felt that the cgs unit of current, the abampere, was too large for convenient use and chose a smaller unit, the *ampere*, for practical usage. The practical unit, the ampere, is one-tenth as large as the abampere. In other words, 10 amperes and 1 abampere are equal strengths of current. As an equation of numbers:

$$10\ I_m = I$$

$$10 \times \text{number of abamperes} = \text{number of amperes.} \qquad (15)$$

In the mks system, all electrical units have the same name and value as the corresponding practical unit. Thus the ampere as defined above is the same as the mks ampere. In the mks system the ampere is defined as that current existing in a conductor when a force of 1 newton (a newton is 10^5 dynes) per meter length is exerted on a conductor placed in and perpendicularly to a uniform magnetic field of 1 weber per square meter.

Following the definition of current strength, the force on a conductor placed perpendicularly to a magnetic field is directly proportional to the length of conductor in the field, to the current flowing in the conductor, and to the flux density of the field. Hence, in cgs units

$$F = B I_m l \qquad (16)$$

Dynes = gausses × abamperes × cm.

In mks units

$$F = B I l \qquad (17)$$

Newtons = webers per square meter × amperes × meters.

Example. Find the force on a conductor 100 cm long when carrying 15 amp and placed in and perpendicular to a uniform field of 5000 gausses.

From equation 16, $F = 5000 \times \dfrac{15}{10} \times 100 = 750{,}000$ dynes

From 17, $F = \dfrac{5000 \times 100^2}{10^8} \times 15 \times \dfrac{100}{100} = 7.5$ newtons

If the conductor makes an angle θ with the magnetic field (Fig. 5), the effective length of conductor is that component perpendicular to the field. In general,

$$F = BI_m(l \sin \theta), \qquad \text{or} \qquad F = (B \sin \theta)I_m l. \qquad (18)$$

Equation 18 shows that either the perpendicular component of the length with respect to the field or the perpendicular component of the field with respect to the conductor may be used.

Fig. 5. Conductor Placed in a Magnetic Field Making an Angle with the Lines of Force.

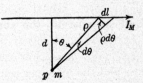

Fig. 6. Pole m at a Perpendicular Distance d from a Straight Wire Carrying a Current.

Magnetizing Force at a Point Due to a Straight Wire Carrying a Current. The magnetizing force at point p (Fig. 6), a perpendicular distance d from the conductor, is the force on a unit pole at the point (page 353). Let a unit pole m be placed at the point in question. If the current is flowing as shown, the direction of the force on a north pole at p is into the paper:

$$df = \frac{mI_m \rho d\theta}{\rho^2}. \qquad (19)$$

Note that $\rho d\theta$ is the component of dl perpendicular to ρ, the radius vector. Equation 19, known as the **law of Biot-Savart**, is empirical and is justified by the fact that all experimental evidence sustains it. Due to a conductor of infinite length, we have a total force F given by the formula

$$F = \int_{-\pi/2}^{\pi/2} \frac{mI_m}{\rho^2}\, \rho d\theta = \int_{-\pi/2}^{\pi/2} \frac{mI_m}{\rho}\, d\theta \tag{20}$$

$$= \int_{-\pi/2}^{\pi/2} \frac{mI_m}{d/\cos\theta}\, d\theta = \frac{2I_m}{d}, \qquad \text{since } m = 1. \tag{21}$$

Therefore in air

$$B = H = F = \frac{2I_m}{d} \qquad \text{gausses.} \tag{22}$$

Equation 22 holds closely where d is small compared to the length.

Example. Given two long parallel wires each carrying 10 amp and spaced 5 cm apart, as shown in Fig. 7. Find the force between them per centimeter of length. The flux density at B due to A is

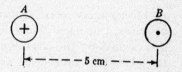

Fig. 7. Cross-Section of Two Long Parallel Wires Carrying a Current.

$$\frac{2I}{d} = 2 \times \left(\frac{10}{10}\right)\left(\frac{1}{5}\right) = \frac{2}{5} \qquad \text{gauss,}$$

and

$$F = BI_m l = \left(\frac{2}{5}\right)\left(\frac{10}{10}\right)(1) = \frac{2}{5} \qquad \text{dyne per centimeter length.}$$

Quantity of Electricity. The quantity or charge of electricity passing a point on a conductor is equal to the product of the current and the time in seconds during which its flows:

$$Q = It \tag{23}$$

If the current is varying,

$$Q = \int i\, dt. \tag{24}$$

Also

$$\frac{dQ}{dt} = i. \tag{25}$$

When the current is expressed in abamperes, the unit of the resultant quantity is the abcoulomb.

$$\text{Abcoulombs} = \text{abamperes} \times \text{seconds}$$

Similarly, the use of the ampere as the unit of current gives the coulomb which is the mks unit of charge or quantity.

$$\text{Coulombs} = \text{amperes} \times \text{seconds}$$

Electromagnetic Induction and EMF. A change of flux linking a coil of wire induces an electromotive force (abbreviated emf) in the coil. The change of flux linkages may be produced by (1) a variation of the field strength, (2) by a movement of the field with respect to the coil, (3) by a movement of the coil with respect to the field, or by a combination of any two or all of these factors. The fundamental requisite for the production of the emf by electromagnetic induction is the change in flux linkages in the coil. By way of illustration, if the coil of Fig. 8 be moved with its plane always perpendicular to a uniform field so that no part of the coil is ever moved out of the field, there will be no change in flux linkages within the coil and no emf induced. However, if the coil is moved out of the field or rotated out of its original plane so as to change the flux linkages, an emf will be induced in it.

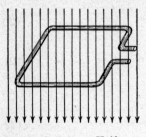

Fig. 8. Coil in a Uniform Field.

Electromotive force is measured by the difference in electric potential it produces. Difference of electric potential or potential drop between two points is measured by the work done in moving a unit charge from one point to the other. For static fields and electrical circuits the path followed by such motion is immaterial. In these instances the law of conservation of energy asserts that the difference in potential energy of the charge at the two points is independent of the way in which the charge arrived at the points. Furthermore, this difference in potential energy must be equal to the work done on or by the charge. It follows that only one difference of potential exists between two points at any one time. *The difference of potential between two points is 1* **cgs unit,** *or* **abvolt,** *when one erg of work is done in carrying a charge of one abcoulomb between the points.* Hence

$$V_m = \frac{W}{Q_m} \tag{26}$$

$$\text{Abvolts} = \frac{\text{ergs}}{\text{abcoulombs}}.$$

Since emf is measured by the drop in potential it can establish, emf is numerically equal to V_m but opposite in sign.

The cgs unit, the abvolt, is a very small unit, so that a practical unit, called the volt, has been in general use for many years.

1 volt is equivalent to 10^8 abvolts.

The volt is the mks unit of potential difference and may be defined as the difference of potential between two points when 1 joule of work is required to move a positive charge of 1 coulomb from the point of lower to that of higher potential. That this relation is correct may be verified by remembering that the abcoulomb being 10 coulombs would require 10 joules or $10 \times 10^7 = 10^8$ ergs of work in moving it between the same two points. As given by equation 26 this represents 10^8 abvolts which has been defined previously as 1 volt.

An emf of 1 abvolt is induced by a uniform change of 1 flux linkage per second. Similarly, a volt is induced by a uniform change of 10^8 flux linkages per second. In terms of the mks system, the volt would be said to be induced by a uniform change of 1 weber turn per second.

Since emf is measured by the difference of potential it can produce, it may be considered as a *cause* and the potential difference as the *result*. According to this conception of emf, a battery due to its chemical actions, a generator due to the changes of flux linkages in its windings, and a thermocouple due to heating, produce emf's. In accordance with this conception of emf, the voltage across a resistance due to a current flowing through it should be called a **potential drop** or **difference** rather than an emf. The potential drop is caused by the current flowing through the resistance which, in turn, is caused by an emf somewhere in the circuit.

The emf produced in a circuit by electromagnetic induction causes a current to flow when the circuit is closed. Experimental and other reasonable evidence proves that the current produced by electromagnetic induction always takes a direction that will cause a reaction opposing the change which produces it. This statement is called **Lenz's law.** In simple words, **Lenz's law** states that an *induced current always opposes the action which produces it.* This law is of fundamental importance in analyzing numerous problems in inductive circuits and machines. To illustrate how Lenz's law may be applied, assume that the flux in Fig. 8 is decreasing in magnitude. According to this law, a current would flow if the circuit of the coil were closed and would produce a magnetizing effect that would tend to prevent the reduction of flux. This would require a current in such a direction that it alone would cause a flux in the same direction as that of the field flux. Grasping the conductor of the coil in the right hand (Ampere's right-hand rule) with the fingers about the conductor in the direction of the flux that the coil alone tends to produce, causes the thumb to indicate the direction of current flow in the coil. This direction is clockwise as viewed from above the coil. If the circuit is open, the emf would be in such a direction as to cause a current to flow as shown above if the coil were closed. If the field is strengthened, the current flows in the opposite direction, *tending* to weaken the field, or neutralize the increase.

Positive and Negative Potentials. These are arbitrary terms. That terminal of a voltage source from which positive electricity or the proton is urged in the external circuit is called the **positive terminal.** One part of a circuit is at positive potential with respect to a second part of the circuit when positive electricity *tends* to move from the first to the second.

Magnitude of Induced EMF. The magnitude of an emf induced by electromagnetic induction is proportional to the rate of change in flux linkages. The relationship may be developed as follows. In Fig. 9, two conducting rails AB and CD are connected electrically by AC. An uninsulated wire EG is free to slide on these rails. A uniform field of flux density B exists over the area $ABDC$ and the wire EG is assumed to be moving at a uniform velocity V as indicated. The flux linking the coil $AEGC$ is changing, and an emf is being induced which, in turn, causes a current I to flow in the rails and the conductor EG. According to Lenz's law, this current produces a reaction opposing the movement of the wire EG. Hence the force $F = BI_m l$ (equation 16) exists due to the magnetic reaction between the field and the current in the wire. From equation 26

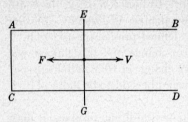

Fig. 9. Conductor Moving in a Magnetic Field.

$$W_{\text{ergs}} = E_m Q_m$$
$$dW = E_m dQ_m = E_m I_m \, dt.$$
But $$dW = Fds = BI_m lds.$$
Therefore $$BI_m lds = E_m I_m \, dt,$$

$$E_m = Bl\frac{ds}{dt} = Blv. \tag{27}$$

When there are N turns in series, each turn has a conductor like EG in Fig. 9 which produces the same force, and the total force is $BI_m lN$. Therefore the emf for N turns in series is

$$E_m = BlvN \qquad \text{abvolts} \tag{28}$$
or $$E = BlvN10^{-8} \qquad \text{volts.} \tag{29}$$

In equation 29, lv is the area swept out per unit time and Blv is the change in flux linking the N turns of the coil per unit time. We may express this in the form

$$Blv = \frac{d\phi}{dt}$$

Substituting this value in equation 29, we find

$$E = N\frac{d\phi}{dt}10^{-8}. \tag{30}$$

This equation states that the emf is proportional to the rate of change of flux linkages with respect to time and is numerically correct. Lenz's law states that a change in flux produces an emf that tends to cause a current which opposes the change. To denote this opposition a negative sign usually precedes the right member of the equation 30. Thus

$$E = -N\frac{d\phi}{dt}10^{-8} \text{ volts} \tag{31}$$

The negative sign means that the induced emf is in a circuit direction which opposes any change in flux linkages. For example, if flux is going into the paper through the coil $AEGC$ and is increasing in magnitude, the induced emf will be in the direction $ACGE$. On the other hand, if the flux is going into the paper but decreasing in magnitude, the emf will be in the direction $AEGC$. Thus equation 31 gives the correct magnitude of the emf and also, because of the minus sign, its correct time relation with respect to the flux variation. When $d\phi/dt$ is varying from instant to instant, equation 31 is written

$$e = -N \frac{d\phi}{dt} 10^{-8} \text{ volts} \tag{32}$$

where e is the voltage induced at any instant of time t.

In the mks system of units equation 28 gives the emf in volts when B is expressed in webers per square meter, l in meters, and v in meters per second. Similarly, by omitting 10^{-8} in equation 32, the emf will be in volts if $d\phi$ is expressed in webers. Either 29 or 31 may be used to calculate emf. Equation 29 is generally more convenient when the flux cut is considered, whereas 31 lends itself more readily to the conception of inducing an emf through a rate of change of flux linking a coil. However, as is often done, it is possible to apply equation 31 to the calculation of an emf by the flux cut concept.

Resistance. Resistance is that property of an electric circuit which opposes an electric current when a steady or direct emf is impressed on a closed circuit. The resulting current is proportional to the emf and inversely proportional to resistance. We may state this in the form

$$I_m = \frac{E_m}{R_m} \text{ or } I \text{ (amperes)} = \frac{E \text{ (volts)}}{R \text{ (ohms)}}. \tag{33}$$

This equation is known as **Ohm's law.** The subscript m means that the quantity involved is expressed in the cgs or electromagnetic system of units. Ohm's law may be used to define resistance. Thus

$$R_m = \frac{E_m}{I_m} \qquad \text{abohms} \tag{34}$$

or in the mks or practical system

$$R = \frac{E}{I} = \frac{E_m/10^8}{10 I_m} = \frac{E_m}{I_m} 10^{-9} \qquad \text{ohms.} \tag{35}$$

Hence $\qquad$ Ohms $= \dfrac{\text{volts}}{\text{amperes}}$, $\qquad$ or $\qquad$ **1 ohm $= 10^9$ abohms.**

Resistance depends upon the kind of material, and the length and cross section of the conductor. It is analogous to the resistance to the flow of water through pipes. The resistance of a conductor is expressed by the equation

$$R = \rho \frac{l}{a} \tag{36}$$

where ρ is a constant called the **specific resistance** or **resistivity,** l the length, and a the cross-sectional area of the conductor. When l and a are unity, R is equal to ρ. Therefore resistivity is the resistance of a piece of the material of unit length and unit cross section. If inches are used, the resistivity is the resistance between opposite faces of an inch cube of the material. A similar statement holds when centimeters are used.

A common way of expressing ρ is in ohms per circular mil foot. This is the resistance of a circular rod of the material $1/1000$ inch in diameter and 1 foot long. When ρ in equation 36 is expressed in ohms per circular mil foot, l must be in feet and a in circular mils. A circular mil is an area equal to that of a circle having a diameter of 1 mil or $1/1000$ inch. Hence 1 circular mil is $\pi D^2/4 = \pi/4 \times 1$, or $\pi/4$ square mils. Square mils multiplied by $4/\pi$ give circular mils. The area of a circle in circular mils is equal to the square of the diameter expressed in mils.

The International Annealed Copper Standard of resistivity for copper of 100 per cent conductivity is 10.371 ohms per circular mil foot, 0.67879 microhm-inch, or 1.7241 microhm-centimeter, at 20 C.

The resistance of most materials increases with temperature. Such materials are said to have a positive temperature coefficient of resistance. A few materials, carbon being one of the most common, have resistances which decrease with an increase in temperature. These materials are said to have a negative temperature coefficient of resistance.

The variation of resistance with temperature is approximately linear and is expressed by

$$R = R_0(1 + \alpha t) \qquad (37)$$

where R_0 is the resistance at 0 C, R the resistance sought at temperature t C, and α is the temperature coefficient of resistance. From 37, α may be defined as the increase in resistance per ohm at 0 C per degree (Centigrade) rise in temperature. The value of α varies with the material. For commercial grades of copper, it is near 0.00427, but it varies somewhat with the degree of purity and heat treatment. For some alloys, α is practically zero, and the resistance of such alloys is independent of temperature. These alloys are very useful in the manufacture of electrical instruments. If a ratio of resistances is wanted in terms of the corresponding temperatures, it may be obtained by a division of two equations similar to equation 37.
Thus,

$$\frac{r_1}{r_2} = \frac{r_0(1 + \alpha t_1)}{r_0(1 + \alpha t_2)} = \frac{1 + \alpha t_1}{1 + \alpha t_2} = \frac{\dfrac{1}{\alpha} + t_1}{\dfrac{1}{\alpha} + t_2} = \frac{234.5 + t_1}{234.5 + t_2}. \qquad (38)$$

Equation 38 could have been readily obtained from a graph of equation 37 plotted in Fig. 10, by establishing a proportion from the sides of the similar triangles shown. If the variation of resistance with temperature is linear, it theoretically becomes zero at -234.5 C, as shown. This figure assumes a value of α slightly less than 0.00427. The temperature -234.5 C might be called the **inferred absolute zero** for copper. The ratio of r_1 to r_2, from the similar triangles, is

$$\frac{r_1}{r_2} = \frac{234.5 + t_1}{234.5 + t_2}.$$

Power. From equation 26, $W_{\text{ergs}} = E_m Q_m$. Since power is the time rate of change of work or energy, we may write

$$P = \frac{dW}{dt} = \frac{d(E_m Q_m)}{dt} = E_m \frac{dQ_m}{dt}.$$

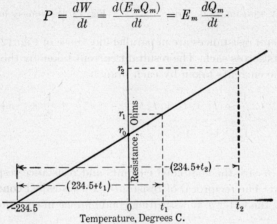

Fig. 10. Variation of Resistance of Copper with Temperature.

From equation (25), $dQ_m/dt = I_m$. Therefore

$$P = E_m I_m \qquad \text{ergs per second,} \tag{39}$$

or

$$P = E_m I_m 10^{-7} \qquad \text{joules per second or watts,}$$

$$= \frac{E_m}{10^8} I_m 10 = EI \text{ watts.} \tag{40}$$

where E is in volts and I in amperes.
From equation 35, $E = IR$.

Then

$$P = IRI = I^2 R. \tag{41}$$

Equation 41 is sometimes used as the defining equation for resistance and is true for either direct or alternating currents.

Series, Parallel, and Series-Parallel Circuits. The current through several resistances in series like those shown in Fig. 11 must be the same. Since the sum of the drops across the several resistances must equal the drop across the whole circuit,

$$V = V_1 + V_2 + V_3 + \cdots = Ir_1 + Ir_2 + Ir_3 + \cdots$$
$$R_0 = V/I = r_1 + r_2 + r_3 + \cdots. \tag{42}$$

Equation 42 shows that the resultant resistance R_0 of any number of resistances in series is the arithmetic sum of the separate resistances.

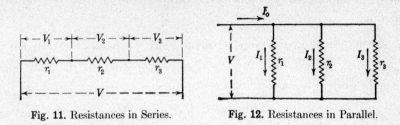

Fig. 11. Resistances in Series.   Fig. 12. Resistances in Parallel.

When several resistances are in parallel like those of Fig. 12, the same voltage drop exists across each. The resultant current taken by the circuit must be the sum of the currents taken by each branch:

$$I_0 = \frac{V}{R_0} = I_1 + I_2 + I_3 + \cdots = \frac{V}{r_1} + \frac{V}{r_2} + \frac{V}{r_3} + \cdots$$

or

$$\frac{1}{R_0} = \frac{1}{r_1} + \frac{1}{r_2} + \frac{1}{r_3} + \cdots \qquad (43)$$

where I_0 and R_0 are the combined currents and resistance respectively of the parallel circuit. The reciprocal of resistance $(1/r)$ is called **conductance** and is designated by the letter g. Substituting conductance in equation 43, we find

$$G_0 = g_1 + g_2 + g_3 + \cdots . \qquad (44)$$

In parallel circuits the reciprocal of the resultant resistance or the resultant conductance is obtained by adding the conductances. The resistance of the parallel combination is obtained by taking the reciprocal of the resultant conductance. The procedure is illustrated by the common and important case of two resistances in parallel. For this case equation 43 becomes

$$\frac{1}{R_0} = \frac{1}{r_1} + \frac{1}{r_2} = \frac{r_1 + r_2}{r_1 r_2}$$

or

$$R_0 = \frac{r_1 r_2}{r_1 + r_2}. \qquad (45)$$

When resistances are connected in series-parallel combinations like the one in Fig. 13, those branches which are in parallel are combined according to equation 43, while the series portions are calculated according to equation 42. The circuit of Fig. 13 may be used as an illustration and solved for currents as follows:

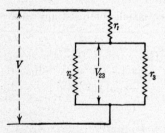

Fig. 13. Series-Parallel Arrangement of Resistances.

or

$$\frac{1}{r_{23}} = \frac{1}{r_2} + \frac{1}{r_3} = \frac{r_3 + r_2}{r_2 r_3} = g_{23}$$

$$r_{23} = \frac{1}{g_{23}} = \frac{r_2 r_3}{r_3 + r_2}.$$

The resistance r_{23} which is the equivalent of r_2 and r_3 in parallel is in series with r_1. Hence

$$r_0 = r_1 + r_{23} = r_1 + \frac{r_2 r_3}{(r_2 + r_3)}, \qquad I_0 = \frac{V}{r_0}.$$

The currents in r_2 and r_3 may be found since I_0 divides between the two branches r_2 and r_3 proportional to the conductances. This is shown by the following equations:

$$I_2 r_2 = I_3 r_3, \qquad \frac{I_2}{I_3} = \frac{r_3}{r_2} = \frac{g_2}{g_3}.$$

Also
$$I_0 = g_{23} V_{23} = g_{23} I_2 r_2$$

$$I_2 = \frac{I_0}{g_{23} r_2} = I_0 \frac{g_2}{g_{23}}.$$

Similarly, $I_3 = I_0 g_3 / g_{23}$.

Substituting the equalities of the conductances, we find

$$I_2 = I_0 \frac{g_2}{g_{23}} = I_0 \frac{1/r_2}{\dfrac{(r_3 + r_2)}{r_2 r_3}} = \frac{r_3}{r_2 + r_3} I_0$$

and

$$I_3 = \frac{r_2}{r_2 + r_3} I_0.$$

The currents could have been found by subtracting the drop in r_1 due to I_0 from the voltage V impressed. This resultant, the drop across the parallel combination of r_2 and r_3, could then be divided by the respective resistances to obtain the currents in the branches.

The simple series-parallel arrangement of resistances does not always exist in networks of resistance, and the procedure illustrated above may not apply. The presence of an emf from either batteries or generators in any branch of a circuit precludes the use of the above method. Such circuits can be solved by Kirchhoff's laws.

Kirchhoff's Laws. Two statements known as **Kirchhoff's laws** were formulated by G. R. Kirchhoff in 1847. These laws are:

1. *The sum of all currents entering a junction in a network equals the sum of those leaving the junction.* Stated in another way, the algebraic sum of all currents taken toward a junction equals zero.

2. *The algebraic sum of the drops of potential around any complete loop in a network equals the algebraic sum of the electromotive forces around the same loop.* Stated in another way, the algebraic sum of all of the potential drops in any closed circuit is zero. This latter statement assumes an emf to be a negative drop.

If the first law were not true, there would be an accumulation of current at a junction in a network, which would increase the charge, and hence the potential.

Nothing like this has ever been found under steady conditions. The second

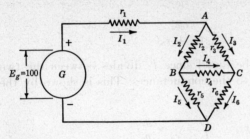

law follows from the definition of emf, that is, emf is measured by the total drop in electrical potential it can establish.

Through the application of Kirchhoff's laws, a set of simultaneous equations may be obtained for any network and they can be solved for the unknown factors. The application of each of these laws may be illustrated by reference to Fig. 14. Applying the first law to the junction A we obtain the equation

Fig. 14. Generator Connected to a Network of Resistances.

$$I_1 = I_2 + I_3.$$

The application of the second law to the loop $GABD$ yields the voltage equation

$$100 = I_1 r_1 + I_2 r_2 + I_5 r_5.$$

The loop $ABCA$, which has no generated voltage in it, may be used as the basis of the following voltage equation:

$$0 = I_2 r_2 + I_4 r_4 - I_3 r_3.$$

A total of six equations is necessary to yield a solution for this example. The correct procedure for obtaining suitable equations for the solutions of a network is worthy of consideration.

A few simple rules aid greatly in establishing the equations for the solution of a network. When setting up equations known as **junction** or **current equations** according to the first law, always use those junctions which yield the least number of additional unknowns. Additional unknowns are those unknown currents which have not previously been incorporated in any current equation. This procedure can be continued as long as at least one additional unknown current can be taken into an equation. It is impossible to obtain any more or less than the required number of current equations if the above rule is followed. The equations known as **voltage** or **loop equations** are set up in accordance with the second law. The simplest loops should be chosen and use should be made of as few additional unknowns as necessary for each equation. These operations are continued until no more additional unknowns can be incorporated in a voltage equation. This procedure will yield no more, and no less, than the required number of voltage equations to effect a solution. As a final check, there should be as many equations as there are unknowns. To illustrate the procedure, the network of Fig. 15 will be considered in detail.

First, arrows are placed on all parts of the circuit designating an *assumed* direction of current flow. The direction assumed is immaterial. If it is wrong, the current calculated will have a negative sign, indicating a flow in the opposite direction. Care must be taken in setting emf's equal to drops to call a

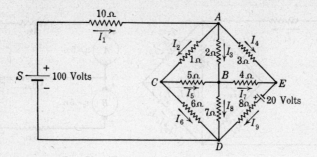

Fig. 15. Battery Connected to a Network of Resistances Showing Assumed Directions of Current Flow.

drop **positive** when the current is in the same direction as that being traced around the loop, and **negative** when tracing against the direction of a current. The equations according to Kirchhoff's first law follow:

$$I_2 = I_6 + I_5, \qquad \text{Junction } C \qquad (1)$$

$$I_1 = I_2 + I_3 + I_4, \qquad \text{``} \quad A \qquad (2)$$

$$I_3 + I_5 = I_8 + I_7, \qquad \text{``} \quad B \qquad (3)$$

$$I_4 + I_7 = I_9, \qquad \text{``} \quad E \qquad (4)$$

Note that the junction B was not used until the junctions C and A had been used, so that the minimum number of unknowns was added at each junction. This would not have been the case had the junction B been taken at the start. The equations using Kirchhoff's second law are:

$$100 = 10I_1 + 1I_2 + 6I_6, \qquad \text{Loop } ACDSA \qquad (5)$$

$$1I_2 + 5I_5 - 2I_3 = 0, \qquad \text{``} \quad ACBA \qquad (6)$$

$$2I_3 + 4I_7 - 3I_4 = 0, \qquad \text{``} \quad ABEA \qquad (7)$$

$$6I_6 - 7I_8 - 5I_5 = 0, \qquad \text{``} \quad CDBC \qquad (8)$$

$$20 = 8I_9 - 7I_8 + 4I_7, \qquad \text{``} \quad EDBE \qquad (9)$$

Since there are no more additional unknowns, the above nine equations are necessary and sufficient, there being nine unknown currents. Solving these equations simultaneously for the unknown currents, we obtain the solution.

Some work may be saved by solving current equations as one labels the diagram, as illustrated in Fig. 16. Under these conditions, the voltage equations are the only ones necessary for the solution. This procedure leaves five unknowns, and the five loop equations are sufficient for a solution.

An example of a solution using Kirchhoff's laws is illustrated by the following problem. A three-wire system is shown in Fig. 17, in which the generator A

has an induced emf of 100 volts and *B* 120 volts. The resistances of the generators, lines, and loads are indicated, and it is desired to find the currents in each line.

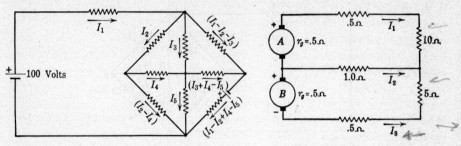

Fig. 16. Network with Assumed Currents Using Minimum Number of Symbols for Currents.

Fig. 17. Generators Supplying a Three-Wire System.

The directions of currents are first assumed and denoted by arrows as shown. Then tracing clockwise the upper and lower loops respectively, the following voltage equations are obtained:

$$100 = 0.5I_1 + 0.5I_1 + 10I_1 - 1I_2 = 11I_1 - I_2$$
$$120 = -0.5I_3 + 1I_2 - 5I_3 - 0.5I_3 = I_2 - 6I_3.$$

The current equation is $I_1 + I_2 + I_3 = 0$.

Solving these three equations simultaneously for I_1, I_2, and I_3, we find

$$I_1 = 9.87, \qquad I_2 = 8.69, \qquad \text{and} \qquad I_3 = -18.56.$$

The negative sign in the solution shows that the direction of I_3 was assumed incorrectly, the current actually flowing toward the negative generator terminal.

The Magnetic Circuit. The magnetic circuit is analogous to the electric circuit. In the magnetic circuit, the magnetic flux, page 353, corresponds to the current in the electric circuit. Reluctance corresponds to electric resistance, and magnetomotive force corresponds to emf. The fundamental equation for the electric circuit is Ohm's law,

$$I = \frac{E}{R} \tag{33}$$

and the analogous equation for the magnetic circuit is

$$\phi = \frac{U}{\mathcal{R}} = \frac{\text{mmf}}{\mathcal{R}} \tag{46}$$

where $\mathcal{R}$ is the symbol for reluctance, U is the drop in magnetic potential, and mmf is magnetomotive force.

Magnetomotive Force. Magnetomotive force is the magnetic stress in a magnetic circuit, which tends to establish a field. It is measured by the total drop in magnetic potential which it produces. Following the analogous definition for potential difference in the electric circuit, *the **difference in magnetic potential** between two points is defined as the work done in moving a unit pole between the two points.* For example, the rise in magnetic potential from B to A in the field of Fig. 18 is the work done on a unit pole in transporting it from B to A. Similarly, the drop in magnetic potential from A to B is equal to the loss in potential energy of a unit pole in falling from A to B. This drop is measured by the work done on a unit pole, and it gives for the defining equation of magnetic potential drop

$$U = \frac{W}{m} \quad \text{gilberts.} \tag{47}$$

When work is expressed in ergs and m in cgs units of pole strength, the drop in magnetic potential is expressed in gilberts.

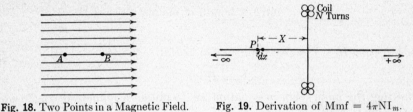

Fig. 18. Two Points in a Magnetic Field.   **Fig. 19.** Derivation of Mmf $= 4\pi NI_m$.

Magnetomotive force is measured by the drop in magnetic potential and is analogous to emf in the electric circuit. Algebraically,

$$\text{mmf} = -U. \tag{48}$$

Magnetomotive force may be conceived as a cause which results in the production and maintenance of a flux.

A coil of wire carrying a current of I_m abamperes will produce an mmf equal to $4\pi NI_m$ gilberts. This statement may be proved as follows. Assume a coil of N turns as shown in Fig. 19. Let a unit magnetic pole P be moved from a distance of x equal to minus infinity through the coil to a distance of plus infinity. At an infinite distance from the coil, the field strength due to a pole from equation 11 is zero, and the flux that passes through or links with the coil is zero. Since the pole is moved from a point where the linkages with the coil are zero through the coil to another point where the linkages are zero, the total change in flux linkages must be due to all of the flux produced by pole P, namely 4π lines. The emf induced in the coil by this change is $E_m = -\,Nd\phi/dt$. If a current of I_m abamperes is maintained in the coil to produce an mmf, the power represented by the induced voltage in conjunction with this current is

$$E_m I_m = -\,NI_m \frac{d\phi}{dt}.$$

The energy or work is

$$\int E_m I_m\, dt = \int -\,NI_m\, d\phi.$$

From the law of conservation of energy, this must be the work done in bringing the pole from minus to plus infinity. Hence

$$W = \int -\,NI_m d\phi = -\,NI_m \int d\phi \quad \text{ergs.} \tag{49}$$

But $\int d\phi = 4\pi$, the total number of lines from the unit pole is 4π, and therefore $W = -4\pi NI_m$ ergs or gilberts which, by definition, is the total drop in magnetic potential, U. From equation 48,

$$\text{mmf} = -U = 4\pi NI_m. \tag{50}$$

If the current is expressed in amperes, mmf $= 0.4\pi NI$. Since no assumption was made regarding the path traversed, the drop in magnetic potential around a closed loop is independent of the path taken.

On page 353, it was stated that the unit of magnetizing force H is the oersted which is equivalent to a gilbert per centimeter. Thus magnetizing force H must be directly related to magnetomotive force which has the gilbert as its unit. Thus

$$U = \frac{W}{m} = \frac{\text{force} \times \text{length of magnetic circuit}}{m} = \frac{fl}{m}.$$

Substituting $H = f/m$, we find

$$U = Hl. \tag{51}$$

Omitting the minus sign in equation 48, to obtain a numerical equality and using equation 50, we have

$$mmf = 4\pi NI_m = Hl \tag{52}$$

that is,

$$\text{Gilberts} = 4\pi N \times \text{abamperes} = \frac{\text{gilberts}}{\text{cm}} \times \text{cm} = \text{oersteds} \times \text{cm}$$

Reluctance. A qualitative and somewhat unscientific definition of reluctance is *that property of space which resists the establishment and maintenance of magnetic flux.* Reluctance is measured by the drop in magnetic potential between equipotential surfaces caused by 1 maxwell of flux. The defining equation arises from the fundamental equation (46, page 370) of the magnetic circuit:

$$\mathcal{R} = \frac{U}{\phi}. \tag{53}$$

Thus the reluctance is unity when 1 maxwell causes a drop of magnetic potential of 1 gilbert. Reluctance depends upon the dimensions of the magnetic circuit and may be expressed by a formula analogous to that for resistance. Thus

$$\mathcal{R} = \frac{U}{\phi} = \frac{Hl}{BA}$$

and for air, where $H = B$,

$$\mathcal{R} = \frac{l}{A}. \tag{54}$$

Since U is numerically equal to mmf, equation 53 may be written in the form

$$\phi = \frac{\text{mmf}}{\mathcal{R}}. \tag{55}$$

This relation is analogous to Ohm's law for the electric circuit and is sometimes referred to as *Ohm's law for the magnetic circuit.*

The reciprocal of reluctance is called **permeance** and may be thought of as the ease with which a material allows flux to be established when an mmf acts upon it.

Magnetization of Materials. All materials may be classified on the basis of their magnetic properties, as diamagnetic, nonmagnetic, and paramagnetic. Substances in which the flux density is less than it would be in a vacuum are called **diamagnetic.** Those materials in which the flux density is the same as in a vacuum are called **nonmagnetic.** Paramagnetic substances are those in which the flux density is more than it would be in a vacuum. Some substances, such as copper, are so slightly diamagnetic as to be negligible from a practical standpoint, and are ordinarily classed as nonmagnetic. Iron and its alloys are the most common paramagnetic substances, and are sometimes called **ferromagnetic.**

Magnetization of Iron. When some form of iron is substituted for air in a magnetic field, the flux increases to many times it original value and the iron is

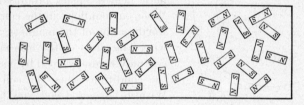

Fig. 20. Unmagnetized Bar of Iron.

said to be **magnetized.** The exact nature of this phenomenon is not definitely known, though there are several theories for explaining the action taking place. The older conception held that each molecule of iron was in itself a small magnet, having a north and a south pole. A random arrangement of these little magnets was assumed when the iron was not magnetized. This arrangement is pictured in Fig. 20, and gives a zero resultant magnetic effect. When the iron was magnetized, the little molecular magnets were assumed to orient them-

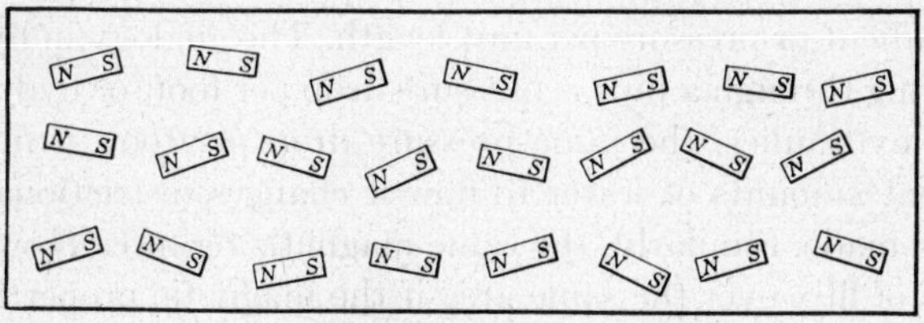

Fig. 21. Magnetized Bar of Iron.

selves like a number of small magnets, so that they would all act in the same general direction as illustrated in Fig. 21.

Another and more modern explanation is based on the electron theory. The ferromagnetic materials are thought to contain crystals having electronic orbits whose planes are capable of orientation in any position. When the material is not magnetized, the orbits are assumed to be arranged in a random fashion such that they nullify each other as far as any external magnetic evidence is concerned. When the material is magnetized, a portion of these electronic orbits change their arrangement so as to make their magnetic actions additive. Some evidence indicates the change in orientation occurs by groups, with all of the orbits in one crystal or portion of a crystal of the material changing at one time. When all of the electronic orbits capable of being oriented are so arranged, the material is said to be **saturated with magnetism.** These theories represent magnetization as a physical geometric grouping of molecules or electronic orbits.

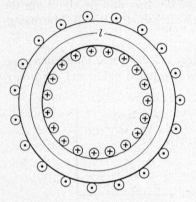

Fig. 22. Coil Wound on An Iron Core.

The basis for calculating a magnetic circuit containing iron will be explained for the iron ring shown in Fig. 22. Let $l =$ length of the magnetic path along the center of the annulus, and $H =$ the magnetic field intensity produced by the coil. When current flows in the coil as indicated, the direction of the magnetic field is clockwise. The effect of the iron core inside the coil may be understood by considering first the conditions when the coil is air-cored. With an air-cored coil and field intensity H, the flux density is numerically equal to H, equation 8. The total drop in magnetic potential around the coil which is equal to the mmf, is Hl. This may be expressed in the form

$$U = Hl. \tag{56}$$

For a given coil of a fixed number of turns, the mmf depends upon the current flowing. Therefore the magnetizing field ($H = \text{mmf}/l$) depends only upon the current for a given coil. The magnetizing field H (gilberts-per-centimeter or oersteds), is the drop in magnetic potential per unit length. It is the magnetic potential gradient or pressure per unit length. The analogy in hydraulics when water is flowing through a pipe is pressure drop per foot, or hydraulic potential per foot. In hydraulics, the same pressure drop per foot, if maintained, will cause different amounts of water to flow if changes in frictional resistance of the pipes are made. Similarly, the same magnetizing force H will cause different amounts of flux over the same area if the magnetic properties of the medium are changed. In other words, different flux densities (B) will result. Now, assume that an iron core be substituted for the air core without any change in the coil or its current. The insertion of this core will cause the flux density B to increase many times, even though the magnetizing force remains constant.

For the air core, the flux density B was numerically equal to H, but after the iron core was inserted, B was numerically many times greater than H. The ratio of B to H is defined as the *permeability* of the magnetic circuit, and is designated by the Greek letter μ:

$$\mu = \frac{B}{H}. \tag{57}$$

Strictly speaking, this is relative permeability as explained on page 352. For the cgs system where the units affected are chosen so as to make the absolute permeability of free space unity, the relative permeability becomes numerically equal to the absolute permeability for the material in question. On this account and since the permeability given in published characteristics of magnetic material is actually relative permeability but customarily called **permeability,** the word "relative" will be dropped. In the mks system absolute and relative permeability are not numerically equal. In addition to there being no recognized agreement on what to do with 4π in the mks system, the system is not so practicable in the calculation of magnetic circuits involving air and iron paths as methods based on cgs and English units. Hence for our purposes the mks system will not be used in magnetic circuit calculations.

Equation 57 is valid only when B is expressed in gausses and H in gilberts-per-centimeter or oersteds. The iron core has a higher permeability than the air core and permits a greater flux density with the same magnetizing force. Neither the total drop in magnetic potential nor the magnetizing force has been changed by the addition of the iron core. The drop in magnetic potential is always Hl. For the iron core, if B is known, equation 10 shows $H = B/\mu$, and equation 56 becomes

$$U = \frac{B}{\mu}l. \tag{58}$$

Equation 58 is valid for air, iron, or any other material. In the case of air, μ is 1 and equation 58 becomes

$$U = Bl = Hl$$

since B has been shown numerically equal to H in air. For the same magnetizing force H, different values of flux densities B will exist, depending upon the material comprising the magnetic circuit. Conversely, for the same value of flux density B, different values of magnetizing force H may exist, depending upon the composition of the magnetic circuit.

The reciprocal of permeability μ is called the **reluctivity.** Permeability and reluctivity have the same relation to the magnetic circuit as conductivity and resistivity do to the electric circuit.

When the mmf per unit length H of the magnetic circuit is not constant, the (total) mmf of the circuit must be obtained by taking the summation of the product of H and dl. Thus

$$\text{mmf} = 4\pi N I_m = \int H dl. \tag{59}$$

This equation states that *mmf is the line integral of the magnetizing force around the magnetic circuit.*

The expression for reluctance given by equation 54 must be modified when applied to an iron-cored magnetic circuit. Since for magnetic substances, $H = B/\mu$ and U is Hl, reluctance becomes

$$\Re = \frac{U}{\phi} = \frac{(B/\mu)l}{AB} = \frac{l}{\mu A}. \tag{60}$$

Equation 60 is general and is valid for air or all other kinds of cores provided the proper value of μ is used. This is exactly analogous to resistance as given equation 36, where ρ corresponds to $1/\mu$.

Calculation of the Magnetic Circuit. The calculation of the magnetic circuit is based on the equations of the preceding article. When mmf is substituted for U in equation 60, a slight transformation gives

$$\phi = \frac{\text{mmf}}{l/\mu A} = \frac{4\pi NI_m}{l/\mu A} = \frac{0.4\pi NI}{l/\mu A} = \frac{0.4\pi NI}{\Re}. \tag{61}$$

This equation is sometimes called **Ohm's law for the magnetic circuit** because of its analogy to that equation for the electric circuit. It would seem to follow that reluctances in series, parallel, or series-parallel might be combined just as resistances were on pages 365 to 367. Two differences between the electric and magnetic circuit tend to complicate what would otherwise be a simple procedure. First, the magnetic circuit is not restricted and there is a leakage of flux around iron paths. Second, the reluctance of most magnetic materials is a function of the flux density. Hence it is generally impossible to find the reluctance or permeability until the flux density is known, and vice versa. A graphical or semigraphical form of solution may be used to overcome this difficulty.

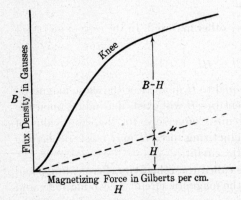

The Magnetization Curve. The magnetization or B–H curve illustrated in Fig. 23 shows the relation between flux density and magnetizing force. The typical magnetization curve of a completely demagnetized piece of iron starts at $B = 0$ and $H = 0$, and may be divided into four sections. The first section is a curve concave on its upper side which straightens out into a second, or linear section. The third section consists of a reversed curve which likewise straightens out into a fourth section which approaches a linear form having a smaller upward slope. The dotted line shows the curve for air. The difference $(B-H)$ between the ordinates of the two curves (iron and air) for any given

Magnetizing Force in Gilberts per cm.
H

Fig. 23. Magnetization or B–H Curve.

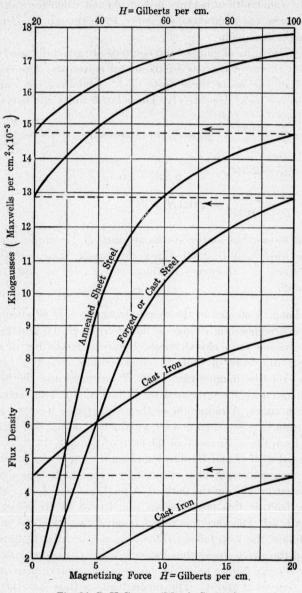

Fig. 24. B–H Curves (Metric System).

value of H is the increase in flux density due to the iron. $B-H$ increases rapidly at first and then approaches a constant value. When $B-H$ becomes a maximum, the iron is said to be saturated magnetically. In the practical sense, saturation of a magnetic substance is said to exist when the value of B is well above the knee of the magnetization curve, even though $B-H$ may not have reached a maximum value.

The magnetic units of gausses and oersteds are generally used by physicists and others in the derivation of fundamental equations. The engineers often use slight modifications of these units, such as kilolines per square inch and ampere-turns per inch, respectively. These latter units are derived as follows:

$$H = \frac{0.4\pi NI}{l_{\text{cm}}} \text{ gilberts/cm or oersteds} \qquad \frac{NI}{l_{\text{cm}}} = \frac{H}{0.4\pi},$$

$$l_{\text{cm}} = 2.54 l_{\text{in.}} \qquad \frac{NI}{2.54 l_{\text{in.}}} = \frac{H}{0.4\pi},$$

$$\frac{NI}{l_{\text{in.}}} = \frac{2.54 H}{0.4\pi} = 2.021 H = H''. \tag{62}$$

Equation 62 shows that ampere-turns per inch H'' is simply another unit of magnetizing force and is 2.021 times the magnetizing force expressed in oersteds. Typical $B-H$ curves in these two classes of units are shown in Figs. 24 and 25.

Hysteresis Loop. A change in the magnetizing force H is not always accompanied by a corresponding change in flux density B. To illustrate, assume a coil of wire wound on a closed magnetic circuit consisting of a completely demagnetized iron core of uniform cross section. When a current is sent through the coil, the magnetizing force H increases and the flux density B increases along curve 1 represented by Of in Fig. 26. This curve is called the **magnetization curve.** A reduction of the magnetizing force to zero after the point f is attained is accompanied by a reduction of the flux density B along the curve 2 from f to a. Reversal of the current through the coil causes curve 2 to be continued with H and B following along the curve abc. After reaching the point c, the magnetizing field is reduced to zero, which causes the density B to follow the curve 3 along the path cd. A final reversal of the current and the magnetizing field at this point causes the density B to follow the curve 4 along the path def. The variation of the magnetizing force has caused the flux density to follow the loop $fabcdef$. This loop is called the **hysteresis loop.** An inspection of the curve shows that for each value of magnetizing force H, the flux density B has a higher value on the descending curve than on the ascending branch (curves 2 and 4). The magnetization thus lags the magnetizing force. Magnetic hysteresis* is that property of materials which causes different flux densities for the same value of magnetizing force when this value is attained by increasing and decreasing magnetic fields.

* Hysteresis comes from the Greek word "hysteros" meaning to lag behind.

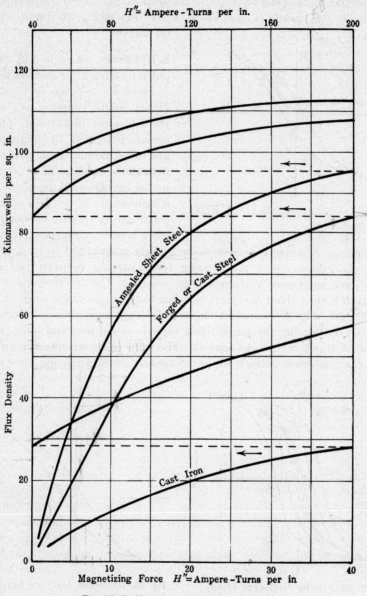

$H'' =$ Ampere - Turns per in.

Kilomaxwells per sq. in.

Flux Density

Magnetizing Force $H'' =$ Ampere - Turns per in

Annealed Sheet Steel

Forged or Cast Steel

Cast Iron

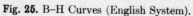

Fig. 25. B–H Curves (English System).

If after having been magnetized to a value M, Fig. 26, the magnetizing field is decreased to zero, the flux density falls to Oa. This value of flux density is known as **residual magnetism**.

Coercive force *is that value of reversed magnetizing force H which is necessary to bring the flux density to zero.* The coercive force in Fig. 26 is represented by Ob and Oe.

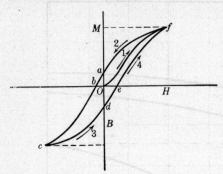

Fig. 26. Magnetization Curve and Hysteresis Loop.

B-H Curves. Since in Fig. 26 three different curves, for positive values of B, show the relation between B and H, one might properly ask which is the one most often used. The B–H curves published by manufacturers are called **normal induction** or **magnetization curves.** They are determined by placing a sample of iron in a symmetrically cyclicly magnetized condition by varying the magnetizing force between equal positive and negative limits. A material is said to be **cyclicly magnetized** when it has been under the influence of a magnetizing force varying between two definite limits until successive hysteresis loops coincide. The limiting value of flux density B is the value taken corresponding to the magnetizing force employed. For example, Fig. 27 shows three hysteresis loops. Loop number 1 is the result obtained by varying the magnetizing force between plus and minus H_1 until successive traces of the loop coincide. The value of B corresponding to point x gives the flux density which is plotted against the magnetizing force H_1. The

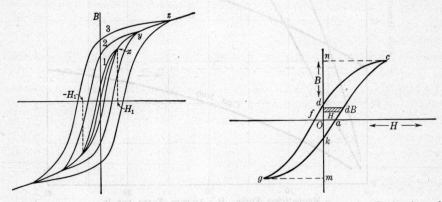

Fig. 27. Illustrating Method of Determining the Normal Magnetization Curve.

Fig. 28. Hysteresis Loop for Derivation of Hysteresis Loss.

magnetizing force is then changed and a similar procedure used to secure additional values of B and H as indicated by points y and z. Plotting of the values of B and H thus obtained gives the normal magnetization or $B-H$ curve for the material. Such curves are the ones customarily employed in magnetic circuit computations.

Hysteresis Loss. The area enclosed by the hysteresis loop is a measure of the energy loss due to hysteresis. This can be shown by the use of the following symbols and equations applied to Fig. 28. Let l denote the length of the magnetic circuit in centimeters, A the cross-section of the magnetic circuit in square centimeters, B the flux density in gausses, N the number of turns of the coil on the magnetic circuit, W_h the work or energy representing the hysteresis loss in ergs, I_m the current in the coil in abamperes, and V the volume of magnetic circuit. The following equations may be written:

$$E_m = N\frac{d\phi}{dt} = NA\frac{dB}{dt},$$

$$4\pi NI_m = Hl, \qquad I_m = \frac{Hl}{4\pi N}, \qquad \text{Power} = E_m I_m$$

$$dW_h = E_m I_m \, dt = NA\frac{dB}{dt}\frac{Hl}{4\pi N} = \frac{Al}{4\pi}HdB$$

$$W_h = \frac{Al}{4\pi}\int HdB \text{ ergs.}$$

This integral for the loop of Fig. 28 when evaluated from g to kac and then from c to dfg represents the area of the hysteresis loop and the energy loss for a complete cycle of variation of flux density. Since Al equals the volume of the magnetic circuit V, $W_h = (V/4\pi)$ (area of loop). For f cycles per second, the power loss is $W_h \times f$. Since the area of the loop is proportional to some power of the maximum flux density B_m, the power loss P_h is

$$P_h = K\frac{V}{4\pi}fB_m{}^x = K_h VfB_m{}^x \tag{63}$$

where K_h is a constant depending upon the material and units chosen and is called the **hysteresis coefficient**, while x is known as the **Steinmetz exponent**.

For modern grades of iron used in electrical machinery, and for flux densities ordinarily employed, x has a value in the vicinity of 2. For the grades of iron formerly used, x was about 1.6, and on this account it is quite customary to see the exponent given as 1.6. In passing, it should be noted that while the exponent is greater in modern steels, the coefficient K_h is less. The result is a lower actual hysteresis loss for a given volume of iron but a more rapid variation of hysteresis loss with change in flux density. Inserting the commonly used value of x, equation 63 becomes

$$P_h = K_h VfB_m{}^{1.6}. \tag{64}$$

It should be noted that equation 64 is based on a uniform flux density throughout the volume V and that the value of x is empirical. This equation should not be applied when the flux densities differ from those used in general practice unless a suitable value of the Steinmetz exponent x is substituted.

Hysteresis loss may be likened to a molecular friction in the magnetic circuit which causes an energy loss in the form of heat. Materials, such as silicon steel, which have relatively slender hysteresis loops, give a low hysteresis loss per unit volume, while materials such as cast iron, which show broad hysteresis loops, have large energy losses.

Eddy-Current Loss. The changing of flux-linkages always induces an emf in an electrical circuit. The changing of flux within an electrical conductor may produce a change of flux linkages in local closed circuits within the mass of the conductor. The emf induced in these small local circuits will cause local currents to flow. These local currents may be likened to the local eddies within a stream of water and are called **eddy currents.** The eddy currents passing through the resistance of the mass of the conductor produce heat (I^2R), and the energy loss involved is called **eddy-current loss.** Eddy currents are usually conceived as existing in the iron portions of a magnetic circuit, though they do exist in any form of solid material which is a conductor of electricity. In accordance with Lenz's law, eddy currents always flow in such a direction as to set up a magnetic reaction opposing the change of flux which produces them.

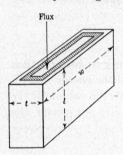

Flux

Fig. 29. Portion of a Lamination Showing Path of Eddy Current.

The loss due to eddy currents may be shown to depend upon several factors. In Fig. 29, one section of a magnetic circuit is shown with an arrow indicating the direction of the flux. The symbols on this figure are as follows: l denotes the length of the magnetic circuit taken parallel to the lines of flux, t the thickness of the section, w the width of the section, and B_m the maximum flux density. The portion of the iron extending the full length of the section which is crosshatched forms a closed electrical path for the eddy current and may be considered as an elemental conductor. Variation in the flux induces in this element an emf (E). The current caused by this emf is E/r, where r is the resistance of the element. The power developed in this elemental conductor under the assumption that the resistance of the element is high compared to its inductance, is $E \times I$. Hence

$$P = E^2/r. \tag{a}$$

The emf induced in the element is *proportional* to the total maximum flux through the section and the variation of this flux with respect to time. The latter factor is directly proportional to f, the number of cycles of flux variation per second. Hence

$$E = K\phi_m f,$$
$$E = K(wtB_m)f. \tag{b}$$

The resistance is *proportional* to the length of the path w of current flow and inversely proportional to the cross-section tl, Hence

$$r = K'\frac{w}{tl}. \tag{c}$$

Substituting equations c and b in equation a, we have

$$P_e = \frac{E^2}{r} = \frac{K^2(wtB_m)^2 f^2}{K' \dfrac{w}{tl}} = K_1 t^2 B_m^2 f^2 (wtl).$$

Since wtl is the volume (V) of the section of iron, we find

$$P_e = K_1 t^2 B_m^2 f^2 V. \tag{65}$$

Equation 65 shows how the various dimensions of the section and other factors affect the eddy-current loss. This loss can be greatly lessened by reducing the thickness (t) of the section and by increasing the number of sections or laminations so as to keep the volume of iron constant. This explains why the iron parts of the magnetic circuits of electrical machines are often laminated. The individual laminations must be insulated electrically from each other, and their planes should be parallel to the direction of flux. This insulation is provided by the formation of iron oxide on the surface of the iron during the process of annealing, or by dipping the laminations in insulating varnish or shellac.

The derivation of equation 65 assumes a uniform distribution of flux throughout the lamination. The value of K_1 depends on the wave form of the flux variation and will remain constant as long as the variation of flux with time is the same. Because of avoiding the use of calculus and the discussion of effective values of alternating-current waves, the above derivation is not rigorous, but the final expression is the same as that obtained by a more thorough method.

Calculation of the Magnetic Circuit in Iron. When iron is present in the magnetic circuit, B/H, or μ, is not constant. The permeability varies with the flux

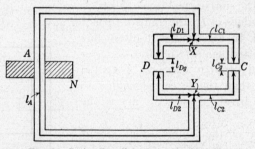

Fig. 30. Series-Parallel Magnetic Circuit.

density and is greater at the lower densities. There may be different values of H for the same flux density due to hysteresis and, consequently, different values of permeability. In general, the permeability used for magnetic materials corresponds to B/H as obtained from the magnetization curve rather than from the hysteresis loop. For the reasons given on page 376 calculations of the magnetic circuit are usually made in conjunction with the magnetization or $B-H$ curves. The application of this method is illustrated by the following example. It is desired to find the mmf of the coil N necessary to produce a certain flux in the magnetic circuit, shown in Fig. 30, at junction points X

and Y. A value of flux through the branch D is assumed and the density B calculated from the cross section of this leg. The value of H for this density B is found on Fig. 24. Then

$$U_{XDY} = Hl_{D1} + Bl_{D_g} + Hl_{D2}.$$

Other values of flux are assumed and the corresponding values of U_{XDY} determined. These assumed values of ϕ_D corresponding to the calculated values of U are then plotted as shown in Fig. 31. The branch C is handled similarly

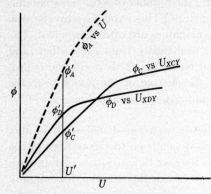

and values for it plotted as shown. Since the branches C and D are in parallel, the flux through A will be the sum of the fluxes in D and C corresponding to the same drop in magnetic potential U'. Thus $\phi_A' = \phi_D' + \phi_C'$. For ϕ_A' the density in the branch A is determined and the corresponding H is found on Fig. 24. $U_A' = Hl_A$. Since the branch A is in series with the combined branches D and C, the drop in magnetic potential U_A must be added to the drop U_{XDY},

Fig. 31. Variation of Flux with Drop in Magnetic Potential for Parts of Fig. 30.

or U_{XCY}, to obtain the total drop. For a flux ϕ_A' in branch A, the total drop in magnetic potential, $U_T' = U_A' + U_{XDY}'$,

and this drop is equal to the total mmf, $0.4\pi NI$ gilberts. The ampere-turns required to produce a flux ϕ_A' in the circuit of Fig. 30 are $U_T/(0.4\pi)$.

By plotting the sum of the branch fluxes at certain values of U against the corresponding values of U, the ampere-turns for any desired flux in A, D, or C may be found. In Fig. 31, the resultant flux ϕ_A is shown plotted against the drop U_{XDY} or U_{XCY}. The total drop in magnetic potential will be greater than the U corresponding to ϕ_A in this figure by the drop U_{XAY} due to the flux ϕ_A.

The solution of the simple series circuit shown in Fig. 32 involves the same principles as those that were illustrated in the preceding example. For any assumed value of flux, the

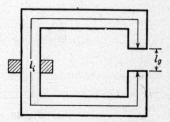

Fig. 32. Series Magnetic Circuit.

density is calculated and the corresponding value of H is read from the curve of Fig. 24. The total drop in magnetic potential is

$$U_T = Hl_i + Bl_g = 0.4\pi NI,$$

whence $NI = U_T/(0.4\pi)$.

The flux corresponding to a given mmf is determined by first plotting a curve of ϕ against U_T for several assumed values of ϕ and then reading the value from the curve. The analytical method for the solution of the two problems just discussed is one of trial and error, and is not to be recommended.

The preceding calculations assumed no flux outside the iron circuit (no leakage flux) except through the air gaps. In the air gaps, the flux lines were assumed to be parallel. If the cross sections of the magnetic circuits vary, U for each portion of constant section is determined separately, and the drops in series added. The $B-H$ curves may be plotted in terms of English units, namely, ampere-turns per inch and maxwells per square inch, as shown in Fig. 25. In terms of these latter units, the drop in the iron part of the circuit of Fig. 32 is

$$U_i = NI_i = \left(\frac{AT}{\text{in.}}\right) l_{i \text{ in.}} \tag{66}$$

For the air gap $U_{\text{gilberts}} = 0.4\pi NI = B_{\text{gausses}} l_{g \text{ cm.}}$

$$NI_g = \frac{Bl_g}{0.4\pi} = \frac{1}{0.4\pi} \left(\frac{B_{\text{max. per sq. in.}}}{2.54^2}\right) \text{ (air gap in inches} \times 2.54)$$
$$= 0.3133 B_{\text{max. per sq. in.}} \, l_g \quad \text{(English system)} \tag{67}$$

where B is in maxwells per square inch and l_g in inches. The total ampere-turns for the English system of units are

$$NI_i + NI_g = \left(\frac{AT}{\text{in.}}\right) l_{i \text{ in.}} + 0.3133 B_{\text{max. per sq. in.}} \, l_{g \text{ in.}}$$

Self-Inductance. Self-inductance is that property of a coil or other electric circuit which opposes any change in the current. **Self-inductance** is defined mathematically as the rate of change of flux linkages in a circuit with respect to the current in that circuit:

$$L = N \frac{d\phi}{di} \tag{68}$$

where L is the symbol of self-inductance. The differential $d\phi$ represents the change in flux caused by the change of current di; and N represents the number of turns with which the flux $d\phi$ links.

The unit of self-inductance is the *henry*. The **henry** exists in an electric circuit when the *rate of change of flux linkages with respect to the current in amperes is 10^8*:

$$L_{\text{henrys}} = N \frac{d\phi_{\text{maxwells}}}{di_{\text{amperes}}} 10^{-8}. \tag{69}$$

Also in the mks system

$$L_{\text{henrys}} = N \frac{d\phi_{\text{webers}}}{di_{\text{amperes}}} \tag{70}$$

Since the coordinates B and H of the magnetization or $B-H$ curve (see Fig. 23) are proportional respectively to ϕ and I, it is apparent that self-inductance $N\dfrac{d\phi}{di}$ is proportional to the slope of these curves. When flux is directly proportional to current, that is, when the magnetization curve is a straight line through the origin, self-inductance is a constant and equal to

$$L_{henrys} = \frac{N\phi_{maxwells}}{I_{amperes}}10^{-8} = \frac{N\phi_{webers}}{I_{amperes}} \qquad (70)$$

A useful relation in the study of commutation and one which is sometimes used as the defining equation of self-inductance, is derived as follows. Dividing equation 31 by equation 68, we find

$$\frac{e}{L} = \frac{-N\dfrac{d\phi}{dt}10^{-8}}{N\dfrac{d\phi}{di}10^{-8}} = -\frac{di}{dt}$$

$$e = -L\frac{di}{dt}, \quad \text{or} \quad L = \frac{-e}{di/dt} \qquad (71)$$

$$\text{volts} = \text{henrys} \times \frac{\text{amperes}}{\text{sec}}.$$

Thus a circuit has a self-inductance of 1 henry when 1 volt is induced by a current changing at the uniform rate of 1 ampere per second.

The effect of self-inductance in an electric circuit is analogous to that of mass or inertia in mechanics. Self-inductance opposes any change of current in a circuit. The opposition is exerted through the induction of an emf (equation 71) in the circuit which opposes that change in emf causing the change in current. When the current tends to increase, the emf of self-inductance is opposite to the current; when decreasing, the emf is in the same direction as the current.

The variation of self-inductance with the number of turns on a coil is important. For a coil with N turns, on a magnetic circuit of length l, cross-section a, and a permeability of μ, the self-inductance is derived as follows:

$$\phi = \frac{\text{m.m.f}}{\Re} = \frac{0.4\pi NI}{l/\mu A} = \frac{0.4\pi NI\mu A}{l}$$

$$L = \frac{N\phi 10^{-8}}{I} = \frac{0.4\pi N^2\mu A}{l}10^{-8} \text{ henrys.} \qquad (72)$$

Equation 72 shows that the self-inductance of a coil having a magnetic circuit of constant dimensions and permeability varies as the *square of the number of turns*.

Mutual Inductance. The rate of change of flux linkages in one coil, with respect to the current in another coil is defined as **mutual inductance**. When the current in the coil 1 of Fig. 33 is changed, it causes a change in the flux produced by it. If the coil 2 is placed so that any of the flux of the coil 1 links it, mutual inductance exists between the coils 1 and 2. This mutual inductance is equal to the rate of change of flux linkages in the coil 2 with respect to the change of current in the coil 1. It is never possible for all of the flux produced by the coil 1 to link the coil 2, although the amount of flux linking the coil 2 due to the coil 1 may be within a small fraction of 1 per cent of the total flux produced by the coil 1. In this latter case the coils are said to be **closely coupled.**

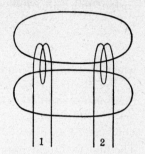

Fig. 33. Flux Linking Two Separate Coils of Wire.

Mutual inductance is also measured in henrys. When the rate of change of flux linkages expressed in maxwells-turns in circuit 2 with respect to a change in current in amperes in circuit 1 is 10^8, the mutual inductance is 1 henry. In the mks system 1 henry of mutual inductance exists when the rate of change of flux linkages in circuit 2 per unit current in circuit 1 is 1 weber-turn per ampere. Thus

$$M_{\text{henrys}} = N_2 \frac{d\phi_{12\,\text{maxwells}}}{di_{1\,\text{amperes}}} 10^{-8} \tag{73}$$

where $d\phi_{12}$ is the change of flux produced by coil 1 which links coil 2.

The change of current in coil 1 causes a change of flux linking coil 2, which, in turn, induces an emf in coil 2 called the **emf of mutual inductance.** This emf in coil 2 is

$$e_2 = -N_2 \frac{d\phi_{12}}{dt} 10^{-8} \tag{74}$$

Dividing equation 74 by 73 and solving for e_2 give the induced emf

$$e_2 = -M \frac{di_1}{dt} \tag{75}$$

Similarly, the emf of mutual induction in coil 1 is

$$e_1 = -M \frac{di_2}{dt} \tag{76}$$

For both equations 75 and 76 the emf is in volts when M is in henrys and di/dt is amperes per second. If induced voltage drops are desired, the minus signs in equations 75 and 76 are omitted.

Energy Stored in a Magnetic Field. A magnetic field represents a definite amount of energy. The energy required to build up a field comes from the electric circuit. Since $e = -L\,di/dt$, the component of the impressed emf supplied to overcome this back voltage due to self-induction is $v = L\,di/dt$. The power expended in energizing the coil is

$$p = vi = L \frac{di}{dt} i.$$

The energy is $dw = p\,dt = L(di/dt)i\,dt$. The total amount of energy delivered by the electric circuit and stored in the magnetic field when increasing the current to a value I is

$$w = \int_0^I Li\,di = \tfrac{1}{2}LI^2 \text{ joules} \tag{77}$$

when L is in henrys and I in amperes.

For the two coils in Fig. 33 carrying currents I_1 and I_2 respectively, the total energy stored in the field may be shown to be

$$\tfrac{1}{2}L_1I_1^2 + \tfrac{1}{2}L_2I_2^2 + MI_1I_2 \text{ joules.} \tag{78}$$

The first two terms represent the energy stored due to the self-inductance of the coils 1 and 2 respectively, and the third term shows the energy stored due to the mutual inductance of the two coils.

Index